HOW YOU TOO CAN DEVELOP A RAZOR-SHARP MIND AND A STEEL-TRAP MEMORY

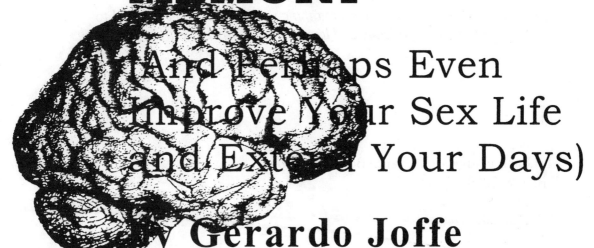

(And Perhaps Even Improve Your Sex Life and Extend Your Days)

by Gerardo Joffe

Turn to page 443 of this book and see how you can get it for absolutely free!

This book is dedicated to:

Priscilla – *the constant support and inspiration*
Michael – *who is always in my heart*
Rachel and Joe – *always hanging in there for Dad*

to:
Jeffrey Kawai – *without whom nothing would have happened*, and to
Eve Ward – *who patiently and lovingly word-processed the whole thing*

ISBN 0-930992-01-6

Publisher: Jomira/Advance, Advance Books Division
              470 Third Street, #211
              San Francisco, CA 94107

Table of Contents

Foreword

Please do not skip this Foreword -- it is an important part of the whole. This Foreword will tell you how this book will change your life.

Before you go on, I'll have to tell you about myself, because I am living proof of the efficacy of what I am going to teach you. As of this writing, I am 79 years old. I am the founder and president emeritus of a substantial direct-marketing business (Haverhills), the founder/ president of a national philanthropy (FLAME, Facts and Logic About the Middle East), and the president of another philanthropy, Friends of the Danish Jewish Museum.   I go to work every morning and put in an eight-hour to ten-hour day. I play vigorous tennis four times a week. I am the author of several books, and have at least two more in the works right now.

Why do I tell you all this? To show you that, if you get off your mental behind, if you put your brain to work, if you exercise it daily and keep working on and improving it, you too -- especially if you latch onto this "secret" at an earlier age than I did -- will be able to enjoy a vigorous, interesting, healthy, long, and, in all likelihood, affluent life.

Surely, you don't doubt that a sharp mind is a main requirement to be successful in business or in any endeavor in which you may or will be engaged. The smart person, the one whose mind is indeed razor-sharp and whose memory is indeed like a steel trap, will always win the competitive race against those who are less endowed. When you get through with this book, you will indeed have such a mind and you will have such a memory.

I am not a medical doctor and cannot of course give you medical advice. But I am convinced, and your experience will certainly also bear this out, that the human brain (yours and mine) while not a "muscle", does certainly behave like one in many respects. Sit on your couch, preferably with a six-pack and a bag of potato chips, and watch the tube. I can almost guarantee you that, just like a muscle that you don't exercise, your brain will become flabby and will eventually deteriorate. Exercise your brain vigorously and it will be effective and supple, just as if you had been "lifting weights" with it in a program of regular exercise.

I promise you that this book will give your brain the most rigorous workout it ever had. There will be times that you will want to cry "uncle" and will wish to give up and not go any further. Don't do that! I promise you that your perseverance will be well rewarded.

While we are on this topic, I want to say one more thing: I have never known anybody who really rigorously exercised his or her mind -- by my methods or by any other means -- who was afflicted with Alzheimer's disease. I just don't think that can happen to a brain that is rigorously put through its paces every day. Do you?

Two more things: On the cover of this book I tell you that it might lead you to better sex and might even extend your life. Puffing? Not entirely, but let me tell you why:

We don't like to talk about our own sex lives, but it's somewhat important that I at least mention it. It's not quite like it was when I was 20 years old. But let me just say that my wife (of 47 years) is always smiling. There is no Viagra in the house.

It is a proven scientific fact that smart people have better sex. And the smarter, the better the sex. That flies somewhat in the face of "popular wisdom", which holds that "uninhibited primitives" have the best sex of all. But it just isn't so. They may do a lot of grunting and sweating, but they don't have good sex. The opposite is true. The smarter you are, the better your brain functions, and the better your brain functions, the longer lasting and the better and more interesting your sex life is likely to be. Believe it!

But how about longer life? Yes, that is the really good part: Another "scientific fact", and one proven in literally millions of cases, is that those who have consistently good and regular sex live longer than those who don't. How is that for a "bonus"? So you see, by having bought this book, and by sticking with it and faithfully going through the lessons and doing the exercises on a daily basis, you will hone your mind to razor sharpness, will develop a "steel-trap" memory, will improve your sex life, and, in all likelihood, you will live longer. What a bargain for $29.95!

But, that isn't all. Turn to page 444 and you will find a <u>Merchandise Certificate in the amount of $30</u> that you can apply to any purchase of $60 ($59.95) or more from Haverhills. So the book turns out to be free -- in fact, you will be making a nickel.

Now to the book itself.

It consists of five sections:

I. <u>Review of Arithmetic</u>. There are things you did know but have forgotten, and things you should know, but never did. And there are some "tricks" that will make life a little easier. (What you will learn right off the bat about adding and subtracting will alone be worth many times the price of this book).

II. <u>The 16-Level Paradigm of Multiplication</u>. That is the "guts" of this book. Here is where you will sharpen your brain through ruthless "manipulation of numbers".

III. <u>A Few Full Trips Through the 16-Level Paradigm.</u> In this section we go together through the full 16-Level Paradigm on six problems. I take you level-by-level and step-by-step through the whole procedure on all six problems.

IV. <u>The Algebra of the 16-Level Paradigm</u>. This is "optional" and only for those who may be interested. In this section, I explain to you the algebraic bases that underlie the methods that we have learned in Section II. It's quite interesting and really very simple. So, unless you got "freaked out" against algebra in high school, you may wish to tackle it.

There are also a few "algebra bonuses" – excursions into permutations/combinations, probability, and equations. Some of this material is related to what we have done in this book. Some of it is unrelated but quite interesting. There are also a few problems for you to solve by yourself.

V.   <u>Final Wrap-up and Odds & Ends</u>. In this short final section I give you your farewell homework, with my guidance part of the way. I show you how you can get your <u>Certificate of Accomplishment</u>. There is also your <u>Merchandise Certificate</u>, which enables you to get this book for FREE --- get your money back. What a deal!

I shall ask you to do some pretty heavy mental lifting in the course of this book. Stick with it and don't give up. You will be greatly rewarded. And if you get all the way through and have done your exercises for a couple of months, you will be eligible for a <u>Certificate of Achievement</u>. Look at page 440 for details.

Good luck, and with best wishes for a sharp mind and a splendid memory.

Gerardo Joffe

P.S.: A small bonus, really a parlor trick: When you get through with the heavy stuff, I'll show you (in Section V) how you can instantly determine the day of the week for any date from January 1, 1900 to December 31, 2099. It's amazing!

And, as we say in the advertising business, that isn't all: In Section IV, I show you how you can make a small but steady income with the "propositions" that I explain to you. Well, I may be exaggerating a little – but you should be able to win some very interesting bar bets.

Section I

REVIEW OF ARITHMETIC

As I said in the Foreword, in this section we are reviewing things about arithmetic that you should know but may have forgotten. I hope that you will also learn a few new procedures that will be useful to you, not just in the exercises in Section II that follows, but that will also prove most helpful in your daily life.

Addition

That is of course the most basic operation. You may think that you know all about that, and you may be tempted to skip this part. But don't! Chances are that you will learn something new and quite important.

Let's take an easy example:

$$
\begin{array}{r}
11,225 \\
+\quad 2,318 \\
+\quad 5,472 \\
+\quad 358 \\
+\quad 13,692 \\
\hline
\end{array}
$$

33065

Let's call out loud how we would usually handle this.

We start with the column on the right; once we've added that, we move on to the left -- one column at a time. Here goes:

    5 - 13 - 15 - 23 - 25   -- Put down 5, carry 2
    4 - 5 - 12 - 17 - 26   -- Put down 6, carry 2
    4 - 7 - 11 - 14 - 20   -- Put down 0, carry 2

6

3 - 5 - 10 - 13   -- Put down 3, carry 1[*]

2 - 3   -- Put down 3

Thus, the result will be 33,065. You have handled this correctly and you have got the right result.

But this book is about how to do figures in your head, and though, as you will see, we shall primarily be concerned with multiplication, and not with addition, we have to learn how to add correctly, in our head, and efficiently. So I'll teach you how to add columns of figures in your head. You will find it quite easy and, once you have mastered it, extremely helpful.

The basis of addition (and as you will see later, also of subtraction and multiplication) in your head is to start from the left and not from the right.

Let's see how this will work in the example we just had.

$$
\begin{array}{r}
11,225 \\
+ \quad 2,318 \\
+ \quad 5,472 \\
+ \quad\quad 358 \\
+ \quad 13,692 \\
\hline
\end{array}
$$

Starting from the left (and taking the first two columns together) we say:

11, 13, 18, 31 (thousand).

We then go to the next column (the hundreds) and say:

Thirty-one two, thirty-one five, thirty-one nine, thirty-two two, thirty-two eight.

I'll write this out for you, because that's what I want you to say in your head -- forget about saying out (loud in your head) the thousands. It wastes time and will tend to confuse you.

---

[*] Many people, I hope you among them, will realize that the last (the left-most column) has only two entries, and can therefore be taken together with the preceding one. Thus, instead of saying 3-5-10-13 they will say 13-15-20-33 and will put 33 down as the last sum.

We then go to the next column (the tenners) and continue as follows: thirty-two eight twenty, thirty-two eight thirty, thirty-two nine hundred, thirty-two nine fifty, thirty-three oh forty.

We then go to the last (the oner) column and finish up as follows: thirty-three oh forty-five, thirty-three oh fifty-three, thirty-three oh fifty-five, thirty-three oh sixty-three, thirty-three oh sixty-five (don't sound out "thousand") -- which is of course the result.

The result is the only thing you'll put down if you wish to put anything down at all. Many, if not most, times it will suffice for you to just have the result in your head.

Describing this process makes it sound cumbersome and complicated. But it's really very easy once you get used to this new way of doing things.

Let's try another example:

$$
\begin{array}{r}
2,387 \\
+\quad 14,283 \\
+\quad 647 \\
+\quad 8,962 \\
+\quad 3,715 \\
+\quad 21,224 \\
\hline
51,218
\end{array}
$$

By the "standard" method, adding from right to left and "carrying", we get the correct result of 51,218. But there is no way, of course, that we could do this addition in our head by using this method.

Let's go from left to right. Again, I'll call out for you the sequence of additions. It sounds different in your head than when I write it down. For instance, when I put down 48.3 (which means 48,300) I sound "forty-eight three" in my head. You will get the knack. If you do this yourself, it will be much faster. I assure you that once you have understood this method --

it will take a little practice -- you will be able to perform these additions in your head as fast or faster than somebody doing it with a pencil or perhaps even with an adding machine.

So here goes:

2 - 16 - 24 - 27 - 48 (000) → 48.3 - 48.5 - 49.1 - 50.0 - 50.7 - 50.9 (000) → (don't say silently the word "thousand" or the period. Say "fifty (pause) nine" -- not "fifty-nine".) Go on with fifty (pause) nine eighty (50,980), fifty-one oh sixty (51,060), fifty-one one (51,100), fifty-one one sixty (51,160), fifty-one one seventy (51,170), fifty-one one ninety (51,190) → (now to the last column, the oners) → 51,197, 51,200, 51,207, 51,209, 51,214, 51,218.

Do this example over again until you fully understand it and have it down totally pat.

Here are three more examples to try on your own.

$$
\begin{array}{r}
6,320 \\
+ \quad 12,472 \\
+ \quad 5,319 \\
+ \quad 16,280 \\
\hline
\end{array}
$$

and

$$
\begin{array}{r}
21,340 \\
+ \quad 12,450 \\
+ \quad 7,316 \\
+ \quad 6,975 \\
\hline
\end{array}
$$

and

$$
\begin{array}{r}
17,283 \\
+ \quad 815 \\
+ \quad 6,328 \\
+ \quad 14,761 \\
\hline
\end{array}
$$

Make up your own examples and practice, practice, practice. You will find that being able to add quickly in your head is one of the most useful things that you will ever learn. It's something that you will be able to use every day.

One more thing about addition:

In many cases, precision is not required; approximation will suffice.

Let's have another look at the first example that we have worked with. Assume it's money and that the last two places in each case are pennies. Let's say that these are daily receipts of a business. The owner wants to know how much money he has taken in, but he doesn't care about the pennies.

Here is the first example again, expressed as money:

$$\begin{array}{rr} \$ & 112.25 \\ + & 23.18 \\ + & 54.72 \\ + & 3.58 \\ + & 136.92 \\ \hline \end{array}$$

Following the same method we have used before, beginning with the left-most column, but adding only the dollars, we get $328. But now we <u>make another important and fundamental assumption -- namely, that the average entry in the two "pennies" columns will be $.50, fifty cents!</u> And the larger the number of entries (in this case, we have only five entries) the more closely it will approximate "50", provided, of course, that the numbers are random, i.e. that there is no preponderance of "00" or anything like that.

So, in this case, we have five entries, and assuming that the average is $.50, we can say that the pennies will add up (approximately, but quite closely) to 5 x $.50 = $2.50. Adding that to the $328, we get $330.50 as our "approximation". As you can see, that differs only by $.15 from the exact result, very close and totally satisfactory for this businessman's purposes.[*]

---

[*] In case you're interested in this sort of thing, the error is .15/330.65 x 100 = .045%, very small indeed.

One other point: While this may seem almost unbelievable to you right now, <u>I can</u> <u>absolutely guarantee you that, by the time you get through with this book, you will be able to do</u> <u>this sort of thing in your head and in seconds</u>. Really!

Here is how it would go (in your head): 112 - 135 - 189 - 192 - 328 - add $2.50 →

$330.50. Total time: ten seconds!

Let's quickly look at the second example we had and let's do it in our head right away.

Again, we think of it in terms of dollars and cents and do the "approximation"

$	23.87
+	142.83
+	6.47
+	89.63
+	37.15
+	212.24

Let's "sound it out silently" in our heads, as follows:

23-165-171-260-297-509. There are six entries at "approximately" $.50 each, so that adds

another (6 x $.50) $3, giving you an "approximate" total of $512 (Remember the exact total? It

was 51,218 or, in dollar terms, $512.18, so that is another very small error -- .035%).

By the way, don't fret if you can't add these things "instantly", as I just showed you.

Keep practicing and it will come, probably very soon. In the meantime, you may do it more

slowly, as we did in the beginning, but always starting on the left: 2-16-24, etc..

So that's it about addition. I believe that what you have learned so far is very worthwhile

and extremely useful. Do the practical examples that I have given you, both exactly and

approximately. Then make up your own examples, and practice, until, I hope, you will indeed

very soon be able to add such columns of figures in your head -- exactly or approximately -- but

in any case in your head, without pencil and paper.

Now let's look at the opposite of addition.

Subtraction

Now that you have mastered addition (I am confident that you have practiced, as I have urged you, and that you are indeed proficient in the methods that I have taught you), let's tackle the opposite of addition: subtraction.

Many people are totally "freaked out" by subtraction. They just refuse to tackle it at all. They tend to panic if confronted with a problem in subtraction. They try to avoid it if they can, and are deeply grateful for calculators to relieve their anxieties.

The main difficulty, and the reason for this, is perhaps the way subtraction is taught in most American schools.

Let's look at a simple example and see how it's done:

$$
\begin{array}{r}
78,976 \\
- \quad 35,423 \\
\hline
\end{array}
$$

You learn to go from right to left, and (sounding out) to go through the following steps:

6 minus 3 is 3   -- Put down **3**

7 minus 2 is 5   -- Put down **5**

9 minus 4 is 5   -- Put down **5**

8 minus 5 is 3   -- Put down **3**

7 minus 3 is 4   -- Put down **4**

So there is your answer: 43,553. Not too bad, and not too difficult.

But, you realize, of course, why this was comparatively easy. You didn't have to "borrow" anything. Your troubles start with the "borrowing".

Let's take another example:

$$60,134$$
$$-\ \ 57,468$$

Again, as we learned in school, we start from the right and proceed as follows:

We can't subtract 8 from 4, because 8 is greater than 4; therefore, we'll have to "borrow" 1 from 3. We say that 14 - 8 = 6.   We put down **6**.

Having borrowed 1 from 3, we have to subtract 6 from 2. But that doesn't work either. So, again, we have to "borrow", this time from the 1 in the next column, leaving only 0. So we subtract 6 from 12, which is 6.   We put down **6**.

Now we have to go to the next column and attempt to subtract 4 from 0, which of course doesn't work. So we'll have to "borrow" once again, this time from the 0 in the next column, leaving -- what? Here is where many people give up altogether, and either reach for a stiff drink or for a calculator. But of course you have to go to the next column and borrow 1 from the 6, leaving only 5. Now, if you are still with us, you subtract 4 from 10. We put down **6**.

Then you subtract 7 from 9.   We put down **2**.

Having subtracted 1 from 6, you'll have 5, and 5 minus 5 of course is 0. In any case, somehow or another you came up with the result of 2,666. That happens to be correct, but you're not entirely sure of it.

That was really difficult and exhausting, and not too many people get it right on the first (or perhaps even on the next) try.

Now, let me show you how to <u>really</u> do it, how to take the pain out of subtraction. It is by <u>subtracting through adding.</u> What? Subtracting through adding? Yes, you will see!

Let's take the same example we just had:

$$
\begin{array}{r}
60,134 \\
-\ 57,468 \\
\hline
\end{array}
$$

We start again from the right, but we don't attempt to take away 8 from 4. We think of the 4 as 14, and ask ourselves how much it is from 8 to 14. We say that 8 and **6** is four**teen**. We put down **6**.

Now, in this vastly improved subtraction through addition, <u>every time you say (in your head) ten, eleven, twelve, or any of the teens, you add one to the next bottom number on the left.</u>

Let's see how it works in this case.

We have already seen that 8 and **6** is four**teen**. We have put down the 6, but having said **teen**, we add 1 to the 6 in the bottom of the next column, making it 7. Since 3 is smaller than 7, we make it 13, and say 7 and **6** is thir**teen**.   We put down the **6**.

Having said **teen**, we add 1 to the 4 on the bottom of the next column, making it 5. The 1 on top becomes 11, and we say 5 and **6** is 11.   We put down the **6**.

Having said **eleven**, we add 1 to the 7 in the next column, making it 8. The 0 on top becomes 10, and we say 8 and **2** is **10**.   We put down the **2**.

Having said **10**, we add 1 to the 5 in the last column; 6 plus 0 is 6. So that is the end of it. The result is **2,666**.

As I explain this to you, step-by-step, it sounds difficult and tedious. But it is really very simple. Please try it, and you will never again use your old method for subtraction. With the addition method it's almost impossible to make a mistake.

Let's try another one, the first example we had in this chapter. It was very easy, because no borrowing was involved.

$$78,976$$
$$-35,423$$

You should be able to write this answer down almost immediately, without doing any "figuring". But let's sound it out and go through the process:

3 plus **3** is 6   -- Put down **3**

2 plus **5** is 7   -- Put down **5**

4 plus **5** is 9   -- Put down **5**

5 plus **3** is 8   -- Put down **3**

3 plus **4** is 7   -- Put down **4**

So the answer is **43,553**.

In this example, we didn't have to add 1 to any of the numbers. That made it very easy. Let's try two more problems, a little more difficult ones.

$$86,473$$
$$-64,768$$

8 plus **5** is 13 (thir**teen**)-- Put down **5** (add 1 to bottom figure of next column)

7 plus **0** is 7   -- Put down **0**

7 plus **7** is 14 (four**teen**) -- Put down **7** (add 1 to bottom figure of next column)

5 plus **1** is 6   -- Put down **1**

6 and **2** is 8   -- Put down **2**

The answer is **21,705**

One more:

$$124,732$$
$$-18,267$$

7 plus **5** is 12 (**twelve**)   -- Put down **5** (add 1 to bottom figure of next column)

7 and **6** is 13 (thir**teen**) -- Put down **6** (add 1 to bottom figure of next column)

3 and **4** is 7   -- Put down **4**

8 and **6** is 14 (four**teen**)   -- Put down **6** (add 1 to bottom figure of next column)

2 and **0** is 2   -- Put down **0**

0 and **1** is 1   -- Put down **1**

And the answer is **106,465**

Here are three more, for you to practice yourself:

$$\begin{array}{r} 86,320 \\ -\ 47,172 \\ \hline \end{array}$$

and

$$\begin{array}{r} 152,419 \\ -\ 38,582 \\ \hline \end{array}$$

and

$$\begin{array}{r} 236,415 \\ -\ 182,287 \\ \hline \end{array}$$

After you have done these, make up your own examples. Practice on at least two or three every day until this advanced method of subtraction has become totally second nature to you.

You may be a little impatient by now, because this book is about doing figures in your head, and here we are teaching you this pencil-and-paper method. Please be patient; we'll come to doing subtraction in our head in just a minute, but I thought it would be very important for you to learn -- and to make totally your own -- this important method of doing subtraction by addition.

Before we get to subtracting in our head, we need to learn an important technique, namely subtracting by complements.

Complements are the numbers that make complete, not always, but for our purposes, mostly to 100.

For instance:

- 63 is the complement to 37

- 52 is the complement to 48

- 16 is the complement to 84

- 23 is the complement to 77

- 41 is the complement to 59, etc., etc.,

because in each case, the two numbers complement each other to 100.

Here are the complements to 10. You know them, of course, though you may perhaps never have thought of them in those terms.

- 1 is the complement to 9

- 2 is the complement to 8

- 3 is the complement to 7

- 4 is the complement to 6

- 5 is the complement to 5

and so on.

Why are these complements important and useful? We'll see in a minute.

Suppose you want to subtract (in your head) 23 from 47.

As with all "head" methods, we start from the left.

We say 40 minus 20 is 20, and 7 minus 3 is 4, therefore, 47 - 23 = 20 + 4 = 24.

It's just a little more difficult if you wish to subtract 57 from 82, because, while you can subtract 50 from 80, you can't subtract 7 from 2.

Here's where complements come in. Instead of attempting to subtract 57 from 82, add the complement of 7 (the 7 of 57) namely 3, which makes it 60. Add the same complement (3) to 82, which makes it 85. Then subtract 60 (remember, we have complemented 57 to 60) from 85, which is very easy and gives us 82 - 57 = 85 - 60 = 25.

Let's try another one like this:

72 - 34

The complement of 4 is 6. So this becomes 78 (72 + 6) - 40 (34 + 6) which is 38.

Or: 297 - 48

Complement 48 to 50 (add 2), add the same 2 to 97, making that 99. 99 - 50 = 49. So, 297 - 48 = 249.

Let's work with complements to 100, which is much more frequent, and therefore much more useful.

Let's say 432 - 267

Most people would have a very hard time doing this in their head, but it is a simple matter with complements.

We need to complement 267 to the next 100, which is 300, and we have to add 33 (the complement of 67) to get to it. You increase 432 by the same amount, which gives you 465. Perform the easier operation of subtracting 300 from 465, and you have the result: 165.

Like some other things we have talked about so far in this book (and many more that we shall still talk about), this sounds very complicated when one describes it, but it's really very easy once you understand it and know what the complements are. Without having to think about it, you must know (and if you don't know yet, practice!) that the complement of 16 is 84, of 64 it's 36, of 81 it's 19, etc. Once you know that, it'll literally take you just seconds to solve such subtraction problems.

Let's try a few more:

653 – 287 add complement 13 and make it

666 – 300   =   366

or 2,332 – 1,652 add complement 48 and it becomes

2,380 – 1,700 =   680

or 825 – 434 add complement 66 and it becomes

891 – 500   =   391

By the way, how did you add 66 to 825? If you don't have the answer to this mini-problem immediately, if you have to figure it out, I hope that you remember what you learned, namely, to add from the left.

825 + 60 → 885 + 6 → 891

The complement method is most useful in subtraction, and almost necessary when you have to cross the "threshold" of a hundred, as in all those previous examples. If you don't cross such a threshold, you don't either need to work with complements at all, or just with complements to ten. Always remember: Start from the left. For instance:

648 – 32

You don't have to cross a threshold; since 48 is greater than 32, you won't have to go below 600. So you say simply   648 – 30 → 618 -2 → 616

or   1,254 – 27

You won't have to cross the "100 threshold" because 54 is greater than 27. But (the final) 7 is greater than the (final) 4. So it might be easier for you to work with the complement of 10, by adding 3 to both 1,254 and to 27, as follows:

$$1,254 + 3 \rightarrow 1,257 - 30 \rightarrow 1,227$$

Easy, isn't it?

Now try a few more on your own:

743 - 58	Complement to 100
1,823 - 16	Complement to 10
752 - 73	Complement to 100
1,843 - 22	No complement needed
1,262 - 89	Complement to 100
843 - 29	Complement to 10

Before we close this chapter, let's see how we can handle subtraction of larger numbers (such as 4- or 5-digit numbers) in our head.

The "trick" is to divide the problem into two parts and use complements as needed.

For instance:

$$
\begin{array}{r|r}
43, & 544 \\
- \quad 16, & 358 \\
\hline
\end{array}
$$

The most convenient place to divide is after the thousands. You can quickly see that 43 (000) - 16 (000) is 27 (000). (But if that's a little hard for you, you can do that part by complements, adding 4 (complement of 16 to 20) to both 43 and 16, giving you 47 - 20 → 27 (000).

That leaves 544 - 358. We complement 358 to 400 by adding 42, and of course add it also to 544. That gives us 586 - 400 = 186, bringing the total to 27,186.

You didn't realize you could do that in your head, did you? And once you get the knack, and practice it, you'll be able to do this kind of thing in seconds, really just by looking at it.

Let's try one more:

$$
\begin{array}{r|r}
67, & 152 \\
- \quad 45, & 375 \\
\hline
 &
\end{array}
$$

We follow the same procedure, dividing after the thousands. But we notice by inspection that we have a little problem here, because 375 is greater than 152, so we can't subtract it. Here is how you do it: "Borrow" 1,000 from 67,000 and your problem becomes:

66 (000) - 45 (000) + (1,152 - 375).

We know how to handle this: 66 - 45 = 21 (000)

That leaves 1,152 - 375: We complement 375 to 400 by adding 25 -- we also add it of course to 1,152; we get 1,177 - 400 = 777.

And the solution to the problem becomes:

21,000 + 777 = 21,777

I am going to give you a few problems of this kind for you to work on yourself. Remember:

- You have to do it in your head; forget about pencil and paper (you may check your answer, if you wish, with pencil and paper or with your calculator).

- Always start from the left.

- For large numbers, divide the problem at a convenient place, usually, but not necessarily, at the thousands.

- Use complements as needed.

And here are four sample problems for you on which to practice. Of course, you can also make up many more of your own.

$$
\begin{array}{r}
43,292 \\
-\ \underline{16,825}
\end{array}
$$

$$
\begin{array}{r}
4,681 \\
-\ \underline{3,219}
\end{array}
$$

$$
\begin{array}{r}
57,212 \\
-\ \underline{18,002}
\end{array}
$$

$$
\begin{array}{r}
3,694 \\
-\ \underline{2,387}
\end{array}
$$

Here is something else that you can do with subtraction by addition that is simply impossible by the "standard" subtraction method.

Take for instance the case in which you have to subtract several numbers from another one.

Suppose a person's income after taxes is $8,754

Let's put that down together with his expenses.

Income	$	8,754
Alimony	$	(1,500)
Rent	$	(1,250)
Food	$	(880)
Clothing	$	(250)
Car Payment	$	(840)
Insurance	$	(220)

Entertainment	$	(250)
Club Membership	$	(180)
Others	$	(240)

How can we do this in one swoop -- first with pencil and paper?

We start adding the expenses (the negatives), beginning (from the bottom upward) in the rightmost column, then subtracting (by the method that we have learned) from the top (income) number, as follows:

1. 0 → 0 and **4** is 4   Put down **4**

2. 4 → 12 → 17 → 19 → 23 → 28 → 36 → 41 and **4** is 45   Put down **4**

3. Now carry 4 (for 40) into the next column, and continue as follows:

    4 → 6 → 7 → 9 → 11→ 19 → 21 → 29 → 41 (take the full 12, instead of just the 2) → 56 (taking the whole 15) → 56 and **31** is 87   Put down **31**

There is no way that you could do that in one operation by the "standard" method of subtraction that you have been using so far. The only way you could do it would be to first add up all the expenses as follows:

8.754

Alimony	$	(1,500)
Rent	$	(1,250)
Food	$	(880)
Clothing	$	(250)
Car Payment	$	(840)
Insurance	$	(220)
Entertainment	$	(250)
Club Membership	$	(180)
Others	$	(240)
Total Expenses	$	5,610

and then subtract that amount from the income as follows:

$$\begin{array}{r} \$ \quad 8{,}754 \\ -\ \$ \quad 5{,}610 \\ \hline \$ \quad 3{,}144 \\ \hline\hline \end{array}$$

Complicated, isn't it? It is so very much easier by the addition method.

This is a most valuable procedure that you should make your own.

Can you do this in your head! Of course!

Go back to the original set-up of this problem, with the income amount on top and, of course, let's start from the left.

Here we go.

First, two columns: 15, 27, 35, 37, 45, 47, 49, 50, 52.

Third column: 52 5, 53 3, 53 8, 54 2, 54 4, 55 7, 56 1

Last column is zero, so it's 5,610

Now we have to subtract that from 8754 (in our head, of course). We know how to do that.

$$\begin{array}{r|l} 87 & 54 \\ -\ 56 & 10 \\ \hline \end{array}$$

It turns out to be easy – nothing has to be borrowed.

87 – 56   =   31

54 – 10   =   44

8754 – 5610 =   3144

Easy, wasn't' it?

24

Here are two more such examples for you to practice on:

$$
\begin{array}{r}
23{,}482 \\
(2{,}951) \\
(13{,}260) \\
(6{,}815) \\
(43) \\
(274) \\
\hline
\end{array}
$$

and finally:

$$
\begin{array}{r}
122{,}615 \\
(18{,}394) \\
(19{,}217) \\
(853) \\
(16{,}817) \\
(1{,}254) \\
\hline
\end{array}
$$

Make up some examples of your own and practice this very helpful method.

I hope you have enjoyed this chapter. Keep practicing, every day!

Now on to multiplication.

Multiplication

As you will see in Section II of this book, Multiplication is what this is all about. But it's not just simply about multiplying numbers. You will learn many different ways of how to arrive at the same goal -- the purpose being, just like the title of this book promises, to sharpen your mind and to develop your memory.

But before we go into that, I must ask you, and <u>I must insist, that you totally, thoroughly, and without hesitation, know your basic multiplication table</u>. For the time being, just to 10 x 10, as you learned in school, but eventually, to at least 20 x 20 (preferably 25 x 25). Up to 10 x 10, you must be able to respond instantly; to 20 x 20 or 25 x 25, you may hesitate a second or two (but not more!). I'll show you how to do that.

As though you didn't know it, here is the multiplication table, just as you learned it in grammar school (you'll find the answer where the factors intersect):

	1	2	3	4	5	6	7	8	9	10
1	1	2	3	4	5	6	7	8	9	10
2	2	4	6	8	10	12	14	16	18	20
3	3	6	9	12	15	18	21	24	27	30
4	4	8	12	16	20	24	28	32	36	40
5	5	10	15	20	25	30	35	40	45	50
6	6	12	18	24	30	36	42	48	54	60
7	7	14	21	28	35	42	49	56	63	70
8	8	16	24	32	40	48	56	64	72	80
9	9	18	27	36	45	54	63	72	81	90
10	10	20	30	40	50	60	70	80	90	100

You should be able to answer immediately and without any hesitation:

$$6 \times 9 =$$
$$8 \times 5 =$$
$$4 \times 7 =$$
$$6 \times 4 =$$
$$7 \times 8 =$$

If this causes you any hesitation at all, you must practice this before you go any further. You cannot possibly tackle Section II or anything else that follows in this book if you don't have the basic multiplication table down absolutely pat.

How about the extended multiplication table -- to (at least) 20 x 20? Although, after a while, that will be as easy for you as the "basic" multiplication table is now, I don't expect you (yet!) to manage that. Instead, I'll show you a technique (a "trick", if you will) of how to do these multiplications so quickly that you indeed will only "hesitate" a second or two before you come up with the answer. This is a technique on which we shall elaborate and build on in Section II.

Assume you want to know what, say, 14 x 21 is. Here is how you proceed:

Step 1: Multiply 10 x 21.Obviously it's **210**.

Step 2: Multiply 4 x 20. Obviously it's **80**.

Step 3: Multiply 4 x 1. Obviously it's **4**.

We add these intermediate results and we get the total of **294**.

Explaining these simple steps makes it appear a little difficult and cumbersome. But, of course, they are simplicity itself. Let's try it one more time with another such example.

Oh, by the way, in this and in <u>all</u> examples that follow in this book, <u>always put the smaller factor (number to be multiplied) first and the larger factor second</u>.

All right, let's try it with 23 x 15, which we change to 15 x 23.

Following the same method, and starting out with 10 x 23 = 230, we get:

$$10 \times 23 \rightarrow 230 \xrightarrow{+5x20=100} 330 \xrightarrow{+5x3=15} \underline{\textbf{345}}$$

It shouldn't take you more than two seconds to do that.

Let's take an example in which both factors are in the 20's, for instance, 23 x 27.

Instead of taking 20 x 27 to begin with, which you will be doing eventually, you might wish to break it down even further if this is still a little difficult for you.

You can first take 2 x 20 (40), then 2 x 7 (14), add that up, and multiply by 10 (which means adding a 0 and brings you to 540); then do 3 x 27 by first doing 3 x 20 (60) and then 3 x 7 (21), and adding it all up, getting the answer of 621 -- altogether four transactions. But they are so very fast that you should really (or will soon be able to) do it in seconds. Let's do it.

$$2 \times 20 \rightarrow 40 \xrightarrow{+2x7=14} 54 \xrightarrow{x10} 540 \xrightarrow{+3x20=60} 600 \xrightarrow{+3x7=21} \underline{\textbf{621}}$$

I give you one more that I'll just write out for you as I go through the mental process, without describing it in detail, as we just did:

23 x 29

$$2 \times 20 \rightarrow 40 \xrightarrow{+2x9=18} 58 \xrightarrow{x10} 580 \xrightarrow{+3x20=60} 640 \xrightarrow{+3x9=27} \underline{\textbf{667}}$$

So, you'll have to know instantly the basic multiplication table. That is an absolute MUST for this book and for life. And you can "fake" your knowledge of the extended multiplication table -- to 20 x 20, or even 30 x 30 -- by using the method I've just shown you. You should be able to arrive at the answers in seconds and lend the impression, to yourself and to others, that you really know all these extended multiplications by heart.

As I said, this book is mostly about how multiplications will sharpen your mind and give you a powerful memory. Stick with it. There is much more to come about this topic.

Division

This book is not about division, so we'll spend very little time with it.

Long division, however, is the bugaboo of most people. Grown men, not armed with calculators, will pale at the thought of having to tackle it. They just don't know how. If they can do it at all, they do it the hard way.

Let's take a simple example:

```
              12,456
      129 | 1,606,824
            129
            316
            258
            588
            516
            722
            645
            774
            774
              0
```

Obviously, this is a made-up example; it's coming out even -- there's no remainder. Most of the time, in long division, there is either a remainder or you can continue dividing to however many decimals you wish.

What we did in the above example was to assess that the <u>divisor</u> (129) went once into the first three digits of the <u>dividend</u> (1,606,824). We therefore multiplied 129 x 1, which is 129, and put it under the 160. We subtracted 129 from 160, which gave us 31. We brought down the next digit (6), which gave us 316. We assessed that 129 goes into 316 twice; and now we multiply 129 x 2: 2 x 9 = 18; put down 8, carry 1, 2 x 2 = 4 + 1 = 5, put down 5; 2 x 1 = 2; put down 2. So we've put down 258. We subtract that from 316 (hopefully by the subtraction by addition method), get 58, bring down the 8, etc., etc.

Here is how to abbreviate the process, by leaving out one line in each of the subtransactions. Let's put down this problem again:

$$
\begin{array}{r}
12{,}456 \\
129 \overline{\smash{\big)}\,1{,}606{,}824} \\
\underline{129} \\
316 \\
\underline{588} \\
\underline{722} \\
\underline{774} \\
0
\end{array}
$$

Here is the abbreviated method.

First, we once again assess that 129 goes once into 160, but instead of writing it down, we say mentally:

1 x 9 = 9 **+ 1** is 10   Put down **1**, carry 1

1 x 2 = 2 **+ 1** (carried) = 3 + **3** = 6   Put down **3**

1 x 1 = 1 **+ 0** (carried) = 1 + **0** = 1   Put down **0** (i.e., nothing)

We now have 31; we bring down 6, and we have 316.

We assess that 129 goes twice (2x) into 316 and, following the same method, we say (mentally):

2 x 9 = 18 + **8** = 26   Put down **8**, carry 2

2 x 2 = 4 + 2 (carried) is 6 + **5** = 11 Put down **5**, carry 1

2 x 1 = 2 + 1 (carried) is 3 + **0** = 3   Put down **0** (nothing)

We now have 58, pull down 8, and have 588.

We assess that 129 goes four times into 588 and, using the same method, say:

4 x 9 = 36 + **2** = 38   Put down **2**, carry 3

4 x 2 = 8 + 3 (carried) is 11 + **7** = 18 Put down **7**, carry 1

4 x 1 = 4 + 1 (carried) is 5 + **0** = 5   Put down **0** (nothing)

That gives us 72. We pull down the 2 and we now have 722. We assess that 129 goes five times into that and, following the same procedure, say:

5 x 9 = 45 + **7** = 52   Put down **7**, carry 5

5 x 2 = 10 + 5 (carried) = 15 + **7** = 22 Put down **7**, carry 2

5 x 1 = 5 + 2 (carried) = 7 + **0** = 7   Put down **0** (nothing)

That brings us to 77. We bring down the last digit (4) and have 774. We assess that 129 goes into 774 six times and proceed:

6 x 9 = 54 + **0** = 54   Put down **0**, carry 5

6 x 2 = 12 + 5 (carried) = 17 + **0** = 17 Put down **0**, carry 1

6 x 1 = 6 + 1 (carried) = 7 + **0** = 7   Put down **0** (nothing)

In other words, this is the end of this division.

Just as other things that we have talked about so far (and many others that we shall talk about later), this sounds like (and probably is) much ado about nothing. But I wanted to be sure that you understand the principle of "abbreviated long division" and make it your own.

Here are two more examples (both come out without remainder) on which you should practice this method.

    1.   286 ⟌ 1,506,648

    2.   654 ⟌ 8,670,732

You will be able to come up with some more. Please practice -- you will find it to have been very much worth your while.

You may wonder why you would need to learn anything like that and, in any case, if you need long division, you can always use your calculator. But, of course, that is not the point. The point of this book is to sharpen your mind. And you can't do that by using a calculator -- any more than you could tone your body by watching a weightlifting movie. And what would you do if, stranded on a desert island (without a calculator), the 273 natives would ask you to distribute 189,736 coconuts equitably among them? If you don't know long division, you would have to go around and around, giving each native one coconut at a time, until they were all distributed. It would probably take you the better part of a week. With long division, especially using this abbreviated method, you would know right away that each native would receive 695 coconuts, with one coconut left over for you.

But let's come down to earth.

One thing you should know how to do and which we shall need as we go along in this book, is to divide, in your head, by small divisors such as 2, 3, 4, and 5. As you get more practice you will be able to handle larger divisions in your head, but right now, let's satisfy ourselves with up to 5.

Also, to make it a little easier at this point, all of the examples I shall give you will come out even, i.e. without remainder. All of the examples will be 4-digit numbers.

Dividing by 2:

Here is an example:

8,222

Split the number into two parts: 8,200 and 22. Since one-half (which is what dividing by 2 is) of 82 is 41, 8,200 divided by 2 is 4,100.

22 divided by 2 is 11. Therefore, 8,222 divided by 2 is the sum of the two, namely 4,111.[*]

Here is another one:

6,742

This is just a little more difficult, because 67 is not divisible by 2. So we break it down into 6,600 and 142.

One-half of 6,600 is	3,300
One-half of 140 is	70
One-half of 2 is	1

Therefore, one-half of 6,742 is the sum of the three: 3,300 + 70 + 1 = 3,371.

Naturally, you probably would not have needed to break it down quite that far. I hope that you would have known instantly that half of 142 is 71, and would have saved one step.

Just one more example:

3,367

---

[*] Since all digits in this example are even, you can really write the result down without going through any figuring: 8/2 = 4; 2/2 = 1. Therefore, 8,222 divided by 2 is 4,111.

Here, neither 33 nor 67 are divisible by 2, both are odd numbers. So the easiest way to do this is to divide 3367 into 3200 + 166 + 1.

We divide each of those three segments by 2 and get 1600 + 83 + ½ = 1,683½

Dividing by 3:

This is a little more difficult, I am afraid. You actually have to do "short division" in your head.

Let's take an easy example:

2,733

Again, we split this number in two – 2,700 and 33. As I said, it's easy, because it comes out so neatly.

Since 27 divided by 3 is 9, 2,700 divided by 3 is obviously	900
33 divided by 3 is	11
Therefore, 2,733 divided by 3 is the sum of the two:	911

Let's try another one that's not quite that easy:

5,559

Splitting the number in two, namely 5,500 and 59, we find that, regrettably, 55 does not divide by three (later in this section, I'll show you how you can tell that immediately). The closest number below 55 that divides by 3 is 54. So we'll split 5,559 into two parts, namely 5,400 and 159.

Since you'll know that 54 divided by 3 is 18, you'll instantly recognize that 5,400 divided by 3 is   1,800

If you cannot tell right away (just yet) how to immediately divide 159 by 3, break it down further into 150 and 9.

150 divided by 3 is   50

and 9 divided by 3 is   3

Therefore, 5,559 divided by is the sum of the three, namely: 1,853

Here are three more problems for you to try on your own, to divide by three, one easy (like our first example), and two more difficult ones (like our last example). All three, however, are divisible by 3, without any remainder:

3,948

6,273

8,880

Dividing by 4:

This is essentially the same as dividing by 2, only that you have to do it twice. You divide by 2 and then divide by 2 once again. For example:

2,448

We know how to divide by 2, and we get 1,224. We do this once again and we get we get 612, which is 2,448 divided by 4.

That was kind of easy, of course, because both 24 and 48 are readily divisible by 4.

Let's take one a little tougher:

2,732

Splitting the number in two -- 2,700 and 32 -- we find that 4 does not go into 27, that the next lower number into which 4 goes is 24. So we have 2,732 = 2,400 + 332.

Since 24 divided by 4 is 6, 2,400 divided by 4 is   600

You might wish to break up 332 into 300 and 32, but, more easily, you simply halve 332 by 2, get 166, and halve it again and get   83

Thus, 2,732 divided by 4 is the sum of the two: 683

Just as I shall teach you later in this section how to tell whether a number is divisible by 3, I'll also show you how to tell instantly whether it's divisible by 4.

On your own, divide the following three numbers by 4 -- in your head, of course! The first is an easy one; the other two are a little more difficult. All three are evenly divisible by 4, without any remainder:

3,684

5,724

3,816

Dividing by 5:

You may think that this may be more difficult than dividing by 3 or by 4, but it's really the easiest.

The reason is that dividing by 5 is the same as multiplying by 2 and dividing by 10.

Let's try a few examples:

2,325

Multiply it by two and it's clear that it's 4,650. Dividing by 10 means taking the 0 away. Thus, 2,325 divided by 5 is 465.

4,795

A little more difficult, but you will quickly see that 4,795 x 2 = 9,590, because 47 x 2 = 94, and therefore 4,700 x 2 = 9,400. That leaves 95 x 2, which you can break down to 90 x 2

(180) and 5 x 2 (10), i.e. 95 x 2 = 190. So, 4,795 x 2 is the sum of those, namely 9,590. We now divide by 10 (take away the 0), and understand that 4,795 divided by 5 is 959.

Here is one even a little more difficult, because in doubling the number to be divided by 5 we go above 10,000. But don't let that freak you out.

6,375

Let's take it one step at a time:

6,000 x 2	=	12,000
300 x 2	=	600
75 x 2	=	150

Therefore, 6,375 x 2 is the sum of the three: 12,750

Dividing by 10 (take the 0 away) we get: 1,275

which is what 6,375 divided by 5 is.

Easy, isn't it?

This is all for division. This is all, at least for our purposes, at least as far as the four basic operations are concerned.

We will now go on to something entirely different.

The Sum of Digits and Casting out 9's

This is an important technique, a good diagnostic tool, which, much to my surprise, is not known to too many people.

I think you will much profit by learning and understanding it.

Take any number, say 12,654.

Now add up the digits in that number. You get progressively:

1 → 3 → 9 → 14 → 18

Add up the number of digits of 18. It's **9**.

Thus, the (ultimate) sum of digits of 12,654 is **9**.

Let's take another number, say 24,398

You do it yourself. You'll find that the sum of digits is 26, which becomes **8**. So the sum of digits of 24,398 is **8**.

Where does "casting out 9's" come in? You can leave out (cast out) the 9's when you add the digits and come up with exactly the same result. For instance, in that last example, instead of adding $2 + 4 + 3 + 9 + 8$, we could have left out the 9 and could have added only $2 + 4 + 3 + 8$. We would have gotten 17, and that would have brought us back to 8. The same thing.

Let's try another one, with more nines in it.

$$96,989$$

Adding up all the digits, we get 41 on the first pass (including the three nines), which reduces to 5. We would have arrived at the same result if we had left out the nines and just added $6 + 8 = 14 \rightarrow$ **5**.

What is the purpose of this and why is this such an important diagnostic tool in arithmetic? Here is why -- two reasons:

1. In any sum, <u>the sum of the digits of the individual entries is the same as the sum of the digits of the result</u>.

2. In any multiplication, <u>the product of the sums of the digits of the factors is the same as the sum of the digits of the multiplication</u>.

This may sound a little awkward and difficult to grasp at first blush. But it's really very easy.

Let me show you.

Take, for instance, the following addition, in which in every case I've put the sum of the digits of each entry next to it.

$$
\begin{array}{rl}
42{,}315 & 6 \\
26{,}823 & 3 \\
9{,}217 & 1 \\
11{,}852 & 8 \\
347 & 5 \\
\hline
90{,}554 & 23 \rightarrow 5 \\
\end{array}
$$

sum of digits: 23 → 5

Amazing, isn't it?

Let's try another one:

$$
\begin{array}{rl}
28{,}205 & 8 \\
15{,}243 & 6 \\
6{,}912 & 9 \\
18{,}370 & 1 \\
\hline
68{,}730 & 24 \rightarrow 6 \\
\end{array}
$$

sum of digits: 24 → 6

So you can see that this is a powerful diagnostic tool. You can quickly tell whether an addition is correct.[*]

Let's see how this works with multiplication. For the purpose of this subject, we are only interested in the role of the sums of digits -- just take my word that the results of the multiplications are correct -- and, of course, you can always check it on your calculator.

For instance:

456 x 3,249   = 1,481,544 → 27 → 9

Sum of digits:

15 → 6 x 18 → 9 = 54   → 9

---

[*] In this, and also in multiplication about which we'll talk in a minute, <u>you do not have a 100% assurance</u> that the result is correct in using the sum-of-digits test only. You can apply other tests that we'll learn about. We may talk about the degree of assurance in the algebra section, <u>but it's very likely to be correct</u>. But if the sum of digits does not correlate, <u>you can be 100% sure that the result is wrong</u>.

$$6 \times 9 \rightarrow \quad = \quad 54 \rightarrow 9$$

Let's try another one:

$$325 \times 278 \quad = \quad 90{,}350$$

Sum of digits:

$$10 \rightarrow 1 \times 17 \rightarrow 8 \quad = \quad 17 \rightarrow 8$$
$$1 \times 8 \rightarrow \quad = \quad 8$$

One small point: In any modification, whether of two or more factors, if the sum of digits of any one of the factors is 9, the sum of digits of the results must be 9. No further inquiry is needed.

For instance, 29,304 x 16,543 x 267. Since the sum of digits is of the first factor is 9, the sum of the digits of the result also must be 9.

And, indeed, it is (no, I don't expect you to do <u>that</u> in your head). Check it out on your calculator. The result is 129,435,211,224 and, or course, as expected, the sum of digits of this result is36 → 9.

Here is another example with more than two factors, for instance:

$$145 \times 378 \times 857 = \quad 46{,}972{,}170 \rightarrow 36 \rightarrow 9$$

Sum of digits:

$$1 \times 9 \times 2$$

$$18 \rightarrow 9 \quad = \quad 36 \quad \rightarrow 9$$

Astonishing, isn't it? This is not a "parlor trick"; it is an important analytical test. Be sure that you fully master it and apply it.

As you will see in just a little while, the technique of sum of digits is also indispensable in the determination of divisibility of numbers.

Powers and Squares

You probably remember from your school days what powers are. They are numbers with a little number (it's called an "exponent") on top. The exponent tells us how many times a number is to be multiplied by itself.

For instance, 7^5 (7 to the 5th power) means 7 x 7 x 7 x 7 x 7

or 8^4 (8 to the 4th power) means 8 x 8 x 8 x 8

By far the most important powers, and the only ones that we shall be concerned with in this book, are the second powers, like 23^2, which means 23 x 23. Second powers are usually called "squares". 23^2 is called "23 squared".

Third powers, such as 5^3, which is 5 x 5 x 5, also have a name. They are called "cubes". They are important, but they play no role in what we are going to do in this book.

There is a reason that these are called "squares" and "cubes" respectively. Let me show you.

1	2	3
4	5	6
7	8	9

This is 3 to the 2nd power, $3^2 = 3$ x 3. As you can see, it is a square with sides of 3 units each. I've counted for you: $3^2 = 3$ x 3 will give you 9 unit squares.

How about cubes? Here is a picture of the outside of a cube of 4 units length on each side.

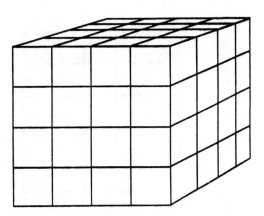

You can't see the inside of the cube, unfortunately, but you can tell by looking at it that there are 4 x 4 = 16 little cubes in the bottom layer and 16 such cubes in each of the layers above it. So we have 4 x 16 = 64. 4^3, 4 cubed = 64.

But back to squares, which is what we are going to work with in this book.

Having already burdened you with having to learn the extended multiplication table, I regret to have to put another load on you.

You will have to learn the squares, to at least 20 squared, 20^2. Don't despair, it really is not that bad. Let's look at it.

1^2	=	1	6^2	=	36	11^2	=	121	16^2	=	256
2^2	=	4	7^2	=	49	12^2	=	144	17^2	=	289
3^2	=	9	8^2	=	64	13^2	=	169	18^2	=	324
4^2	=	16	9^2	=	81	14^2	=	196	19^2	=	361
5^2	=	25	10^2	=	100	15^2	=	225	20^2	=	400

Once you have mastered that, we may later go a little further, perhaps to 25^2 or 30^2. But please try to get these down very well so that, when asked, you can immediately call them out without having to think about it.

If you look at these squares a little more closely, you'll find something interesting:

You will find that the square of any number is equal to the square of the preceding number, plus twice that number, plus 1.

For instance, 7^2 (49) is the preceding square (6^2 = 36) plus 6 + 6 + 1, i.e. 36 + 13 = 49.

Or, 5^2 (25) is the preceding square (4^2 = 16) plus 4 + 4 + 1, i.e. 16 + 9 = 25.

Let's see why that is that way.

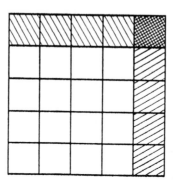

The above is 4^2, which is 16. How does 5^2 relate to that?

You can see that to get to 5^2 from 4^2, we have to add 4 to each side, in other words, 2 x 4, and then add that one square in the corner.

How about if we go down, rather than up, say from 4^2 (16) to 3^2 (9)?

It's pretty much the same, in reverse.

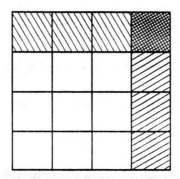

We are taking 4 away from each side. But in doing that, we have taken the corner square away twice, and we'll have to put it back in.

So we find that to get from a square to the next lower square, we subtract that base number twice and add back 1.

For instance: $8^2 = 64$.

How much is 7^2 (if we didn't know)? Well, you take 8 away twice from 64, which brings you to 48, and then you add 1 back in, which brings you to 49, which is of course what 7 squared is.

The same principle applies also if the difference between the numbers is more than 1.

Let's take for instance 5^2. How does it relate to 8^2?

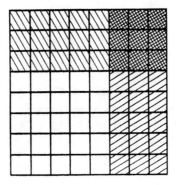

42

As you can see, we'll have to take away twice 3 x 8, but since we have taken this 3^2 corner away twice by doing so, we have to add it back in. Look at the picture.

So we have: $64 - 2 (3 \times 8) + 3^2 = 64 - 48 + 9 = 25$ which is of course what 5^2 is.

And, you can of course use the same diagram to visualize the reverse, namely how to get from, say, 5^2 to 8^2. You add 3 x 5 twice, and then add the "corner" -- 3^2. So we have: $8^2 = 25 + (3 \times 8) - 3^2 = 25 + 48 - 9 = 64.$[*]

Since you by now certainly know your squares to at least 10, you also know all squares (of full tens) to 100, because all you have to do is to add two zeroes.

For instance:

3^2	=	9	30^2	=	900
5^2	=	25	50^2	=	2,500
9^2	=	81	90^2	=	8,100

Now suppose you need to know what the square of 34 is.

Here is how you proceed:

$30^2 = 900$

Since 4 x 2 (remember, you have to double the difference between the "base" and the number, the square of which you wish to find) is 8, you get 8 x 30 (240) and then add the square of 4 (the difference between 30 and 34), which is 16.

Therefore, the square of 34 is:

$900 + 240 + 16 = 1,156.$

---

[*] Here is an important and interesting fact about squares: The sum of consecutive odd numbers, beginning with 1, is always a square, with the number of such numbers being the base of the square. For instance; $1 + 3 = 4 = 2^2$; or $1 + 3 + 5 + 7 + 9 = 25 = 5^2$; or, $1 + 3 + 5 + 7 + 9 + 11 + 13 + 15, + 17 + 19 = 100 = 10^2$. Have a look at the diagrams on page 41 and see why it has to be that way.

Here is another one. Let's try

$$53^2$$

50^2	=	2,500
53 - 50	= 3	
2 x 3	= 6	
add 6 x 50	=	300
add 3^2	=	9
Total	=	2,809 is the square of 53.

This also works backward, of course. For instance,

$$56^2$$

56 is close to 60, so we start from there.

60^2	=	3,600
60 - 56	= 4	
2 x 4	= 8	
subtract 8 x 60	=	(480)
add 4^2	=	16
Total	=	3,136 is the square of 56.

How did we subtract mentally 480 from 3,600? It's easiest, of course, by subtracting with complements. Instead of subtracting 480, we add 20, and subtract 500. Therefore, 3,600 - 480 = 3,620 - 500 = 3,120.

Let's try another one:

$$88^2$$

We know that it must be 90 squared (8,100) - 4 x 90 (360) + 2^2 (4), i.e. 7,744.

You understand of course that I need for you to do these squares in your head -- no pencil and no paper!

Here are a few examples for you to try by yourself (I am giving you a few hints)

83^2 go up from 80 -- $80^2 + (6 \times 80) + 9$

64^2 go up from 60

78^2 go down from 80 -- $80^2 - (4 \times 80) + 4$

47^2 go down from 50

As you can see, you can determine almost instantly any square up to 100^2 by using this method -- starting from a square that is a multiple of 10, adding or subtracting twice the product of that base, and the difference between the base and the number whose square is sought, and finally, adding the square of the difference between the base and the number whose square you seek.

I promised you that I wouldn't give you any algebra in this section, and I am going to keep my word. We'll express it algebraically in Section IV. But, in the meantime, really understand and practice these squares. It is one of the most common and important procedures in arithmetic and, for what will be following in Section II.

Two more things about squares:

A special case, but a very useful one, is that of squares of numbers ending in 5.

Here is the rule:

> *To get the square of a number ending in 5, take the square of the number formed by the digit(s) preceding the 5, add that number to the square, and tag on 25 behind it.*

Sounds complicated? It's really easy:

For instance, say **45^2**.

We square the number before the 5, which is 4. That square is 16. And then we add 4, which brings us to 20. We tag 25 on the end of that and get 2,025, which is indeed the square of 45.

Let's try another one:

$$75^2$$

Since 7^2 is 49, and adding 7 to that gives us 56, hanging a 25 at the end of it gives us 5,625, which is the square of 75.

And, since you know your squares (I hope, up to at least 20 squared), we can immediately and without thinking about it determine the squares of larger numbers ending in 5, such as:

$$185^2$$

The number before the 5 is 18. We know that 18^2 is 324, and adding 18 to that gives us 342. We "hang on" 25 and get 34,225 as the square of 185.

You see what wonderful things you have already learned -- and that's really only the beginning.

You will recall that we learned to get squares of numbers that had some distance from multiples of 10 by thinking of, say, 63 as 60 + 3, and of, say, 48 as 50 - 2.

Now, knowing how to square numbers ending in 5, we have another departure point for quickly finding squares and, as we'll see later, also for other things.

Let's say you need the square of

87

From what we have just learned, we know that the square of 85 is 7,225.

87 is 2 more than 85, so we have to take double that amount (which is 4) multiply it by 85, which is 340, and adding that to 7,225 gives us 7,565. We now have to add the square of the

difference between 85 and 87 (2, which is 4). This brings the whole thing to 7,569. That is indeed the square of 87.

How about arriving at the same thing, the square of 87, by working it down from 90, instead of working it up from 85?

No problem!

We have 90^2, which is	8,100
We <u>subtract</u> (3 x 2) = 6 x 90	(540)
We add 3^2 =	<u>9</u>
and get	<u>7,569</u>

Remember, you have to do this (just like everything else in this book) in your head. You know by now, of course, how to subtract 540 from 8,100. You do it by complements. The complement (to 600) of 540 is 60, so we add 60 to 8,100, which is 8,160, and subtract 600, giving us 7,560. Now we add $3^2 = 9$, and we have 7,569, which we know to be the square of 87.

So you can take your choice in any case, whichever you think is easier -- working up or working down.

Squares are especially easy, and you should be able to spit them out almost immediately, for numbers that are one removed from 10's or from 5's.

If you look for the square of a number 1 larger than the "base", <u>add twice the base, and add 1</u>.

If you look for the square of a number 1 smaller than the "base", <u>subtract twice the base, and add 1</u>.

That, starting either from 5 or from 0, takes in all numbers ending in 1, 4, 6, and 9.

For instance, the square of 41: It's 40^2 (1,600) + 2 x 40 (80) + 1 = 1,681.

Or, the square of 59: It's 60^2 (3,600) - 2 x 60 (120) + 1 = 3,481

Or, the square of 76: It's 75^2 (5,625) + 2 x 75 (150) + 1 = 5,776.

Or the square of 84: It's 85^2 (7,225) - 2 x 85 (170) + 1 = 7,056.

You now know more about squares and how to arrive at them than 99.99% of the population of the United States.

But we aren't quite through yet.

In this book, we have frequent occasion to use squares of numbers ending in ½ (.5) such as, for instance, 15½ , 74½, etc. Here is the rule:

To get the square of a number that is larger by ½ than the base number,

simply <u>add the base to the square of the base</u>... and add .25.

Also, to get the square of a number that is smaller by ½ than the base,

simply <u>subtract the base from the square of the base</u>...and add .25.

For instance:

$15½^2$ is 15^2 + 15 (+ .25) = 225 + 15 (+ .25) = 240 (.25)

Or $73½^2$ is 73^2 + 73 (+.25) = 5,329 + 73 (+ .25) = 5,402 (.25)

But here is the good news (and the reason that in the above examples we put .25 in parentheses): You should know about that .25 of course, but all through this book you may disregard it. The reason is that any time you will need such a square, we shall immediately subtract the square of another number also ending in ½, and the two will cancel each other out.

For instance, we may have the case of $31½^2 - 9½^2$.

We know that the square of 31 is 961; therefore, the square of 31½ is 31 more (+ .25), namely 992 (.25).

The square of 9½ is the square of 10 (100) less that base (10), so it's 90 (.25).

Subtracting the latter from the former, we get: $31½^2 - 9½^2 = 992 (.25) - 90 (.25) = 902$.

As you can see, we can disregard the .25 in both cases, because they cancel each other out. 992.25 – 90.25 is the same as 992 – 90 = 902.

Before we close this chapter on squares, let me show you another method of how to arrive at the squares of numbers ending in ½. You can do it by starting from a multiple of 10.

Suppose you want to get the square of 63½. First, you get the 3,600, which is the square of 60. It's 3½ from 60 to 63½. Therefore, we take 2 x 3½ = 7, add 7 x 60, which is 420, bringing us to 4,020. Add the square of 3.5, which we know to be 12 (.25). So we add that, and get 4,032 (.25).

Or, say, the square of 78½.

We take the square of 80, which is 6,400, subtract (2 x 1½) 3 x 80 = 240, which brings us to 6,160, and we add 1.5^2, which is 2 (.25). So we get 6,162 (.25).

The squares of the "half numbers" to ten (leaving the .25 out of every case) are:

$½^2$	=	0			
$1½^2$	=	2	$6½^2$	=	42
$2½^2$	=	6	$7½^2$	=	56
$3½^2$	=	12	$8½^2$	=	72
$4½^2$	=	20	$9½^2$	=	90
$5½^2$	=	30			

In each case, the square of such "half numbers" is the square of the base plus the number itself.

It's of course just like the squares of numbers ending in 5, which we have just learned about, but dividing by 100 (10 x 10). So, for instance, we know that $65^2 = 4,225$; therefore, 6.5^2 is 42 (.25).

This was an important lesson because squares are very important, both in "real-life" calculations and in what follows in this book. So please, try to really understand it, study it, and practice it with your best attention.

Divisibility

It is often necessary to be able to assess whether a given number is divisible by another one -- a small one, say, up to 12.

I am going to show you how to do that.

Divisible by 2

Chances are that you know that already or find it so evident that you never have given it any thought.

All __even__ numbers and only even numbers are divisible by 2.

Even numbers are those that end in 0, 2, 4, 6, 8.

Is 248 divisible by 2? Of course, because it ends in an even number.

Is 2,589 divisible by 2? Of course not, because it ends in an odd number.

Divisible by 3

This may be news to you. It's very easy to determine, almost instantly.

> *A number is divisible by 3 if its sum of its digits is either 3, 6, or 9.*

You remember sums of digits, of course.

Is 4,567 divisible by 3? No, because the sum of digits is 4.

Is 2,856 divisible by 3? Yes, because the sum of digits is 3.

Is 46,215 divisible by 3? Yes, because the sum of digits is 9.

Interesting, isn't it?

Divisible by 4

Here is the rule:

> *A number is divisible by 4 if the number formed by the last 2 digits is*
>
> *divisible by 4.*

If you don't already know it, here are the 2-digit numbers that are divisible by 4:

00, 04, 08, 12, 16, 20, 24, 28, 32, 36, 40, 44, 48, 52, 56, 60, 64, 68, 72, 76, 80, 84, 88, 92,

96.

Any number that ends in one of these 25 numbers is divisible by 4.

Study this list and memorize it, or at least be able to recognize the 25 numbers

immediately when you see them.

Is 46,274 divisible by 4? No, because 74 is not divisible by 4.

Is 6,815 divisible by 4? Of course not, because it's an odd number and that certainly can't be divisible by 4. We can forget about it right away.

Is 72,348 divisible by 4? Yes, because the last 2 digits, 48, are a number that is divisible by 4.

Divisible by 5

That's another easy one. You probably know it already or perhaps have never given it much thought.

> *All numbers ending in 0 or in 5, and only those numbers, are divisible by 5.*

Is 2,567 divisible by 5? Of course not! It doesn't end in either 0 or 5.

Are 2,350 and 24,825 divisible by 5? Both are, of course, because they end in 0 and in 5, respectively.

Divisible by 6

Think of 6 as the product of 2 and 3 and it's clear that in order for a number to be divisible by 6 it has to pass the divisibliliy tests for both 2 and 3. In other words:

> *For a number to be divisible by 6, it has to be even, and the sum of its digits*
>
> *must be 3, 6, or 9*

Is 13,415 divisible by 6? Of course not, it's not even. Is 23,358 divisible by 6? No -- it's even, but its sum of digits is 4.

Is 352,812 divisible by 6? Yes, it is, because it is even and its sum of digits is 3.

Divisible by 7

What I want to tell you now is extraordinary. I don't think that there are more than perhaps 1,000 people in the whole United States who know this. Surely if any competent mathematician would set his mind to it, he could come up with this rule. But right now, he wouldn't know it. Ask your high school math teacher whether there is a rule for divisibility by 7. I assure you that he/she will tell you that there is no such rule and that it can't be determined by inspection. But, yes, there is such a rule and yes, it can be determined.

Before we go ahead, you have to know one easy thing, namely the numbers to 100 that are divisible by 7.

To refresh your memory, here are the fourteen numbers to memorize:

07, 14, 21, 28, 35, 42, 49, 56, 63, 70, 77, 84, 91, and 98.

You should practice this and learn these numbers by heart. You should be able to tell immediately whether or not a 2-digit number is divisible by 7.

Now turn to the next page, in which I give you the rule of how to determine divisibility by 7. As I said, you will be one of the very few people who will know how to do that.

> *To determine the divisibility of a number by 7, separate the last 2 digits of that number, double the number formed by the remaining digits and add it to the last two digits. If the result of this operation is a number greater than two digits, repeat the operation, separate the last 2 digits of the number, double the number formed by the remaining digits and add to the last 2 digits. Repeat, if necessary, until the result is reduced to 2 digits. If that 2-digit number is divisible by 7, the original number is divisible by 7. If the 2-digit number is not divisible by 7, the original number is not divisible by 7.*

With that information under our belts, let's proceed.

Take any number, say   **9,978**

You have to split the number in two parts: the last two digits, and the digits before that. In our case:

$$99 \mid 78$$

Now you double the number before the split (99) which becomes 198. Add the 198 to the 78 behind the split and get   276

Again, split the number with the last two digits (76) on one side, and the rest of the number (2) on the other side.

$$2 \mid 76$$

Again, double the 2 and add to the 76. It's 80. 80 is not divisible by 7; therefore, 9,978 is not divisible by 7.

Let's try another one:

92,813

As before, we split it like this:

928 | 13

We double 928 (in our head, of course); it's 1,856. We add the 13 to it and get:

1,869

Again, we split the number and get:

18 | 69

Double 18, get 36, and add to 69, which gives you 105.

Do one final split

1 | 05

And doubling 1, which becomes 2, and adding 5, we get 7, which is of course divisible by 7. Thus, we can be assured that 92,813 is divisible by 7 (it's 13,259).

One more: **86,415**

It goes without saying, of course, that I expect you to do this splitting and adding in your head. O.K.?

I won't spell every step out loud any more; I'll just take you through the process:

$$
\begin{array}{r|l}
864 & 15 \\
17 & 43 \\
& 77
\end{array}
$$

Therefore, 86,415 is divisible by 7 (it's 12,345).

Divisible by 8

That's another one for which many people say there is no rule. But of course there is. And the generally accepted rule is that a number is divisible by 8 if the last three digits are divisible by 8.

But that is a pretty useless rule, because who would possibly be able to memorize all 125 3-digit numbers that are divisible by 8.

I have developed a much better test:

> *In any number of 3 digits or more, the third digit from the right (the hundred) is either even (0, 2, 4, 6, 8) or odd (1, 3, 5,7, 9).*
>
> *If that number is even, for the whole number to be divisible by 8, the last two digits have to be divisible by 8.*
>
> *If that number is odd, the last two digits must be divisible by 4, but may not be divisible by 8, for the whole number to be divisible by 8.*

A little while ago, we had the 25 2-digit numbers that are divisible by 4. Let's look at them again, with those divisible by 8 being bold-faced.

00, 04, **08**, 12, **16**, 20, **24**, 28, **32**, 36, **40**, 44, **48**, 52, **56**, 60, **64**, 68, **72**, 76, **80**, 84, **88**, 92, **96**.

Let's apply our rule to a few examples. I won't waste your time by giving you numbers that are odd or that don't end in a 2-digit number divisible by 4, because you would know right away that such a number would not be divisible by 8.

How about   **32,428**

The last two digits (28) are divisible by 4, but not by 8. Since the third digit from the right (4) is even, this number is not divisible by 8.

Another one: **42,548**

The last two digits (48) are divisible by 8, but the preceding digit (5) is odd, and we know that if the third digit is odd, the last 2 digits must be divisible by 4 (they are), but they may not be divisible by 8. And 48, of course, is divisible by 8.

Therefore, 42,548 is not divisible by 8.

How about   **23,632**

This number is divisible by 8, because the third digit is even and the number formed by the last two digits (32) is divisible by 8.

One last example: **43,112**

Yes, this number is divisible by 8, because the third digit (1) is odd and the number formed by the last two digits is divisible by 4, but not divisible by 8.

Try divisibility by 8 with the following numbers:

36,512
24,828
38,976
128,228
29,160
18,456

Are any of these numbers divisible by 3, by 5, by 6, or by 7? By more than one of these factors? Please test and mark them!

Divisible by 9

This is another easy one, though it may be news to you. It's very similar to the test for divisibility by 3, because it involves the sum of digits. You will remember that the test for divisibility by 3 was that the sum of digits had to be 3, 6, or 9. The test for divisibility by 9 is more stringent:

In order for a number to be divisible by 9, the sum of its digits must be 9.

Let's try a few examples:

11,307

No, it's not divisible by 9. The sum of digits is 3, which means that it is divisible by 3, but not by 9.

111,202

This number, too, is not divisible by 9, because the sum of digits is 7, so that is out.

226,224

Yes -- well, you knew that the third one would be charmed. The sum of digits of this number is 18, which becomes 9. So, 226,234 is indeed divisible by 9 (the answer is 25,136)

Would you like to try a few on your own? Test the following numbers for divisibility by 9:

23,655
27,819
154,348
56,763
182,312

Are any of them divisible by 3, by 4, by 5, by 6, by 7, or by 8?

58

Naturally, you realize that all numbers divisible by 9 are also divisible by 3 (and if they are even, also divisible by 6). And all numbers divisible by 6 are also divisible by 3, of course.

Divisible by 10

I shouldn't really waste your time with that one, because, whatever little involvement with arithmetic you may have had until now, you know of course that:

> *A number, in order to be divisible by 10, has to end in 0.*

Therefore, obviously, 23,460, 2,000, 840 are divisible by 10, and 15,318, 6,255, and 23 are not.

Divisible by 11

When I taught you how to tell divisibility by 7, I told you that there are very few people, even mathematicians, who know how to recognize such divisibility. Divisibility by 11 is almost as unknown, even by people who are otherwise quite knowledgeable in arithmetic.

The rule is:

> *In order for a number to be divisible by 11, the difference of the sums of its alternate digits must either be 0, 11, or a multiple of 11.*

Sounds a little complicated? Yes, it does. But let me show you how it's done and you will see that it's quite easy.

Let's take: **2,547**

In order to make it a little clearer, I shall mark alternate digits in different type.

2,5*4*7

The sum of 2 + 4 is   6

The sum of 5 and 7 is   12

The difference is   6

Therefore, this number is not divisible by 11

Another one: **3*6*,9*8*5**

The sum of 3 + 9 + 5 is   17

The sum of 6 and 8 is   14

The difference is   3

Therefore, this number is not divisible by 11

505,8*0*2

The sum of 5 + 5 + 0 is   10

The sum of 0 + 8 + 2 is   10

The difference is   0

Therefore, this number is divisible by 11

And one last one: **9*3*,8*1*9**

The sum of 9 + 8 + 9 is   26

The sum of 3 + 1 is   4

The difference is   22

which is a multiple of 11, and this number (93,819) is therefore divisible by 11.

Divisible by 12

Do you remember how to test for divisibility by 6? Since 6 had two components ("factors", more about that a little later), namely 2 and 3, it had to fulfill the requirements of divisibility for both:

To be divisible by 6, a number has to be even and its sum of digits has to be 3, 6, or 9.

It's quite similar with 12, whose factors are 2 x 2 x 3, or 4 x 3. Therefore, in order to be divisible by 12, a number has to pass the test of divisibility by 4 and by 3.

> *For a number to be divisible by 12, the number formed by the last two digits has to be divisible by 4 and the sum of digits must be 3, 6, or 9.*

Let's see.

How about   **13,917**

Forget it, don't even test it. This is an odd number and obviously, an odd number can't be divisible by 4, and therefore not by 12.

28,972

This looks promising, because the last 2 digits (72) are divisible by 4. Alas, the sum of digits is 1, so this number is not divisible by 12.

How about   **18,408**

Looks good, because 08 is divisible by 4. How about the second test, the sum of digits. The sum of digits is 3. Therefore, 18,408 is divisible by 12.

We could go on and on with divisibility, but I believe that, for all practical purposes, being able to recognize divisibility up to 12 is as far as you need to go.

But you will be able to go beyond with what you have learned so far, understanding that all numbers, except primes (patience, that comes is in the next chapter), are made up of prime factors, such as 2, 3, 5, 7, 11, etc., just as 6 was made up of 2 and 3, and 12 of 2 and 2 and 3.

Take for instance 14. It's a product of 2 and 7. Therefore, based on what we have already learned, divisibility by 14 has to fulfill the requirements for both 2 and 7. You know of course that in order to be divisible by 2, a number has to be even. To be divisible by 7, it has to come out with a 2-digit number divisible by 7 after following the procedure I've shown you.

Let's take an example: **8,792**

It's even, so it's a good sign; it fulfills one of the requirements.

How about the second test, divisibility by 7? Let's try it.

$$87 \mid 92$$

87 x 2 is 174. We mentally add that to 92 and get

$$2 \mid 66$$

We double 2, get 4, and add that to 66 and get 70. And that is of course divisible by 7. Therefore, 8,792, having passed both tests, is divisible by 14.

The same reasoning holds for 15. It has to pass the test for divisibility by 3 (the sum of digits must be 3, 6, or 9), and the number must end in either 0 or 5, the test for divisibility by 5. Therefore, 1,855 is not divisible by 15, because though it ends in 5 (which makes it divisible by 5), its sum of digits is 1 and the number is therefore not divisible by 15.

29,610, on the other hand, <u>is</u> divisible by 15, because it ends in 0 (it passes the test for divisibility by 5) and the sum of digits is 9, which makes it divisible by 3.

Without taking you step-by-step through it, you can apply the same kind of test for divisibility by 18 (must be an even number and the sum of digits must be 9); of 21 (must have sum of digits of 3, 6, or 9 and pass the test for divisibility by 7), and on and on.

This has been an important chapter. You will find many applications in your life to apply the test for divisibility, and of course it will be important as we go along in this book. Most importantly, perhaps, it will have opened your mind to arithmetic concepts and will have made you look at numbers differently and more knowledgeably than you did before.

Before we close this chapter, I am going to give you a little test. I am going to give you some numbers and you will test them for divisibility.

Some of these numbers may be divisible by only one of the divisors given, others may be divisible by more than one, and others by none. So let's have a look and determine for each number the divisors that apply.

16,284	2, 3, 4, 5, 6, 7, 8, 9, 10, 11, 12, none
28,357	2, 3, 4, 5, 6, 7, 8, 9, 10, 11, 12, none
142,511	2, 3, 4, 5, 6, 7, 8, 9, 10, 11, 12, none
14,352	2, 3, 4, 5, 6, 7, 8, 9, 10, 11, 12, none
63,182	2, 3, 4, 5, 6, 7, 8, 9, 10, 11, 12, none
155,400	2, 3, 4, 5, 6, 7, 8, 9, 10, 11, 12, none
22,378	2, 3, 4, 5, 6, 7, 8, 9, 10, 11, 12, none
62,769	2, 3, 4, 5, 6, 7, 8, 9, 10, 11, 12, none
50,479	2, 3, 4, 5, 6, 7, 8, 9, 10, 11, 12, none
27,408	2, 3, 4, 5, 6, 7, 8, 9, 10, 11, 12, none
18,816	2, 3, 4, 5, 6, 7, 8, 9, 10, 11, 12, none
88,128	2, 3, 4, 5, 6, 7, 8, 9, 10, 11, 12, none

Do you see any that are divisible by 14, 15, 18, 21, 24? If so, mark them.

Now on to something quite different.

Primes and Factors

Prime numbers are those that are only divisible by 1 and by themselves. Here is the list of primes up to 100: 2, 3, 5, 7, 11, 13, 17, 19, 23, 29, 31, 37, 41, 43, 47, 53, 59, 61, 67, 71, 73, 79, 83, 89, 91, 97.

Except for 2, all primes are odd numbers since, obviously, every even number is divisible by 2 and thus would make it ineligible as a prime.

According to the "fundamental principle of arithmetic", every positive integer can be expressed in one and only one way (except for order of factors) as a product of prime numbers.

The primes whose product is that number are its "factors".

Take any number, say   **420**

In order to determine its factors, we apply what we learned about divisibility, starting from the lowest prime number (2). 420 is an even number and we realize that it is divisible by 2. We divide it by 2 and get   210

Since this is still an even number, we realize that we can again divide it by 2. We do that and get   105

This is an odd number and therefore not divisible by 2. We apply the sum-of-digit test to determine whether it's divisible by 3. The sum of digits is 6; therefore, yes, it's divisible by 3. Let's do it. We get   35

The sum of digits is 8, so this is no longer divisible by 3. But it ends in 5; we therefore know that it is divisible by the next prime, namely 5. We divide 35 by 5 and we get

7

which is prime and therefore the last factor of 420

Thus, we find that the factors of 420 are:

2 x 2 x 3 x 5 x 7 or 2^2 x 3 x 5 x 7

Let's try another one: **1,188**

Applying the same test as in the previous example, we find that 1,188 is divisible twice by 2 and that after doing that we get 297. Since the sum of digits of 297 is 9, it is divisible by 9, which means that it is divisible by 3 and again by 3, which brings us to 33.

But the sum of digits of 33 is 6 and it's therefore also divisible by 3, bringing us to 11, which is a prime and therefore the last factor of 1,188.

Therefore, the factors of 1,188 are:

2 x 2 x 3 x 3 x 3 x 11 or 2^2 x 3^3 x 11

Let's do one more, but as you will see, one of the primes is larger than 11, which is the largest we have looked at so far: **6,545**

Since it's an odd number, 2 is obviously not a factor of 6,545. Also, the sum of digits is 2, so it's not divisible by 3. But, since it ends in 5, it's obviously divisible by 5, so we do that and get   1,309

This number is no longer divisible by 5, so we go to the next highest prime, which is 7.

You remember the test for 7, don't you? You split off the last two digits (09), double the digits before the split (13), get 26, and add the 09 to it. That gives you 35, which is divisible by 7, so 7 is a factor.

We divide 1,309 by 7 and get 187

You may wonder how you can possibly divide 1,309 by 7 without using pencil and paper. It's easy. Complement 1,309 to 1,400 by adding 91. 91 is 13 x 7. Since 14 divided by 7 is 2, it's clear that 1,400 divided by 7 is 200. But we want to know how much 1,309 divided by 7 is. Since 91 = 13 x 7 less than 1,400, 1,309 divided by 7 is 13 less than 1,400 divided by 7 -- 13 less than 200. Therefore, 1,309 divided by 7 is 200 - 13 = 187. It takes a little while to explain this. But, I promise you that by the time you get through with this book you will recognize such relationships immediately and will be able to solve a problem such as 1,309 divided 7 in an instant and without giving it a second thought.

We now have to factor   187

We try the test for divisibility by 7 one more time, adding 2 to 87, getting 89, and realizing that that number is not divisible by 7. We therefore go on to the next prime, which is 11.

Do you remember the test for divisibility by 11? We add the first and the third digit and get 8. The second digit is also 8. Therefore, the difference between the two sets of digits is 0, which means that 187 is indeed divisible by 11.

For some of you it may be immediately clear, just by inspection, that 187 divided by 11 is 17. If you can't see it right away (you will be able to see these things immediately before we are through in this book) think of the closest "easy" multiple of 11, less than 187. It's 110 (10 x 11), which leaves 77; and that divided by 11 is 7. Thus, 187 divided by 11 is 17. 17 is a prime and therefore the last factor of 6,545.[*]

Summarizing, the factors of 6,545 are 5 x 7 x 11 x 17.

Every number can be factored into its primes. I give you six examples for you to work out yourself. You always start testing with the lowest prime (2), and then work your way up through 3, 5, etc. Keep in mind that a factor can occur more than once. Check your work by multiplying all the factors. If you've done it right you'll get back the number that you have factored.

Here goes:

1,28	**77,07**
1,36	**16,94**
12,70	**1,33**

Before we close this chapter, one last word about primes. They have for centuries engaged the attention of the most prominent thinkers and mathematicians and there are still many unanswered questions. Two things about primes, however, have been proven and clarified:

❖ The number of primes is infinite.

❖ The number of primes in a given interval diminishes as numbers become larger. For instance, there are more primes between 0 and 100 than there are between 100

---

[*] To check for the factors of a number, you can stop when you get beyond the square root of that number. Just determining the approximate square root will suffice. For instance, in the present cast of 6,545, you realize that the square root (actually 80.901...) must be just a shade over 80. Thus, if we hadn't found 17 to be the last factor, we would have tested the remaining primes lower than 80. Take the next higher odd number (6,547) for instance, you will find that it is not divisible by any of the prime factors from 2 to 79, and you can therefore conclude that 6,547 itself is prime.

and 200; or more primes between 20,000 and 30,000 than, say, between 50,000

and 60,000, etc.[*]

Nobody, however, has yet found a way of creating primes or of predicting how many

primes there are in a given interval, say, between 1 million and 2 million. Would you like to try?

(Just kidding!)

Some Special Cases

Before we finish this section on arithmetic and get into the real meat of this book in

Section II, there are some special cases that I want to acquaint you with.

All of them form the basis of some of the "Levels" that we'll deal with in Section II. But

they are of sufficient importance that you should know about them beforehand; they will come in

handy in many applications.

Multiplying Numbers That End in the Same Digit

There is a simple and quick procedure for multiplying numbers that end in the same digit.

Here is the rule:

> *The product of two numbers ending in the same digit is the product of the*
>
> *numbers before the common last digit, multiplied by 100, plus the sum of*
>
> *those numbers, multiplied by 10, times the common last digit, plus the*
>
> *square of that common last digit.*

---

[*] This does not hold true for the smallest numbers. For instance, there are as many primes between 20 and 30 as between 10 and 20, and more between 40 and 50 than between 30 and 40.

Take for instance:

43 x 73

Here is what you do:

1. Multiply 40 by 70. Since you know that 4 x 7 is 28, you know that

   40 x 70   =   2,800

2. Add 40 + 70 = 110 and multiply that by the last,

   common digit, which in this case is 3.

   110 x 3   =   330

3. Finally, add the square of the last digit, 3^2 =   9

4. Add this up: 43 x 73   =   3,139 ✓

Let's try another one:

68 x 98

Without going into detailed explanation, here is how it works:

1. 60 x 90   =   5,400

2. 150 x 8   =   1,200

3. 8^2 =   64

4. Add this up: 68 x 98   =   6,664 ✓

I do expect you to do that in your head, of course. You must add as you go along, in other

words: $5,400 \xrightarrow{+1,200} 6,600 \xrightarrow{+64} 6,664$.

I don't want to take you beyond handling 2-digit numbers in this course, but just in case you are interested, you should know that you can do this also (in your head) with 3-digit numbers.

For instance:

134 x 24

1.	130 x 20	=	2,600
2.	150 x 4	=	600
3.	4^2	=	16
4.	Add this up: 134 x 24	=	3,216 ✓

And let's do one more:

173 x 53

1.	170 x 50	=	8,500
2.	220 x 3	=	660
3.	3^2	=	9
4.	Add this up: 173 x 53	=	9,169 ✓

Once you learn how to do this, it should literally take you only seconds to do something like this in your head.

But in this, as in many other cases we have already learned and will still learn much more of as we go along, you also have to think of these "shortcuts" or "special methods" as <u>bases</u> from which to reach other results.

Coming back to our previous example (134 x 24 = 3,216), suppose that what you really want to know is how much is, say, 136 x 24, rather than 134 x 24.

Knowing that 134 x 24 is 3,216, a result that you should have arrived at in seconds, you realize that 136 x 24 is 2 x 24 more than 134 x 24. Since you now know that 134 x 24 = 3,216 and since you know of course that 2 x 24 = 48, you can add the two – 3,216 + 48 = 3,264, and you'll know immediately that 136 x 24 = 3,264.

Try some of your own. I'll give you examples of multiplying two numbers ending in the same digit, and then ask you to derive another result using the first one as a base. Here goes:

48	x	88	49	x	88
33	x	63	33	x	66
24	x	104	27	x	104
57	x	97	58	x	97
35	x	75	35	x	78

Multiplying Numbers That Have the Same Initial Digit(s)

This is sort of the counterpart of multiplying numbers that end in the same digit.

Here is the rule:

> *The product of two numbers that have the same initial digits is the square of that common full tenner*[*]*, plus that full tenner times the sum of the last digits, plus the product of those last digits.*

---

[*] Remember; "Full tenners" are 30 or 60, for example, rather than 3 or 6.

For instance:

42 x 49

Here is what you do:

1. Take the square of 40. Of course, that is the square

   of 4 (16) x 100   =   1,600

2. Add the last digits of the two numbers

   (2 + 9 = 11) and multiply by 40   =   440

3. Multiply the last two digits of the two

   numbers with each other: 2 x 9   =   <u>18</u>

4. Add this up: 42 x 49   =   <u>2,058</u>

Let's try another one:

61 x 68

1. 60^2 =   3,600

2. 9 x 60   =   540

3. 1 x 8   =   <u>8</u>

4. Add this up: 61 x 68   =   <u>4,148</u>

Once you get the hang of it this should be one smooth process; in other words, you would not go step-by-step through the individual clicks. In this example, it would go like this and will take really (!) only seconds: $3,600 \xrightarrow{+9\times60=540} 4,140 \xrightarrow{+1\times8=8} 4,148$.

Again, just as with numbers <u>ending</u> on the same digit, this can easily be expanded to 3-digit numbers.

For instance:

132 x 138

Well, as you know of course, $13^2 = 169$. Therefore:

1.	130^2 (=13^2 with two 0's added)	=	16,900
2.	(8 + 2) = 10 x 130	=	1,300
3.	2 x 8	=	16
4.	Add this up: 132 x 138	=	18,216 ✓

And this also, though it looks a little forbidding at first glance, is something you can do in your head. If you can't do it just yet, I can assure you that you will be able to do it by the time you get through with this book.

And here, too, you can use this as a "base" and can easily figure out how much, say, 152 x 138, instead of 132 x 138, is, namely 20 x 138 or 2,760 more than 18,216, which is 20,976. Many other departures from this base are possible, of course, such as 137 x 138, 132 x 158, etc., etc.

How did we add 2,760 to 18,216 (in our heads)? Remember, we always start from the highest number, from the left. So our first step is 18,216 + 2,000, which is 20,216. We then add 700, which brings us to 20,916. And we then add 60, which brings us to 20,976. Really, it's very easy if you do it that way.

I shouldn't scare you with these big numbers, because this book is really about multiplying 2-digit numbers. So let's try it once more with 2-digit numbers.

For instance:

$$73 \times 78$$

Here are the steps:

1. 70^2 $\qquad\qquad\qquad$ = $\qquad$ 4,900

2. $(8 + 3) = 11 \times 70$ $\qquad$ = $\qquad$ 770

3. 8×3 $\qquad\qquad\qquad$ = $\qquad$ <u>24</u>

4. Add this up: 73×78 $\quad$ = $\qquad$ <u>5,694</u>

It's really easy, isn't it? And you can use 73 x 78 as a base. You may wish to know for instance how much 73 x 88 is. Easy: It's 10 x 73 = 730 more than 73 x 78 which you know to be 5,694. How do we add these two numbers in our head? You know how:

$$5,694 \xrightarrow{+700} 6,394 \xrightarrow{+30} 6,424.$$

One thing that you will learn in this book is to recognize opportunities to use shortcuts to arrive at desired results. Working from "bases", which may be multiples of 10, squares of numbers, or arrived at by the methods that we have just learned (same ending digit or same initial digit (s)), multiples of 5 (which we will learn about next), or others that you will learn about, will provide such bases. They will often even allow you to work with 3-digit numbers in your head, without any problem.

Here are a few examples for you to try yourself and in each case a "derivative" from the base. Remember, I expect you to do these exercises in your head. That's what this is all about.

41	x	49	61	x	49
34	x	38	34	x	78
122	x	128	122	x	138
83	x	89	63	x	89
64	x	67	54	x	67

Multiplying Two Numbers that End in 5

This is another of those important special cases which, though they are the basis of one of the levels we shall deal with, should be talked about separately.

Here is the rule of how to multiply two numbers ending in 5. It is of course a special case of the "same ending number" that we have just talked about.

> *To multiply two numbers that end in 5, multiply the digit(s) before the 5, then add one-half of the sum of these digits, disregarding any remainder of ½. If there is no remainder, "hang on" 25; if there is a remainder, "hang on" 75.*

Sounds complicated, but it's really quite easy.

For instance:

35 x 55

1. Multiply 3 x 5	=	15
2. Add 3 + 5 = 8 and divide by 2	=	4
3. Since no remainder, hang on		25
4. Add this up: 35 x 55	=	1,925 ✓

Here is another one:

65 x 95

1. 6 x 9	=	54
2. 6 + 9 = 15 and divide by 2 = 7 (½)	=	7
3. Since there is a ½ remainder, hang on	=	75
4. Add this up: 65 x 95	=	6,175 ✓

Let's try a few with two and three digits:

25 x 175

1. 2 x 17	=	34
2. 2 + 17 → 19 $\xrightarrow{/2}$	=	9
3. Since remainder, hang on	=	<u>75</u>
4. Add this up: 25 x 175	=	<u>4,375</u>

and one with two 3-digit numbers:

135 x 265

1. 13 x 26

Here's how you figure that:

Add 10 x 26 = 260 and 3 x 26 which is 3 x 20 + 3 x 6 = 78 and get		338[*]
2. 13 + 26 → 39 $\xrightarrow{/2}$ 19	=	19
Since remainder, hang on	=	<u>75</u>
3. Add this up: 135 x 265	=	<u>35,775</u> ✓

Tell me, before you bought this book, would you ever have believed that you could have done this sort of thing in your head? Of course not! And, just as in the previous methods that we have learned, you can always use these multiples of 5 as a base for derivative calculations.

I won't load your mind at this time by using 3-digit numbers multiplied as the base, but let's go back once more to 2-digit numbers, for instance:

---

[*] As you get further along, you would have immediately recognized that, since 26 is 2 x 13, 13 x 26 is 13^2 x 2. You know of course that $13^2 = 169$, and that therefore, 13 x 26 is twice as much, i.e. 338.

45 x 85

1.	4 x 8	=	32
2.	4 + 8 = 12 → /2	=	6
3.	Since no remainder, hang on	=	25
4.	Add this up: 45 x 85	=	3,825

Suppose you need to know how much 47 x 85 is. It's easy from that base. It's 2 x 85 (170) more than 3,825. Therefore, 47 x 85 = 3,995. Or you need to know how much 45 x 89 is.

Again, starting from your 45 x 85 = 3,825 base, you realize that 45 x 89 has to be 4 x 45 more. 4 x 45 = 180. 3,825 + 180 is 4,005.

(How do you add mentally 180 to 3,825? Two ways: either add 100 and then 80: 3,825 → 3,925 → 4,005, or add 200 → 4,025 and subtract 20 → 4,005. Use the method that is easier for you. But before you get through with this book, you will figure the answer to such a simple problem out without having given it any conscious thought).

Here are a few examples and derivatives to try on your own:

25	x	65		26	x	5
35	x	95		35	x	98
65	x	125		63	x	125
75	x	85		75	x	87
45	x	155		44	x	155

Square of Half-Sum

For lack of a better term, I'll call this special case "square of half-sum".

It, too, is the basis of one of the Levels we will be learning about. But it is such an important tool that we should learn about it beforehand.

It works best or would be the preferred method of multiplying two numbers if:

❖ they are relatively close together, or

❖ they add up to a multiple of 10.

The rule (it sounds -- like all these things -- somewhat complicated, but it's really quite easy) is:

> *The product of two numbers is the square of one-half the sum of these numbers, less the square of the difference between that half-sum and either of the numbers.*

How do you find the half-sum of two numbers? Two ways:

1. Add the two numbers and divide by 2.

2. (Usually even easier if the numbers are close together.) Assess the difference between the two numbers and add one-half of the difference to the lower number.

For example, let's do a couple of easy ones first.

42 x 46

You can find the half-sum by adding $42 + 46 = 88$ and dividing by 2, which gives you 44.

Or you can, by inspection, assess the difference between the two numbers as being 4 and adding one-half of that (2) to the lower number, which gives you 44.

In either case, the half-sum is 44.

And here is how we solve the problem.

1. 44^2. You know how to do that.

$$40 \times 40 = 1{,}600 \xrightarrow{\;+8\times40=320\;} 1{,}920 \xrightarrow{\;+4^2=16\;} \qquad = \qquad 1{,}936$$

2. Subtract the square of the difference (2^2) $\qquad = \qquad$ <u>(4)</u>

3. Therefore: 42 x 46 $\qquad = \qquad$ <u>1,932</u> ✓

Let's try another one.

32 x 54

The difference is 22; the half-sum therefore is $32 + 11 = 43$.

1. 43^2 (you know how to do it) $\qquad = \qquad$ 1,849

2. Subtract 11^2 $\qquad = \qquad$ <u>(121)</u>

3. Therefore: 32 x 54 $\qquad = \qquad$ <u>1,728</u> ✓

This next one is easy because the last 2 digits add up to 10.

43 x 77

The half-sum is 60. You arrive at it either by adding $43 + 77$, which gives you 120, and one-half of that is 60; or, you can assess the difference between 43 and 77, which is 34, and adding one-half of that (17) to 43, which then again brings us to 60.

We know of course that $60^2 = 3{,}600$ (if you have forgotten how to do that, go back a few pages) and that $17^2 = 289$. We now have to subtract it from 3,600. The easy way to subtract 289 from 3,600 is to add the complement (of 289 to 300) which is 11, to 3,600 → 3,611, and subtract 300, which brings us to 3,311. Thus, $43 \times 77 = 3{,}311$.

Here is one that is a little more difficult, because we'll get a half-sum ending in ½. But we have learned how to handle that, so, not to worry.

54 x 83

1. $54 + 83 = 137$; therefore, half-sum is 68½

2. $68\frac{1}{2}^2 = 70^2 - 3 \times 70 + 1\frac{1}{2}^2$

3. $4{,}900 - 210 + 2\,(.25)$ $\qquad = \qquad$ 4,692

4. $14\frac{1}{2}^2 = 14^2 + 14 = 196 + 14$ (.25) $\quad\quad\quad = \quad \underline{(210)}$

5. Therefore: 54 x 83 $\quad\quad\quad = \quad \underline{4,482}$ ✓

That's about as difficult as it gets, and it wasn't really all that bad, was it?

Let's try another one of the same level of difficulty, namely using squares of numbers ending in ½.

63 x 96

1. Half-sum is 159/2 = 79½.

2. The square of 79½ is $80^2 - 80 = 6,400 - 80$ $\quad = \quad 6,320$

3. The difference is 16½. $16\frac{1}{2}^2 = 256 + 16$ $\quad = \quad \underline{(272)}$

4. Therefore: 63 x 96 $\quad\quad\quad = \quad \underline{6,048}$ ✓

How did we subtract (mentally) 272 from 6,320? By complement, of course. We add 28 (the complement of 272 to 300) 6,320 → 6,348 and we subtract 300 from that, bringing us to 6,048, which is 63 x 96.

Two more examples, one easy one (numbers close together and half-sum not ending in ½, and one more difficult one. I won't guide you step-by-step, just take you through the paces.

61 x 69

1. Half-sum is 65.

2. 65^2 $\quad\quad\quad = \quad 4,225$

3. Difference is 4

4. Subtract 4^2 $\quad\quad\quad = \quad \underline{(16)}$

5. Therefore: 61 x 69 $\quad\quad\quad = \quad \underline{4,209}$ ✓

23 x 88

1. Half-sum is 55½.

2. $55½^2 = 55^2 + 55$ =   3,080

3. Difference is 32½

4. Subtract $32½^2$ $(32½^2 = 1,024 + 32)$ =   (1,056)

5. Therefore: 23 x 88   =   2,024 ✓

This is a very important method, a very important "special case". As you go along in this book, you'll always be on the lookout for short cuts and special cases that will make it easier for you to arrive at your result. This method, just like the others that we have learned about, is one of the really important ones. Be on the lookout!

Before we close, let me give you a little homework, a few examples to do by this "half sum" method on your own. Remember: You must do all of your work in your head -- that's what this book is about. Pencil and paper don't count.

21 x 33

42 x 68

62 x 79

53 x 74

63 x 69

Halves, Quarters, and Eighths

To multiply a number by 25, by 50, or by 75 (and of course by 100), is a special case. Because the numbers correspond to ¼, ½, and ¾ of 100.

And, as you will see in a minute, 12½, 37½, 62½, and 87½ are also "special" because they correspond to one-eighth, three-eighths, five-eighths, and seven-eighths of 100, respectively. Since we shall not be working with very small numbers (usually no numbers under 20) we shall not be dealing with 12½. But we shall be dealing with 37½, 62½, and 87½. And, yes, we'll also be dealing with 100.

Let's look at the diagram that follows. It will show you the relationships of fractions of 2, 4, and 8 in relationship to 100.

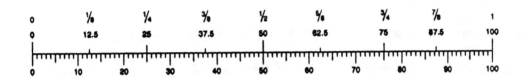

Let's take a very simple case. Assume you wish to know how much 50 x 84 is. Since 50 is (50% = one-half of 100) we simply divide 84 by 2, which gives us 42. We multiply by 100 by hanging on two zeroes and get 4,200. Therefore, 50 x 84 = 4,200.

Suppose we need to know what 25 x 84 is. The process is similar. We need to know how much one-quarter of 84 is. Well, you know of course that one way to find one-quarter is to divide twice by 2. So doing this with 84 we get → 42 → 21. We multiply that by 100 and, presto, 84 x 25 = 2,100.

Let's make it a little more difficult:

25 x 63

63 is not <u>cleanly</u> divisible by 2, let alone by 4, because it is an odd number. But let's divide it anyway -- first by 2, which gives us 31½, and then again by 2, which gives us 15¾. How did we do that? 31 divided by 2 is 15½ and ½ divided by 2 is ¼, so 63 divided by 4 is 15¾,

which is 15.75. Hanging on those two 0's (or, which is the same, leave out the decimal point) and we get 25 x 63 = 1,575.

There is another way of doing this. It may be easier in some cases and it's probably more "scientific".

If you are looking for quarters, determine the most immediately preceding number divisible by 4, the remainder is the remaining quarters.

For instance, in this case (25 x 63), the closest lower number to 63 divisible by 4 is 60. 60 divided by 4 is 15. There is a remainder of 3; therefore, 63 divided by 4 = 15¾.

Suppose you would want to divide 63 by 8. The same reasoning applies. The closest lower number to 63 that is divisible by 8 is 56. 56 divided by 8 = 7. There is a remainder of 7. Therefore, 63/8 = 7⅞.

Once you know how much 25 x 63 is, you can use it as a base and figure quickly how much, for instance, 27 x 63 is. Obviously, it's 2 x 63 or 126 more. So in order to find out how much 27 x 63 is, you have to add 126 to 1,575 -- like this:

$$1{,}575 + 100 \rightarrow 1{,}675 \xrightarrow{+20} 1{,}695 \xrightarrow{+6} 1{,}701.$$

Obviously, you would do this in your head much faster than what it looks like on paper.

How about multiples of 75, which is ¾ of 100? You first figure x 25, which means you divide by 4, then multiply that by 3.

Let's try this, for instance:

75 x 79

(In "real life" you would use the "half-sum" method we learned about. You would right away realize that the half sum is 77 and that the difference is 2. Therefore, 75 x 79 is $77^2 - 2^2 =$ 5,929 - 4 = 5,925. And you remember of course how to quickly arrive at 77^2. It's 80^2 (6,400), less (3 x 2) 6 x 80 = 480 + 9. We arrive at 6,400 - 480 by adding the complement of 20 (480 to

500) to 6,400, which brings us to 6,420, and we then subtract 500 to give us 5,920. Adding 9 brings us to 75 x 79 = 5,925. This sounds cumbersome and complicated if you explain it step by step. But it's really fast and easy if you understand it -- and I know that you do indeed understand it by now).

But this is not "real life". We are "committed" to solve this problem in terms of 75, which we have agreed is ¾ (of 100).

Proceeding as we did with 63, we divide 79 twice and find that 79/4 = 19¾ = 19.75. Or, we could realize that 76 is the largest number divisible by 4 that is lower than 79. 76 divided by 4 is 19. There is a remainder of 3. And, therefore, 79/4 is 19¾ = 19.75.

By whatever means arrived at, we need to multiply that by 3 because we are dealing with 75 and not with 25. We get 3 x 19 = 57 and 3 x ¾ = 9/4, which is 2¼ or 2.25. Adding the two, we get 59.25, multiply by 100 → 5,925, which, as we already know, is indeed 75 x 79.

If one of the factors is very close (within, say, 1½) to one of the eighths -- 37½, 62½, 87½ -- we should work with those.

Let's say we want to multiply:

37 x 81

We realize immediately (I hope) that 37 is very close to (only ½ removed) from 37½ which is ⅜ (of 100). So, as a first step, we have to find out what ⅛ of 81 is. How much is ⅛ of 81? You go to the next number below it that is divisible by 8 and that of course is 80. And an eighth of 80 is 10. An eighth of 1 is ⅛. Therefore, an eighth of 81 is 10⅛. But we need ⅜. So, we multiply 10⅛ x 3 which brings us to 30⅜, which is 30.375. Multiply it by 100 and we have 3,037½. That is 37½ x 81, but we want 37 x 81. That means that we'll have to take ½ of 81, which is 40½, away from that. We can forget the ½'s because they cancel each other out in subtraction. So it's 3,037 - 40. You can either solve that by complements (add 60) → 3,097 and subtract 100 → 2,997 or you can subtract 37 from 3,037 and then subtract another 3, and it will get you in both cases to 237 x 81 = 2,997.

Let's try one that is a little trickier, say:

88 x 94

Again, we realize that the easy way to solve this is by square of half sum $(91^2 - 3^2)$, but, as before, we are "committed" to solve it by quarters or eighths.

We realize that 88 is ½ more than 87½ (which is $7/8$ of 100).

First, we have to divide 94 by 8. The next closest lower number divisible by 8 is 88, and 88/8 = 11. That leaves 6. 6 divided by 8 is 6/8 or ¾. Therefore, 94/8 = 11¾.

Since we are dealing with $7/8$, we have to multiply this by 7, which is $77 + {}^{21}/_4$. ${}^{21}/_4$ is 5¼; therefore, 8¾ x 7 = 77 + 5¼ = 82¼ = 82.25. Multiply it by 100 and you have 8,225. But this is 87½ x 94. In order to find what x 88 is, we have to add ½ of 94, which is 47. Therefore, 88 x 94 is 8,225 + 47 = 8,272.

As we said before, there are of course other ways to solve this problem, including the square of half-sum, but in this case we are committed to eighths, quarters, etc., and how to solve it "the hard way."

Another way to solve this problem with that "commitment" is to go to 100 x 88 and then subtract 6 x 88.

1. 88 x 100   =   8,800

    But we want 88 x 94, so we need to subtract 6 x 88.

    How do we figure that? Easy:

    Step 1:   – (6 x 80)   =   (480)

    Step 2:   – (6 x 8)   =   (48)   →   (528)

2. Therefore: 88 x 94   =   8,272

Which is of course the result we have expected.

And how did we subtract mentally 528 from 8,800? By complement, of course. We add

72 (the complement of 528 to 600) to 8,800, giving us 8,872 and then subtract 600 → 8,272.

Easy, isn't it?

You can use this method also when you are not right "on target" (i.e. if one of your factors

is not exactly a quarter or an eighth), either because it is convenient or because you are

"committed" to it, as we are here and as we shall be in Level 4 of Section II.

Suppose you need:

27 x 48

You know that a quarter (.25) of 48 is 12 → 1,200. And you know that you have to add 2

x 48 = 96 in order to arrive at 27 x 48. Therefore, 27 x 48 = 1,296.

Let's try another one:

72 x 91

72 is close to 75 (which is ¾ of 100). 91 is not divisible by 4. The closest number divisible

by 4 below 91 is 88, and that divided by 4 is 22. That leaves 3, which divided by 4 is ¾.

Therefore, 91/4 = 22¾ . To get to 75 x 91, we need to multiply this by 3. 22¾ x 3 = 66+$\frac{9}{4}$,

which is 68¼ or 68.25 → 6,825. But we don't need 75 x 91. We need 72 x 91. So we have to subtract 3 x 91 from 6,825. 3 x 91 = [(3 x 90) + (3 x 1)] = 273. We subtract 273 from 6,825

(with complement of course). We add 27 (the complement of 273 to 300) to 6,825 and get 6,852.

Subtract 300 and we get 6,552, which is the answer to 72 x 91.

One more, but this time I won't take you step by little step any more.

Let's take:

53 x 71

1. .50 x 71 (½ of 71) = 35.50 → 3,550

2. 3 x 71 = 213

3. Therefore: 53 x 71 = 3,763

Easy, isn't it?

I am going to leave you with a few examples for you to do yourself. You will by now

know several ways of how to reach your result. But in this case you are "committed" to solve

these problems by the quarter/eighth method. Some of these problems will be right on target (25,

50, 75) or next to an "eighth" target (37½, 62½, 87½) or perhaps 100. Others will be a few

notches off. You will solve them by first targeting a quarter or an eighth and then adding or

subtracting the difference.

I have tried to make things as clear as possible. In re-reading this chapter, however, I think

that there might be a difficulty with which you might need a little help. I am hopeful that you will

remember enough of your high school arithmetic to be able to follow this with not too much

difficulty.

Suppose you need ⅝ of 31. First, you have to figure out how much ⅛ of 31 is. Eight goes

into 31 three times, with a remainder of 7. So, ⅛ of 31 is 3⅞. So far, so good. But you need ⅝ of

31. It's clear that it will have to be 3⅞ x 5. The first part (3 x 5 = 15) is easy. How about

multiplying that fraction $\frac{7}{8}$ x 5? $\frac{7}{8}$ x 5 = $\frac{35}{8}$. But (and this is the part that you might find a little

tricky), $\frac{35}{8}$ = $4\frac{3}{8}$. Can you see why? Eight goes into 35 four times, with a remainder of 3. Thus,

$\frac{5}{8}$ of 31 is 15 + $4\frac{3}{8}$ = $19\frac{3}{8}$, or 19.375.

Let's try another one that's a little sticky—say, $\frac{7}{8}$ of 76. The largest number smaller than

76 that is divisible by 8 is 72. Thus, 76 divided by 8 is 9, with a remainder of 4. But 4 divided by

8 is $\frac{1}{2}$. Therefore 76 divided by 8 is $9\frac{1}{2}$. That's $\frac{1}{8}$ of 76. But we need $\frac{7}{8}$ (of 76). That would be

$9\frac{1}{2}$ x 7, or 63 + $\frac{7}{2}$. $\frac{7}{2}$ is $3\frac{1}{2}$. Therefore, $\frac{7}{8}$ of 76 is 63 + $3\frac{1}{2}$ = $66\frac{1}{2}$, or 66.50.

What if we would have needed $\frac{7}{8}$ of 75, rather than of 76? $\frac{1}{8}$ of 75 would be $9\frac{3}{8}$.

Multiplying that by 7 would give us 63 + $\frac{21}{8}$. $\frac{21}{8}$ = $2\frac{5}{8}$. Therefore, $\frac{7}{8}$ of 75 is 63 + $2\frac{5}{8}$ = $65\frac{5}{8}$, or

65.625.

After having solved each problem by the quarter/eighth method, try to solve it also by one

of the other special methods that we have learned. You must arrive at the same answer, of course.

Here goes:

25 x 59

63 x 72

81 x 97

54 x 87

50 x 85

37 x 86

75 x 93

The Special Case of 37

This is a rather minor special case, based on the following:

$$
\begin{array}{rcl}
3 \times 37 & = & 111 \\
6 \times 37 & = & 222 \\
9 \times 37 & = & 333 \\
12 \times 37 & = & 444 \\
15 \times 37 & = & 555 \\
18 \times 37 & = & 666 \\
21 \times 37 & = & 777 \\
24 \times 37 & = & 888 \\
27 \times 37 & = & 999 \\
\end{array}
$$

Since 74 is 2 x 37, we also have the following:

$$
\begin{array}{rcl}
3 \times 74 & = & 222 \\
6 \times 74 & = & 444 \\
9 \times 74 & = & 666 \\
12 \times 74 & = & 888 \\
\end{array}
$$

Just being aware of this can often lead you to good shortcuts.

Suppose you have:

17 x 37

We already know several ways to correctly solve this (such as by square of half-sum ($27^2 - 10^2$) or by same last digits [$(10 \times 30) + (7 \times 40) + 7^2$)], but here we are "committed" to work with 37.

We instantly realize that 18 x 37 = 666. So 17 x 37 is 37 less. To subtract 37 from 666 we add the complement of 37 to 40 (which is 3) to 666 → 669 and subtract 40 → 629, which is 17 x 37.

Or we could have said that 15 x 37 = 555. 17 x 37 is 2 x 37 (74) more.

Therefore, 17 x 37 = 555 + 74 = 629.

How about:

19 x 74

We know that 9 x 74 = 666. We double that to get 18 x 74. How do we double 666? We start from the left: 1,200 + 120 + 12 = 1,332. But we need 19 x 74, which is 74 more. We add that to 1,372 and get 1,406, which is 19 x 74.

Suppose you have:

62 x 74

You know that 6 x 74 = 444. Therefore 60 x 74 = 4,440. Add 2 x 74 = 148 and you have 4,588, which is 62 x 74.

Or:

37 x 87

You know that 37 x 9 is 333; therefore 37 x 90 = 3,330. In order to get to 37 x 87, we have to subtract 37 x 3 which we know to be 111. Therefore, subtract 111 from 3,330. First subtract 100 → 3,230, then 10 → 3,220, then 1 → 3,219, which is 37 x 87.

As usual, I am going to give you a little homework. In the problems that follow, even if you see easier ways to solve them, you are "committed" to work with the "37" method. But, for good practice, always try a second method with each problem – and arrive at the same result, of course.

Try these:

24 x 38

36 x 63

58 x 74

37 x 57

And a few more:

18 x 37

21 x 39

62 x 74

28 x 37

27 x 74

37 x 88

The purpose of this book is not to make you a "lightning calculator". The purpose is just as it says in the title: To give you a razor-sharp <u>mind</u> and a steel-trap <u>memory</u>. And I promise you that you'll get just that if you stick with me all the way.

But even so, when we get through this book, you will inevitably also become a "math whiz" and, if you are so inclined, you will be able to "amaze your friends" with your ability to make lightning calculations. It's simply a byproduct of what you have already learned and what you are still going to learn.

Even now, when you have just learned a few "shortcuts" and "special cases", you should be able to solve many multiplication problems (the bread and butter of "lightning calculators") very quickly, perhaps even in seconds. It's something you may wish to begin to practice -- not in order to amuse and amaze your friends, but for your own benefit, in order to acquire ever-greater facility with numbers.

Let me give you first twelve examples for you to solve, on the basis of the information you already have. I'll tell you in each case what your best approach to the solution is, though in almost all cases there are several good approaches to solving the problem. And after that, I'll give you twelve more examples, but on those you are going to be on your own; you will have to find yourself which is the best way to attack and solve each problem.

So here goes with the first part:

1.   **32 x 62**   --   use "same last digit" method

2.   **33 x 39**   --   use "same first digit" method

3.   **48 x 56**   --   use "square of half-sum" method

4.   **35 x 75**   --   use "ending in 5" method

5.   **37 x 18**   --   use "37" method

6.   **45 x 45**   --   use "square of ending in 5" method

7.   **53 x 53**   --   use "square of any number" method

8.   **36 x 38**   --   use "square of any number" method (36^2) and add 2 x 36 (or use $37^2 - 1^2$)

9.   **53 x 74**   --   use "same first digit" method (53 x 54) and add 20 x 53

10.   **28 x 75**   --   use "eighths and quarters" method -- one-quarter of 28, then multiply by 3 and then by 100

11.   **45 x 73**   --   use "ending in 5 method" (45 x 75) and subtract 2 x 45. You can subtract 2 x 45 (90) by adding 10 and subtracting 100

12.   **43 x 52**   --   use "square of half-sum" method. Half-sum is 95/2 = 47½ and difference is 4½. (There are easier ways to solve this -- for instance 43 x 53 - 43, but I want you to practice squares of numbers ending in ½)

And now you are on your own.

1. **64 x 84**

2. **46 x 75**

3. **28 x 34**

4. **65 x 85**

5. **32 x 38**

6. 24 x 73

7. 18 x 37

8. 38 x 53

9. 34 x 65

10. 51 x 82

11. 27 x 63

12. 49 x 68

All of these can reasonably be solved by more than one of the methods you have learned so far. Try two methods for each problem and compare results. They should be the same, of course.

And here is something else: You should check the accuracy of your results by applying the following two tests

- The ending digit of the product has to be the same as the results of the ending digits of the factors. For instance, in your first problem (64 x 84) the product (result) has to end in 6, because 4 x 4 is 16 and that ends in 6.

- The sum of digits of the product (result) has to be the same as the product of the sum of digits of the factors. For instance, in your first problem (64 x 84) the sum of digits of the factors is 1 and 3, respectively. Therefore, the sum of digits of the product must be 1 x 3, which is 3.

If your result meets both of these tests, you can be virtually assured that it is right. If it fails one or the other of these tests, you can be 100% sure that it is wrong.

This finishes our section on arithmetic. It contains much very helpful and important material. It will be worth your while to go over this material again and again until you find that you are fully in control of it. You will not be able to handle the fairly heavy "lifting" that follows in Section II if you have not understood and mastered what we have dealt with in this section. And remember: It must all be done in your head -- no pencil, no paper!

Section II

THE 16-LEVEL PARADIGM OF MULTIPLICATION

"P aradigm" is a somewhat fancy word, but it does apply here. It is a scheme, or framework, of combinations, for use in grammar, in certain branches of mathematics, and on other occasions.

This section is really the "meat" of this book. You will find some of it pretty difficult going. But I urge you to stay with it even when you may think sometimes that you can't handle it, because your rewards will be extraordinary.

If you stay the course, learn the techniques, and master the examples, you can expect to develop that razor-sharp mind and that steel-trap memory that I promised you.

What we shall learn, the skills we shall develop, sounds simple, but you will see that it can get quite complex. It isn't just ordinary multiplication. We shall take each problem through a 16-level process (paradigm), with each level consisting of two or more steps, for a total of 51 steps. In other words, instead of simply learning how to multiply two 2-digit numbers with each other, we shall learn a rigorous scheme of 51 different ways to do that. In the process (though there may be some pain), you will develop a super-sharp mind and a tremendous memory.

Though this does not mean too much to you at the present time, here are the sixteen levels and the steps at each level. (By the way, going from level to level doesn't mean that it gets harder and harder. Some levels are easier than others. And, any one step within a level may be more or

less difficult than the others.)

The sixteen levels are:

Level 1, 2 Steps
The Easiest

Level 2, 2 Steps
The Classic

Level 3, 5 Steps
Centered Around 5

Level 4, 3 Steps
Powers of 2 or 3, Quarters or Eighths

Level 5, 2 Steps
Flips

Level 6, 2 Steps
Complements to 100

Level 7, 2 Steps
Complement Squares

Level 8, 4 Steps
Halves, Common Denominators, Halves and Doubles

Level 9, 4 Steps
Plus and Minus 10

Level 10, 7 Steps
Flips and Diagonals (Part I)

Level 11, 2 Steps
Skewed

Level 12, 5 Steps
Flips and Diagonals (Part II)

Level 13, 3 Steps
Square of Half-Sum and Centered on 50

Level 14, 2 Steps
Complement to 10

Level 15, 4 Steps
Equal Oners and Tenners

Level 16, 2 Steps
Strip the Tenners

All of this may sound a little like voodoo to you at this time. I agree that, inevitably, the names of some of these steps may sound a little bit strange.

But, I assure you that it will all fall into place for you.

What we shall do in the first part of this Section is to take you through each one of the sixteen levels, so that you understand each one thoroughly and are able to do it yourself.

We shall go through five or six examples at each level, step-by-step, and (as we call it) "click-by-click". At the end of each level, I will give a number of examples for you to work on yourself.

In each case, the calculations have to be performed by the method that the level demands, even if some other (perhaps easier) way to solve the problem may be available. But, intermediate calculations may be performed by whatever means are most convenient to you.

We shall have a few conventions:

❖ In all cases, the smaller number will be the first factor and the larger number will be the second factor. For instance, we shall say 37 x 82, and not 82 x 37.

❖ Although, as I promised you, we shall totally stay away from algebra in this Section, it will be convenient from time to time to designate numbers by letters.

In the above example (37 x 82), we would refer to the digits:

3 = **a**
7 = **b**
8 = **c**
2 = **d**

If we think of or refer to the digit 3 as 30 or to the digit 8 as 80, we shall call it **10a** or **10c**, respectively.

If we should refer to the whole first factor (37, in this case), we will call it **A**; and, if we refer to the whole second factor (82, in this case), we will call it **B**.

❖ In case of any number that we need to remember for later use, we will put a box around it, like this:

$$\boxed{3475}$$

❖ As we have done before, we shall use arrows to show the flow of thinking of how we get from one point to the next. For instance, let's say that we do want to multiply 37 x 82 by the Level 1 method (which we shall learn about immediately). We will do the following:

$$30\text{x}80 \longrightarrow 2{,}400 \xrightarrow{+30\text{x}2=60} 2{,}460 \xrightarrow{+7\text{x}80=560} 3{,}020 \xrightarrow{+7\text{x}2=14} 3{,}034 \checkmark$$

❖ We shall use the Δ symbol (Greek letter "Delta") for differences ("gaps") between numbers, regardless of which number is the larger. For instance, the gap between 25 and 13 is 12, and so is the gap between 13 and 25. We would write it like this:

Δ 25|13 = 12 or
Δ 13|25 = 12

Here are a few examples:

Δ 34|13 = 21

98

$$\Delta\ 15|\text{-}3\ =\ 18$$
$$\Delta\ \text{-}8|\text{-}24=\ 16$$
$$\Delta\ \text{-}4|32\ =\ 36$$

etc.

❖ We shall use a check mark, like this: 3,034✓, to show final results or to confirm that a result that we have obtained is the correct one.

❖ For the sake of convenience, we shall use two terms that don't really exist in the English language. For instance, in our example:

37 x 82

the 3 and the 8 would be the **"tenners",** and the 7 and the 2 would be the **"oners"**.

❖ And finally: In all cases (except Level 10 and Level 12) visualize the problem as being written on one line, for instance:

37 x 82, or

54 x 93.

In Level 10 and Level 12, I shall ask you to visualize them "stacked", for instance:

$$
\begin{array}{r}
37 \\
\text{x }\underline{82}
\end{array}
\quad\text{or}\quad
\begin{array}{r}
54 \\
\text{x }\underline{93}
\end{array}
$$

Naturally, it goes without saying (I know that I am repetitive about this) that everything you will do, anything in this book, is to be done in your head. There will be no pencil and no paper, and certainly no calculator.

Now, let's go to Level 1:

LEVEL 1: *The Easiest*

2 Steps

As we go along, you will learn many ways of how to multiply two 2-digit numbers with each other. In the majority of the cases, in perhaps as many as 80%, the Level 1 method will turn out to be the easiest. Learn it well, practice it faithfully, and you will be able to use it every day, perhaps several times.

Let's take our old friend

37 x 82

as an example.

Here is the rule for Level 1:

> *To multiply two 2-digit numbers with each other, multiply the tenner of the first number with the tenner of the second number, add to that the product of the first tenner with second oner and the product of the first oner with the second tenner, and finally add the product of the 2 oners.*

Sounds complicated? Yes it does, but as you will see as we actually go through it, it is really quite simple and you'll catch on very quickly.

We will have quite a few such "rules" as we go along and they may all sound complicated. But think of it this way: Suppose you would have to explain to an aborigine, someone who had never seen Western-style garments, how to put on a coat. You would have to tell the person which arm to raise, how to position the arm to the arm hole, etc. It would be much, much easier if you could actually show the person how to do that, rather than have to put it into the form of a "rule". So that's pretty much the way it is with what we are doing here.

We call every action we take a "click".

This level has two Steps. In Step 1 we multiply the first number (37 in this case) with the second number (82 in this case), and in Step 2 we reverse this process.

Let's go through the first step slowly.

$$37 \times 82$$

Step 1

You know of course that $3 \times 8 = 24$; therefore $30 \times 80 = 2,400$.

Click 1: 30×80 =   2,400

Click 2: 30×2 $= + 60$ → 2,460

Click 3: 7×80 $= +560$ → 3,020

Click 4: 7×2 $= + 14$ → <u>3,034</u>

Therefore: 37×82 =   <u>3,034</u>✓

So, you add at each click as you go along and say (mentally):

$$2,400 \xrightarrow{+30 \times 2 = 60} 2,460 \xrightarrow{+7 \times 80 = 560} 3,020 \xrightarrow{+7 \times 2 = 14} \underline{3,034} \checkmark$$

I show you this by the "transactional arrow" (streamlining) method to get you used to that and to enable you to perform this and all future operations in one smooth mental movement. If you try it a few times, you will find it to be one smooth, continuous thinking process, with the final result coming out very quickly.

All the operations we have performed are really quite easy and you should have no trouble at all to perform them without further ado. The only even slightly difficult transaction would perhaps be to add 560 to 2,460. How do you do that? Simple:

2,460 + 500 = 2,960; and, 2,960 + 60 = 3,020

Let's do Step 2 of this example. We reverse the action and, in effect, multiply the second number with the first one.

Here goes.

37 x 82

Step 2

Click 1: 80 x 30 = 2,400

Click 2: 80 x 7 = + 560→ 2,960

Click 3: 2 x 30 = + 60 → 3,020

Click 4: 7 x 2 = + 14 → 3,034

Therefore: 37 x 82 = 3,034✓

Do this one, too, by the transactional arrow method which I want you to get used to.

80 x 30 → 2,400 $\xrightarrow{+80x7=560}$ 2,960 $\xrightarrow{+2x30=60}$ 3,020 $\xrightarrow{+2x7=14}$ 3,034✓

Let's try a few more:

23 x 47

Step 1

Click 1: 20 x 40 = 800

Click 2: 20 x 7 = + 140→ 940

Click 3: 40 x 3   = + 120→ 1,060

Click 4: 7 x 3   = + 21 → <u>1,081</u>

Therefore: 23 x 47   =   <u>1,081</u>✓

And,

Step 2

Click 1: 40 x 20   =   800

Click 2: 40 x 3   = + 120→ 920

Click 3: 7 x 20   = + 140→ 1,060

Click 4: 7 x 3   = + 21 → <u>1,081</u>

Therefore: 23 x 47   =   <u>1,081</u>✓

Let me emphasize once again that in reality this should and will go much faster because you will be able (if not right now, certainly very soon) to perform these operations in one continuous, smooth mental movement simply by using the transactional arrow method and will be able to arrive at the result almost as soon as the problem is posed.

In some cases, when the oner of either factor is 7, 8 or 9, it may be more convenient to work with the complement and subtract it.

Take for instance

58 x 73

Instead of thinking of 58 as 50 + 8, let's think of it as 60 − 2 and use that in the Level 1 procedure.

58 x 73
(60 −2) x 73

Step 1

Click 1: 60 x 70	=		4,200
Click 2: 60 x 3	= + 180	→	4,380
Click 3: - 2 x 70	= - 140	→	4,240
Click 4: - 2 x 3	= - 6	→	<u>4,234</u>
Therefore: 58 x 73	=		<u>4,234</u> ✓

With Step 2, since the 3 of 73 is less than 5, we do it the standard way:

Step 2

Click 1: 70 x 50	=		3,500
Click 2: 70 x 8	= + 560	→	4,060
Click 3: 3 x 50	= + 150	→	4,210
Click 4: 3 x 8	= + 24	→	<u>4,234</u>
Therefore: 58 x 73	=		<u>4,234</u> ✓

Let's try another one like that, but this time with the oner of the second factor being 7, 8, or 9.

24 x 57

Step 1

Click 1: 20 x 50	=		1,000
Click 2: 20 x 7	= + 140	→	1,140
Click 3: 4 x 50	= + 200	→	1,340
Click 4: 4 x 7	= + 28	→	<u>1,368</u>
Therefore: 24 x 57	=		<u>1,368</u> ✓

104

Step 2

We now think of 57 as 60 – 3.

24 x 57
24 x (60 – 3)

Click 1: 60 x 20   =   1,200

Click 2: 60 x 4   = + 240   →   1,440

Click 3: - 3 x 20   = - 60   →   1,380

Click 4: - 3 x 4   = 12   →   <u>1,368</u>

Therefore: 24 x 57   =   <u>1,368</u> ✓

Of course, you may always decide to do any Level 1 operation the "normal" way. Working with these complements may be a little difficult for you at first, but you really should try it and practice it; it will prepare you for some of the more difficult calculations that are ahead.

So, let's try one example in which both numbers have high oners and can therefore, advantageously be handled with complements.

38 x 59
(40-2) x (60-1)

Here, compressing to two clicks, as you would actually do after only a little practice.

Step 1

Click 1: 40 x 59   =   40x50 (2,000) + 40x9 (360) =   2,360

Click 2: - 2 x 59   =   →   <u>-118</u>

Therefore: 38 x 59   =   <u>2,242</u> ✓

Or you could say,

Click 1: 40 x 59 = 40x60 (2,400) – 40x1 (-40) → 2,360

Click 2: - 2 x 59 = → $\underline{-118}$

Therefore: 38 x 59 = $\underline{2,242}$ ✓

Step 2

Click 1: 60 x 38 = (60x40) = 2,400 - (60x2) → 2,280

Click 2: - 1 x 38 = → $\underline{-38}$

Therefore: 38 x 59 = 2,242 ✓

Did you see how easy it is?

Let's do one final example, and reduce it to only two clicks.

46 x 82

Step 1

Click 1: 40 x 82: $\xrightarrow{40x80}$ 3,200 $\xrightarrow{+40x2=80}$ 3,280

Click 2: 6 x 82: $\xrightarrow{6x80}$ 480 $\xrightarrow{+6x2=12}$ $\underline{492}$

Therefore: 46 x 82 = $\underline{3,772}$ ✓

Step 2

Click 1: 80 x 46: $\xrightarrow{80x40}$ 3,200 $\xrightarrow{+80x6=480}$ 3,680

Click 2: 2 x 46: → $\underline{92}$

Therefore: 46 x 82 = $\underline{3,772}$ ✓

106

So that's it for Level 1. As I told you in the beginning, it is usually the easiest way to multiply two 2-digit numbers with each other, the preferred method in perhaps of 80% of all cases. So it behooves you to become really proficient in this method. You will be able to use it all the time.

I'll now give you a few examples to work on your own. Work them through both Step 1 and Step 2 in each case and if they lend themselves to it, try to work with the complement method.

And one last hint to checking your work to make sure that your result is correct (remember, no pencil, no paper, no calculator!). Your result must in every case fill two conditions:

1. The last digit must be the same as it would be if you multiplied just the last two digits (the oners) with each other.

2. The sum of digits of the result must be the same as the product of the sums of digits of the two factors.[*]

3. The result must be between the "limits of the tenners." For instance, in the case of 46 x 82, the result must be between 40 x 80 (3,200) and 50 x 90 (4,500).

If your result – in those exercises and in the exercises that follow and in every such

---

[*] If the sum of digits of either factor is 9, you don't have to do anything else; regardless of what the sum of digits of the other factor is, the sum of digits of the result must be 9.

operation -- fulfill these three conditions you can be almost (but no quite 100%) sure that your

result is right. If it fails any of these conditions, you can be 100% sure that your result is wrong.

Let's test a few of the results of the examples that we have worked with.

37 x 82 = 3,034

Test 1: 7 x 2 = 14, last digit is 4✓

Test 2: Sum of digits (37) 1 x (82) 1 = 1   3,034 → 1 ✓

Test 3: Limits of tenners: 2,400 – 3,600 ✓

58 x 73 = 4,234

Test 1: 8 x 3 = 24, last digit 4✓

Test 2: Sum of digits (58) 4 x (783) 1 = 4   4,234 → 4 ✓

Test 3: Limits of tenners: 3,500 – 4,800 ✓

23 x 47 = 1,081

Test 1: Last digit will be 1✓

Test 2: Sum of digits: 5 x 2 → 1✓

Test 3: Limits of tenners: 800 – 1,500 ✓

Now try these on your own:

21 x 64

32 x 57

43 x 72

31 x 83

46 x 67

48 x 79

24 x 53

37 x 92

28 x 67

54 x 61

Have you done those? Did you test them as we have learned? Did they come out all right and passed the three tests? Good! Now make up at least ten more of your own, until you are <u>really</u> confident that you are in control of Level 1. It's very important!

LEVEL 2: *The Classic*

2 Steps

Level 2 is called the "Classic" because it is based on how such problems are solved in algebra.

All right, all right, I promised you that there won't be any algebra in this section, but I just had to nibble at it here to show you what I mean.

Let's again take our friend

37 x 82

and call 3 = a, 7 = b, 8 = c and 2 = d

then we have (10a + b) x (10c + d).

(In algebra that work out to 100ac + 10ad + 10bc + bd.)

And that's what we are going to be doing in Step 1 of Level 2.

The rule for Step 1 of Level 2 is:

> *To multiply two 2-digit numbers, multiply the full tenners*[*]*, add the product of the first full tenner with the second oner. Add the product of the second full tenner and the first oner and finally add the product of the two oners.*

Let's try it for

37 x 82

Click 1:	30 x 80		=	2,400
Click 2:	30 x 2	= 60	→	2,460

---

[*] Remember: The "full tenner" is the tenner digit multiplied by 10, in this case 30, rather than 3, and 80, rather than 8.

Click 3:	80 x 7	= +560	→	3,020
Click 4:	7 x 2	= +14	→	3,034
Therefore:	37 x 82		=	3,034 ✓

This looks pretty much like Step 1 of Level 1, but only because we have run it through four separate clicks. When you streamline it down to two clicks, as you did, in Level 1 you will do this:

Click 1:	30 x 82		=	2,460 ✓
Click 2:	7 x 82	= +574	→	3,034 ✓

Whereas in Level 2, when you streamline it as we shall in a while, you do –

Click 1:	30 x 80		=	2,400
Click 2:	(7 x 80) + (2 x 30)	= +620	→	3,020
Click 3:	7 x 2	= +14	→	3,034 ✓

In Step 2 of this level, we work with complements for both numbers, regardless of whether the oner is small or large.

Here's how it works for 37 x 82, which becomes $(40 - 3) \times (90 - 8)$.

Click 1:	40 x 90		→	3,600
Click 2:	-(40 x 8) – (90 x 3) = -320 - 270	= -590	→	3,010
Click 3:	(-3) x (-8)	= +24	→	3,034
Therefore:	37 x 82		=	3,034 ✓

I'll have to admit that this is a little difficult when you first do it. You might have to practice quite a bit to get over Click 2. If you find it easier, you may at first do this by first subtracting (40 – 8) 320 from 3,600 and then, in the next click, subtract (90 x 3) 270 from that. But eventually, you should do it in three slick consecutive moves.

Let's try

57 x 73

Step 1

Click 1:	50 x 70		=	3,500
Click 2:	(7 x 70) + (3 x 50)	= +640	→	4,140
Click 3:	7 x 3	= +21	→	4,161
Therefore:	57 x 73		=	4,161 ✓

And now, Step 2.

Step 2

57 x 73
or
(60 – 3) x (80 – 7)

Click 1:	60 x 80		=	4,800
Click 2:	- (60 x 7) – (80 x 3) = -420 – 240	= -660	→	4,140
Click 3:	(-3) x (-7)	= +21	→	4,161
Therefore:	57 x 73		=	4,161 ✓

Another one:

$$34 \times 72$$

Step 1

Click 1:	30×70	$=$	2,100
Click 2:	$(4 \times 70) + (2 \times 30) = 280 + 60 = +340$	$\rightarrow$	2,440
Click 3:	$4 \times 2 \qquad\qquad\qquad = +8$	$\rightarrow$	2,448
Therefore:	34×72	$=$	2,448 ✓

Step 2

$$34 \times 72$$
$$\text{or}$$
$$(40 - 6) \times (80 - 8)$$

Click 1:	40×80	$=$	3,200
Click 2:	$-(40 \times 8) - (80 \times 6) = -320 - 480 = -800$	$\rightarrow$	2,400
Click 3:	$(-6) \times (-8) \qquad\qquad = +48$	$\rightarrow$	2,448
Therefore:	34×72	$=$	2,448 ✓

Here's one more.

$$24 \times 87$$

Step 1

Click 1:	$20 \times 87: 2 \times 80 \rightarrow 160 \xrightarrow{+2\times7=14} 174 \xrightarrow{\times10}$	$=$	1,740
Click 2:	$4 \times 87: 4 \times 80 \rightarrow 320 \xrightarrow{+4\times7=28} +348$	$\rightarrow$	2,088
Therefore:	24×87	$=$	2,088 ✓

Step 2

24 x 87
or
(30 – 6) x (90 – 3)

Click 1:	30 x 90			2,700
Click 2:	– (30 x 3) – (90 x 6) = -90 – 540	= -630	→	2,070
Click 3:	(-6) x (-3)	= +18	→	2,088
Therefore:	24 x 87		=	2,088 ✓

And one final example;

42 x 76

Step 1

Click 1:	40 x 76: 40 x 70 → 2,800 — +40x6=240 →			3,040
Click 2:	2 x 76	= +152	→	3,192
Therefore:	42 x 76		=	3,192 ✓

Step 2

42 x 76
or
(50 – 8) x (80 – 4)

Click 1:	50 x 80			4,000
Click 2:	– (50 x 4) – (80 x 8) = -200 – 640	= -840	→	3,160
Click 3:	(-8) x (-4)	= 32	→	3,192
Therefore:	42 x 76		=	3,192 ✓

I know that you'll find this a little harder than Level 1, especially Step 2, of course. But practice subtracting as it is necessary in the second step of the level, freely using the "complement" technique that we have learned. And this, in Step 2, is also the first time that you have to remember numbers that you will use later. As in the last example, for instance, you have to keep the 4,000 in mind which you are working on to work out the sum of 50 x 4 and 80 x 8 which you will then have to subtract from the 4,000 that I hope you will have remembered. When you first do this, you will frequently find that you have forgotten the number that you are supposed to be working on. Don't get too frustrated and don't give up. It's all part of learning and ultimately internalizing these techniques.

And here's your homework. Try all of these with level 2. Also do all of them by the methods of Level 1.

1.	32 x 37
2.	83 x 92
3.	51 x 74
4.	33 x 56
5.	24 x 63
6.	41 x 78
7.	53 x 74
8.	27 x 65
9.	28 x 69
10.	34 x 57
11.	62 x 77

Don't forget to check your results by the two tests that we have learned.

LEVEL 3: *Centered Around 5*

5 Steps

In this level we reduce our problem to how much the result of multiplying two numbers differs from the product of the two numbers if they ended in 5 instead of what they actually end in.

For instance, and coming back to our old friend: 37 x 82, we figure out first how much 35 x 85 is (having ended both numbers in 5) and then by how much 37 x 82 differs from that. That difference is called the "gap" and we denote it by the Greek letter Delta, like this Δ. That is what we do in the first step.

In the second and third steps of this level, we adjust our problem so as <u>to make the respective oners (b and d) add up to 10</u> and arriving at the gap from that. In Step 2, we adjust the second oner (d), and in Step 3 we adjust the first oner (b).

In the fourth and fifth steps of this level, we adjust our problem so as <u>to equal the respective oners (b and d)</u>, and deriving the gap from that.

In Step 4, we adjust the second oner (d). In Step 5, we adjust the first oner (b).

Step 1

Let's see.

37 x 82
35 x 85

Click 1:	Multiply 3 x 8 x 100	=	2,400
Click 2:	Add (3 + 8) and divide by 2 = 5(½)		
Click 3:	5 x 100 = 500	→	2,900
Click 4:	Since 11 is an odd number, hang on 75	→	<u>2,975</u>
Therefore:	35 x 85	=	<u>2,975</u> ✓

You know (or you should know), of course, how to multiply two numbers that end in 5. But in case you don't quite remember, here is once again the rule.

To multiply two numbers that end in 5, multiply the digit(s) before the 5, then add one-half of the sum of these digits, disregarding any remainder of ½. If there is no remainder in the second step, "hang on" 25. If there is a remainder of ½, "hang on" 75.

We have figured out how much 35 x 85 is.

But we don't want 35 x 85. We want 37 x 82. So how do we get from the former to the latter?

The first step is to think of 37 x 85 which is 2 x 85 (170) more than 35 x 85. The second step is to go from here to 37 x 82 which is 3 x 37 (111) less than 37 x 85. So we have +170 - 111 = +59 as our gap (Δ). And we check it for correctness:

$$37 \times 82 = 2,975 + 59 = \underline{3034} \checkmark$$

We know that's right. We've solved this problem before.

In Steps 2 and 3 we adjust the oners so as to add up to 10 -- first by adjusting the second oner (Step 2), and then by adjusting the first oner (Step 3).

Here's the rule.

> ***Having adjusted the oners to add up to 10, the gap (Δ) is plus/minus the difference between the oner of the smaller number and 5, times the difference between the full tenners, minus the square of the gap between the smaller oner and 5.***

Wow! But it's really quite easy.

Let's try this on our example:

37 x 82

Step 2

First we have to make the oners add up to ten; therefore we change 37 x 82 to 37 x 83. Naturally, the result would have to be adjusted at the end by subtracting 1 x 37 to bring us to the final gap (Δ) which we know to be +59.

Click 1:	Δ between the oner of the lower number (7) and 5 = 2		
Click 2:	Δ between the tenners is (80 – 30) = 50		
Click 3:	2 x 50	=	100
Click 4:	- square of Click 1 = - (2 x 2)	=	- 4
Therefore:	Δ before adjusting is	=	96 ✓

But we have to subtract 37 to get to the final gap (Δ).

$$96 - 37 = \underline{59} \checkmark$$

118

Step 3

37 x 82

38 x 82

In this step we adjust the oner of the lower number (7) and make it 8, so as to make the two oners add up to ten. (8 + 2 = 10) Our problem then becomes 38 x 82 and the difference (gap, Δ) will be overstated by 1 x 82, for which we have to adjust.

So here goes.

Click 1:	$(8 - 5) = 3$		
Click 2:	$(80 - 30) = 50$		
Click 3:	$3^2 = 9$		
Click 4:	$(3 \times 50) - 9$	=	141
Click 5:	Adjust by subtracting 82	=	- 82
Therefore:	Final Δ	=	59 ✓

Naturally, once you get the hang of it you will do all of this in one smooth continuous movement rather than clicking five times.

In Steps 4 and 5, we adjust the oners so as to make them equal. In Step 4 we adjust the second oner and in Step 5 we adjust the first oner. Here's the rule.

Having adjusted the oners to be equal, the gap (Δ) is plus/minus the sum of the full tenners plus 10, times the difference between the common oner and 5, plus the square of that difference.

Let's see. Again, with

$$37 \times 82$$
$$37 \times 87$$

Step 4

We adjust the second oner to equal the first oner (7) and get 37 x 87. Naturally, in order to find the real gap (Δ) we'll have to subtract 5 x 37 = 185 (the difference between 37 x 87 and 37 x 82) at the end.

Let's go through it click by click:

Click 1:   7-5 = 2

Click 2:   80 + 30 + 10 = 120

Click 3: $2^2 = 4$

Click 4:   (2 x 120) + 4   =   244

Click 5:   Adjust by subtracting 5 x 37   =   -185

Therefore: Final Δ =   59 ✓

Step 5

We adjust the lower oner to 2, so as to get 32 x 82. At the end we'll have to add 5 x 82 = 410, because 32 x 82 will be understated by that.

$$37 \times 82$$
$$32 \times 82$$

So let's try it.

Click 1:   2 –5 = -3

Click 2:   80 + 30 + 10 = 120

Click 3: $(-3)^2 = 9*$

*The square of a negative number is positive. Please accept that for right now.

Click 4:	(-3 x 120) + 9	=	-351
Click 5:	Adjust by adding 5 x 82	=	<u>410</u>
Therefore:	Final Δ	=	<u>59</u> ✓

(A word of explanation: In the operation -351 + 410, we added the larger positive number to a smaller negative number.) It is often easier to turn things around, by subtracting the negative number from the positive one, in this case 410 - 351. And we know how to easily do that: by complement. We add 49 (the complement to 351 to get to 400) to both numbers and get

$$459 - 400 = 59$$

While we are at it, also remember: If you <u>subtract</u> a number from a negative number, the negative number becomes larger in absolute terms.

For instance:

$$- 5 -7 = -12$$

(If you find this puzzling, considering the following: You owe $5 and then you owe another $7: It is clear that you own $12, isn't it.)

When you <u>add</u> a number to a negative number, the negative number becomes smaller in absolute terms or becomes a positive number (if the number you added is larger than the negative number to which you added it).

For instance:

$$-12 + 8 = -4$$

and

$$-12 + 17 = +5$$

Again, if you are a little puzzled, think of it in terms of money as above, and it will be quite clear to you.

You may be getting a little confused by now, a little dizzy, with all those gaps and Δ's. The purpose in every case is to come back to the original gap --- the gap between the result of the problem itself and what the result would have been if both factors had ended in 5. In Section IV on algebra we'll give individual suffixes to the different Δ's and that may make it a little clearer.

We have now run through our full cycle of Level 3, all five steps. We shall now do a few examples, but instead of going click by click, we shall streamline as we go along just as I expect you to do after just a little practice.

For example:

47 x 68

We solve this by Level 1 ("easiest") method, as follows:

$$50 \times 70 = 3,500 \xrightarrow{-3 \times 70 = -210} 3,290 \xrightarrow{-2 \times 47 = -94} \underline{3,196} \checkmark$$

Step 1

Reduce the oners to 5's.

47 x 68 becomes
45 x 65

Without going through the steps, you should now know just by inspection and after having mentally multiplied $4 \times 6 = 24$ and then added $4 + 6 = 10$ and dividing that by 2 which gives you 5, and adding that to 24 gives you 29, and (since there's no remainder) hanging on 25, that

45 x 65 = 2,925

To arrive at final Δ:

- Add: 2 x 65 (to get 47 x 65)   =   +130

- Add: 3 x 47 (to get 47 x 68)   =   <u>+141</u>

- **Therefore:**   Final Δ =   <u>+271</u> $\checkmark$

122

Is that right? Let's check it out:

- 47 x 68   =   3,196

- 45 x 65   =   -2,925

- Therefore: Final Δ =   <u>271</u> ✓

Step 2

We make oners add to 10.

47 x 68 becomes
47 x 63
We'll have to add (5 x 47) = $\boxed{235}$ at the end.

- 7 – 5 = 2

- 60 – 40 = 20

- 2 x 20   =   40

- -(2^2)   =   -4

- Add $\boxed{235}$ →   235

- Final Δ →   271 ✓

Step 3

We make oners add to 10.

47 x 68 becomes
42 x 68
We'll have to add (5 x 68) = $\boxed{340}$ at the end.

- 2 – 5 = -3

- $60 - 40 = 20$

- $- 3 \times 20$ $=$ -60

- $-(3^2)$ $=$ -9

- Add $\boxed{340}$ $\rightarrow$ $\underline{340}$

- Final Δ $=$ $\underline{271}$ ✓

Step 4

We equalize oners.

47 x 68 becomes
47 x 67

We'll have to add $(1 \times 47) = \boxed{47}$ at the end.

- $7 - 5 = 2$

- $40 + 60 + 10 = 110$

- 2×110 $=$ $+220$

- $+2^2$ $=$ $+4$

- $+ \boxed{47}$ $=$ $\underline{+47}$

- Final Δ $=$ $\underline{271}$ ✓

Step 5

We equalize oners.

47 x 68 becomes
48 x 68

We'll have to subtract $(1 \times 68) = \boxed{68}$ at the end.

124

- $8 - 5 = 3$

- $60 + 40 + 10 = 110$

- 3×110 =   +330

- 3^2 =   +9

- Subtract $\boxed{68}$ → $\underline{-68}$

- Final Δ = $\underline{271}$ ✓

Another example:

43 x 79

We solve this by Level 1 method, as follows:

$$40 \times 80 \to 3,200 \xrightarrow{-1 \times 40 = -40} 3,160 \xrightarrow{+3 \times 79 = 237} \qquad \underline{3,397} ✓$$

Now, reduced to 45 x 75.

We know, by inspection and without having to go through any steps that

$$45 \times 75 = 3,375$$

Step 1

Now, to find final Δ.

- Subtract: 2×75 (to get to 43 x 75)   =   -150

- Add: 4×43 (to get to 43 x 79)   = $\underline{+172}$

- Final Δ = $\underline{22}$ ✓

Let's check it.

- 43×79 =   3,397

- 45 x 75 = -3,375

- Final Δ = 22 ✓

Step 2

Make oners add to 10.

43 x 79 becomes
43 x 77
We'll have to add (2 x 43) = 86 at the end.

- 3 – 5 = -2

- 70 – 40 = 30

- -2 x 30 = -60

- $-(-2^2)$ = -4

- Add 86 → +86

- Final Δ = 22 ✓

Step 3

Make oners add to 10.

43 x 79 becomes
41 x 79
We'll have to add (2 x 79) = 158 at the end.

- 1 – 5 = -4

- 70 – 40 = 30

- -4 x 30 = -120

- $-(4^2)$ $\quad = \quad$ -16

- Add $\boxed{158}$ $\rightarrow$ $\quad$ +158

- Final Δ $\quad = \quad$ <u>22</u> ✓

Step 4

Equalize oners.

43 x 79 becomes
43 x 73
We'll have to add (6 x 43) = $\boxed{258}$ at the end.

- $3 - 5 = -2$

- $40 + 70 + 10 = 120$

- -2×120 $\quad = \quad$ -240

- $+(-2)^2$ $\quad = \quad$ +4

- Add $\boxed{258}$ $\rightarrow$ $\quad$ +258

- Final Δ $\quad = \quad$ <u>22</u> ✓

Step 5

Equalize oners.

43 x 79 becomes
49 x 79
We'll have to subtract (6 x 79) = $\boxed{474}$ at the end.

- $9 - 5 = 4$

- $40 + 70 + 10 = 120$

- 4×120 $\qquad = \qquad$ 480

- $+4^2$ = 16

- Subtract $\boxed{474}$ → -474

- Final Δ = 22✓

(How do you do this in your head? It's super-simple, of course: $480 - 474 = 6$. $6 + 16 = 22$. Presto!)

Here's another one.

54 x 83

We find by Level 1:

$50 \times 80 \rightarrow 4,000 \xrightarrow{+50 \times 3 = 150} 4,150 \xrightarrow{+4 \times 83 = 332}$ 4,482 ✓

Step 1

Reduce the oners to 5.

(You know how to do that.)

55 x 85 = 4,675

To arrive at final Δ:

- Subtract: 1×85 (to get to 54×85)   = - 85

- Subtract: 2×54 (to get to 54×83)   = -108

- Final Δ = -193✓

Let' check it:

- 54×83 =   4,482

- 55×85 =   -4,675

- Δ =   -193✓

Step 2

Make oners add to 10.

54 x 83 becomes
54 x 86

We'll have to subtract (3 x 54) = $\boxed{162}$ at the end.

- 4 – 5   = -1

- 80 – 50 = 30

- -1 x 30   =   -30

- $-(1^2)$ =   -1

- Subtract $\boxed{162}$ →   <u>-162</u>

- Final Δ   =   <u>-193</u> ✓

Step 3

Make oners add to 10.

54 x 83 becomes
57 x 83

We'll have to subtract (3 x 83) = $\boxed{249}$ at the end.

- 7 – 5   = 2

- 80 – 50 = 30

- 2 x 30   =   60

- $-(2^2)$ =   -4

- Subtract $\boxed{249}$ →   <u>-249</u>

- Final Δ   =   <u>-193</u> ✓

Note: How do you subtract 249 from 56? First, turn it around and make it 249 – 56. Then, work with the complement of 56, which is 44, to make it 100. Add 44 to 249 → 293. 293 – 100 = 193. Since you have reversed signs at the beginning, you must now reverse signs again and 193 becomes –193 ✓.

Step 4

Equalize oners.

54 x 83 becomes
54 x 84

We'll have to subtract (1 x 54) = 54 at the end.

- $4 - 5 = -1$

- $80 + 50 + 10 = 140$

- $-1 \times 140 \qquad = \qquad -140$

- $+1^2 \qquad = \qquad +1$

- Subtract 54 → $\underline{-54}$

- Final Δ $\qquad = \qquad \underline{-193}$ ✓

Step 5

Equalize oners.

54 x 83 becomes
53 x 83

We'll have to add (1 x 83) = 83 at the end.

- $3 - 5 = -2$

- $80 + 50 + 10 = 140$

- $-2 \times 140 \qquad = \qquad -280$

130

- $+(-2^2)$ = +4

- Add $\boxed{83}$ → $\underline{+83}$

- Final Δ = $\underline{-193}$ ✓

(Shortcut to subtraction: Turn it around and make negatives positive and vice versa: 280 - 4 = 276; 276 - 83 (add complement) = (276 + 17) – (83 + 17) = 293 – 100 = 193. Then turn it around again: 193 → -193.)

Are you getting the hang of it? Let's just try one more together before we go on to something else.

27 x 58

Solving it the easy (Level 1) way:

$$30 \times 60 \to 1,800 \xrightarrow{-3x60=-180} 1,620 \xrightarrow{-2x27=-54} \underline{1,566} \checkmark$$

(Remember: 1,620 – 54 = 1,620 + 46 – 100 = 1,566.)

Step 1

Reduce the oners to 5.

25 x 55 = 1,375
(You know how.)

To arrive at Δ:

- Add 2 x 55 (to get 27 x 55) = 110

- Add 3 x 27 (to get 27 x 58) = $\underline{+81}$

- Final Δ = $\underline{191}$ ✓

Let's check it.

- 27 x 58 = 1,566

- 25 x 55   =   <u>-1,375</u>

- Final Δ =   <u>191</u> ✓

Step 2

Make oners add to 10.

27 x 58 becomes
27 x 53
We'll have to add (5 x 27) = 135 at the end.

- $7 - 5 = 2$

- $50 - 20 = 30$

- 2 x 30   =   60

- $-(2^2)$ =   -4

- Add 135   →   <u>+135</u>

- Final Δ =   <u>191</u> ✓

Step 3

Make oners add to 10.

27 x 58 becomes
22 x 58
We'll have to add (5 x 58) = 290 at the end.

You know the clicks, so let's streamline it.

$-3 \times 30 \rightarrow -90 \xrightarrow{-(3^2)=-9} -99 \xrightarrow{+[290]}$ <u>191</u> ✓

Step 4

Equalize oners.

27 x 58 becomes
27 x 57
We'll have to add (1 x 27) = 27 at the end.

Streamlining:

$$2 \times (50 + 20 + 10) \rightarrow 160 \xrightarrow{\ +2^2=4\ } 164 \xrightarrow{\ +[27]\ } \qquad \underline{191} \checkmark$$

Step 5

Equalize oners.

27 x 58 becomes

28 x 58

We'll have to subtract (1 x 58) = $\boxed{58}$ at the end.

Again, streamlining:

$$3 \times (50 + 20 + 10) = 240 \xrightarrow{\ +3^2=9\ } 249 \xrightarrow{\ -[58]\ } \qquad \underline{191} \checkmark$$

So that is it for Level 3. We are really getting into the action now. If you have followed these five examples and worked them through with me, especially when we get at the end to the streamlining process, you should by now feel your mind already having become a little sharper and your memory improved. But don't be impatient, there is much more to come.

To really nail down this level, here is some homework for you to try in Level 3. There will be extra bonus points, of course, if you also work these examples with Level 1 and Level 2.

For this level, we work only with the "gap" (Δ). In each case (in Step 1) you also have to work out the actual solution to the problem. As I told you before, in most cases the easiest way to do this is by the Level 1 method -– either going up or going down from a tenner for instance, thinking of 58 as of 60-2. In some of the examples that follow, I am giving you a hint of how the underlying problem can be solved by one of the alternative methods that we have learned.

Here goes.

1. **28 x 73**   **Easiest way: (28 x 75) – (2 x 28).**

2. **53 x 87**   **Easiest way: (50 x 87) + (3 x 87).**

   Note: In this example, since 3 + 7 = 10,

   Steps 2 & 3 will be one single step.

3. **44 x 67**   **Easiest way: Level 1: 44 x 67 = (40 x 67) + (4 x 67).**

4. **25 x 63**   **Easiest way: Take one-quarter of 63 by dividing**

   by 2 and then again dividing by 2.

5. **41 x 83**   **Easiest way: Level 1: (40 x 83) + (1 x 83).**

6. **33 x 92**   **Easiest way: (30 x 92) + (3 x 92).**

7. **52 x 69**   **Easiest way: (50 x 69) + (2 x 69).**

8. **36 x 73**   **Easiest way: $(36^2 \text{ x } 2) + 36$.**

9. **37 x 84**   **Easiest way: (Remember the special case of 37.) 90 x 37 – 6 x 37.**

10. **39 x 69**   **Easiest way: Remember the special case of both factors ending**

    in the same digit.) $(30 \text{ x } 60) + (9 \text{ x } 90) + 9^2$.

LEVEL 4: *Quarters and Eighths*
3 Steps

This is a fairly easy level, so if you found Level 3 with its five Steps a little exhausting, this will come as somewhat of a respite.

This level has two parts, which really don't have too much to do with each other. The first part is Step 1; the second part is Step 2 and Step 3.

In Step 1, we locate one of the powers of 2 or 3 (or multiples of them) that is equal or almost equal to one of the factors. We use that as a multiplier, <u>by mentally going through the Power Points</u> then add or subtract any differences.

Have a look at this graph in which I have marked the Power Points and the applicable multiples.

The power points are: 16 (we won't need it, because we don't work with numbers lower than 20), 27, 32, 48, 54, 64, 81, 96.

Using these powers, you must go through the power points, as follows:

Suppose you need 24 x 32. 32 is the 5th power of 2. So here's what you do mentally:

$$24 \rightarrow 48 \rightarrow 96 \rightarrow 192 \rightarrow 384 \rightarrow 768$$

$$(x\,2)\ (x\,4)\ (x\,8)\ (x\,16)\ (x\,32)$$

or if you need 56 x 81: 81 is the 4th power of 3. So here is what you do in your head:

$$56 \rightarrow 168 \rightarrow 504 \rightarrow 1,512 \rightarrow 4,536$$

$$(\text{x } 3) \quad (\text{x } 9) \quad (\text{x } 27) \quad (\text{x } 81)$$

How do you keep track of the powers so you won't get confused while you are in, say, the 3rd or 4th power and you are doubling or tripling. Easy: Do it on your fingers! No, I don't mean that you should count on your fingers like a child. But, visualize your fingers as you go along. You think of your thumb first for the first power (2 or 3), your index finger for the second power (4 or 9), your middle finger for the third power (8 or 27), your ring finger for the fourth power (16 or 81), your pinky for the fifth power (of 2 only, 32), and the thumb once more for 64 (the 6th power of 2). That is the highest you'll have to go. 96, which you will seldom use as an anchor, is 3 x 32, 3 x 2^5.

Let's try an example:

28 x 83

We have two choices: We can either go with 27 --

27 x 83 and then add 1 x 83 = 83,

or, we can go with 81 --

27 x 81 and then add 2 x 27 = 54.

It's a tossup; they are equally easy. So just for practice (we will not do that in our "real examples"), let's do both.

1.   **28 x 83 becomes**
                                                         27 x 83

27, of course, is the 3rd power of 3. Here we go.

$$83 \rightarrow 249 \rightarrow 747 \rightarrow \underline{2,241} \checkmark$$

$$(\text{x}3) \quad (\text{x } 9) \quad (\text{x}27)$$

One advantage in working with powers of 3 is that you can very quickly test your results, because the sum of digits <u>must</u> be 9, at the least after doing 3x twice. If it is not, you've made a mistake. 2,241 of course passes this test.

But we don't want 27 x 83; we want 28 x 83, so we will have to add 1 x 83 = 83. Thus, 28 x 83 = 2,241 + 83 = 2,324 ✓

2.   **28 x 83 becomes**
                                                                 28 x 81

81 is the 4th power of 3, so let's do it.

$$28 \rightarrow 84 \rightarrow 252 \rightarrow 756 \rightarrow 2,268$$

$$(x\,3) \quad (x\,9) \quad (x\,27) \quad (x\,81)$$

We are pleased to note that the sum of digits of 2,268 is 9. So we are pretty sure that this is correct, especially since the last digit is 8, which is of course what it should be.

But we don't want 28 x 81; we want 28 x 83. We will therefore have to add 2 x 28 = 56. Thus, 28 x 83 = 2,268 + 56 = <u>2,324</u> ✓

That's it for Step 1.

In Step 2, we will locate the closest eighth, quarter, or half of the first factor and work with it. We then finish the calculation by adding or subtracting the difference between that and the real factor.

Have a look at this graph.

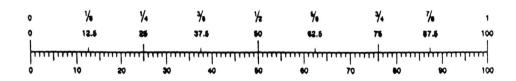

As you can see, the target points are 25, 37½ , 50, 62½ , 75, 87½, and 100. We will use the eighths (37½, 62½, and 87½) only when we are very close to them, say not more than 1½ removed. For instance, we can use the eighths if the factor is between 36 and 39, 61 and 64, 86 and 89, because it's a little tricky.

In Step 3, we do the same thing, only we work with the second factor.

For instance, let's do the same problem:

28 x 83

We would in Step 2 figure 25 (one quarter) x 83 and then add 3 x 83. To get the quarter of 83 (which is not readily divisible by 4 we can use either of two methods: 1. We divide 83 twice by 2 → 41½ → 20¾ $\xrightarrow{\text{x100}}$ 2,075, or 2. We realize that the closest number below 83(00) that is divisible by 4 is 80 (00) → 20 (00), and that 3 divided by 4 is ¾ or .75. So, again it comes out to 2,075. Practice with both methods and with the examples and it will become easy to you.

But now we have 25 x 83. Since we need 28 x 83, we'll have to add 3 x 83 = 249. Therefore (by Step 2 of Level 4), 28 x 83 = 2,075 + 249 = 2,324. (You know how to add this in your head: Start from the left --- 2,075 + 200 → 2,275 $\xrightarrow{+40}$ 2,315 $\xrightarrow{+9}$ 2,324 ✓

By the way, would you like to test the result?

First, you test the last digit of the result, which is 4. Is that right? Yes, because the product of the last digits of the problem itself -- 8 x 3 = 24 also ends in 4.

So far so good. Now do the sum-of-digits test:

28 x 83 = 2,324 → 2 ✓

(1) x (2)   → 2 ✓

So you can be almost 100 percent sure that you have it right.

In Step 3, we'll work with 83, which is the other factor of:

28 x 83

The closest quarter or eighth is 75, so we will go with that. 75, of course, is 3 x 25 or ¾. So we will have to first figure what a quarter of 28 is. That's easy, because 28 is cleanly divisible by 24; it's 7. Therefore, ¾ of 28 is three times that or 21. Thus, 28 x 75 = 2,100.

But we need 28 x 83, which is 8 x 28 = 224 more. Therefore, 28 x 83 = 2,100 + 224 →

<u>2,324</u> ✓

Let's try a few more examples:

38 x 76

You realize immediately, of course, that 76 is 2 x 38 and that, if you were not committed to solve this problem by the parameters of Level 4, we would simple say that 38 x 76 = 38 x 38 x 2 or 38^2 x 2. We know how to arrive quickly at 38^2. It's 40^2 - (4 x 40) + 2^2. (If you don't remember how to do that, please go back to the Section II.) $1,600 \xrightarrow{-4 \times 40 = -160} 1,440$

$\xrightarrow{+2^2 = 4} 1,444$. But, we must do it with Level 4, so let's do it.

Step 1

I think it's easiest to hit on 81 (which is the 4th power of 3):

38 x 76 becomes
38 x 81

We will then have to subtract 5 x 38 = 190 from our result.

$$38 \xrightarrow{\text{x3}} 114 \xrightarrow{\text{x3}} 342 \xrightarrow{\text{x3}} 1,026 \xrightarrow{\text{x3}} 3,078 - \boxed{190} \quad \rightarrow \quad \underline{2,888} \checkmark$$

$$(3 \text{ x}) \qquad (9 \text{ x}) \qquad (27 \text{ x}) \qquad (81 \text{ x})$$

Step 2

The closest quarter or eighth to 38 is 37½, Which is ³⁄₈. So we have:

38 x 76 becomes
37½ x 76

We will have to add ½ x 76 = $\boxed{38}$ at the end.

First we will have to figure out what ⅛ of 76 is. The closest lower number to 76 that is divisible by 8 is 72. 72 divided by 8 is 9. The remainder is 4. 4 divided by 8 is ⁴⁄₈ or ½. Therefore, 76 divided by 8 is 9½. We need ³⁄₈ of 76, so that is 3 x 9½ = 28 ½. Multiply by 100 and you have 2,850. Thus, 37½ x 76 = 2,850. But we are ½ of 76 (38) short of our result, so we add that.

$$38 \times 76 = 2{,}850 + \boxed{38} = \underline{2{,}888} \checkmark$$

Step 3

The closest quarter or eighth to the second factor (76) is, of course, 75. So we say:

38 x 76 becomes
38 x 75

and add 1 x 38 = $\boxed{38}$ at the end.

How do we get one quarter of 38? Easiest is to divide twice by 2, $38 \xrightarrow{/2} 19 \xrightarrow{/2}$ 9.5. Three quarters is 3 times that, 28.5, but again, we have to add 38 to the end. Therefore, 38 x 76 = 28.5 x 100 + $\boxed{38}$ = $\underline{2{,}888}$ $\checkmark$

(You will notice that we had to add 38 in both Step 2 and Step 3. That is not what usually happens; it's a coincidence and very much the exception.)

Another example:

54 x 63

Step 1

54 is 2 x 27, so let's go with that.

$$63 \xrightarrow{x3} 189 \xrightarrow{x3} 567 \xrightarrow{x3} 1{,}701 \xrightarrow{x2} 3{,}402 \checkmark$$

$$(x\,3) \qquad (x\,9) \qquad (x\,27) \qquad (x\,54)$$

Of course, we could have also gone with 64 (2^6) and then subtracted 1 x 54 = 54. Try it!

Step 2

54 x 63

The closest quarter or eighth to the first factor (54) is 50 (one-half).

$$50 \times 63 = 3{,}150$$

$$4 \times 63 \; = \; \underline{\;\;252\;}$$

$$\rightarrow \qquad 54 \times 63 = \underline{3{,}402} \;\checkmark$$

Step 3

54 x 63

The closest quarter or eighths to the second factor is 62½ (three eighths). We will have to add ½ of 54 = $\boxed{27}$ at the end.

- ⅛ of 54 = $6\tfrac{6}{8}$ = $6\tfrac{3}{4}$

- ⅝ of 54 = 5 x $6\tfrac{3}{4}$ = $30\tfrac{15}{4}$ = $33\tfrac{3}{4}$ = $\xrightarrow{\;\;x100\;\;}$ 3,375

- Add $\boxed{27}$ → $\underline{\;\;27}$

- 54 x 63 = $\underline{3{,}402}\;\checkmark$

Another one:

62 x 93

In this example, too, if it weren't for our commitment to solve this problem by Level 4, we would immediately notice that 62 = 2 x 31, that 93 = 3 x 31 and that therefore 62 x 93 = 31^2 x 6. We know that $31^2 = 30^2 + (2 \times 30) + 1^2 = 900 + 60 + 1 = 961$. We want 6 x 961: 6 x 900 = $\rightarrow$ 5,400 + $\xrightarrow{\;+6x60=360\;}$ 5,760 $\xrightarrow{\;+6x1=6\;}$ $\underline{5{,}766}\;\checkmark$

This is the kind of thing that you will immediately recognize by the time you get through with this book. Many multiplications of two 2-digit numbers have such shortcuts available. Look for them and, even though this is not the purpose of this book, you will inevitably become a math whiz.

Step 1

62 x 93

The closest power of 2 or 3 (or multiple) is 64 so we should be using it. But, just for purposes of practice, let's make it a little more difficult and choose 96 which is 3 x 32, 3 x 2^5. We will have to subtract 3 x 62 = $\boxed{186}$ from the result.

Let's go:

$$62 \xrightarrow{\text{x2}} 124 \xrightarrow{\text{x2}} 248 \xrightarrow{\text{x2}} 496 \xrightarrow{\text{x2}} 992 \xrightarrow{\text{x2}} 1{,}984 \xrightarrow{\text{x3}} 5{,}952$$

$$(2\,x) \qquad (4\,x) \qquad (8\,x) \qquad (16\,x) \qquad (32\,x) \qquad (96\,x)$$

We have to subtract $\boxed{186}$. 62 x 93 → 5,952 – 186 = <u>5,766</u> ✓

You know of course how to subtract 186 from 5,952: Add 14 (the complement to 200) and subtract 200. 5,952 + 14 – 200 = 5,966 – 200 = <u>5,766</u> ✓

Step 2

62 x 93

What is the quarter or eighth closest to 62? It is of course 62½.which is ⅝.

So we have to determine what ⅝ of 93 is. The closest lower number divisible by 8 is 88. 88 divided by 8 is 11, and there is a remainder of 5. So, 93 divided by 8 is 11 ⅝. We want ⅝ so that would be 5 times as much or 55²⁵⁄₈ or 58⅛ or 58.125. Multiply that by 100 and you have 5,812.5 or 5,812½ which is what 62½ x 93 is. We want 62 x 93, which is ½ of 93 = 46 ½ less.

Since you will be subtracting ½ from ½, you may forget the half on both numbers because they will cancel each other. Therefore $5,812½ - 46½ = 5,812 - 46 = \underline{5,766}$ ✓

As some of the other things we have learned so far, this sounds quite complicated, but really only because I take you step by step. Keep practicing what you have learned so far and what you will be learning and I assure you that it will take you, really, only seconds to perform such operations.

Step 3

62 x 93

What is the closest quarter or eighth to 93? Well, the closest is 87½. It's just 5½ away from 93. But as I have told you, you should perhaps avoid the eighths unless you are very close (as just now, when we used ⅝ = 62.5, instead of 62). But how about 100? It's pretty close to 93.

So our problem becomes:

$$62 \times 93 = (62 \times 100)) - (62 \times 7)$$

62 x 100 is of course 6,200. And 62 x 7 is (420 + 14) = 434. Therefore, 62 x 93 = 6,200 – 434. Easy subtraction, because the complement of 434 (to 500) is 66. Therefore, 62 x 93 = 6,200 – 434 = 6,266 – 500 = $\underline{5,766}$ ✓

Let's do one last one:

43 x 58

Do you see right away how you would solve this in less than five seconds in "real life"? Maybe not just yet, but if you don't now you will be able to see these things very soon.

Here is the "insight". Instead of 43 x 58, think of 43 x 57, which adds up to 100. The half sum is 50 and the gap between 50 and either of the factors (43 or 57) is 7. So, by the rule of square of half sum that we have learned (if you don't quite remember go back and review it – it's really quite important) 43 x 57 is $50^2 – 7^2 = 2,500 – 49 = 2,451$. We need 43 x 58, so we'll have to add 1 x 43 = 43 and get <u>2,494</u> ✓

But once again, this is not "real life". We are committed to solve this problem by Level 4 method. I just wanted to show you the kind of thing you should look out for if you had to solve such a problem the quickest and easiest way.

But back to Level 4.

Step 1

43 x 58

The closest or most convenient power of 2 or 3 (or multiple) to 58 might be 48 (3×2^4) or 64 (2^6). I think we should go for 48 because of the convenience. It is 10 x 43 = $\boxed{430}$ less than 43 x 58 and we will therefore have to add that at the end. And of course it's easy to multiply numbers by ten (just hang on a zero) and we add that at the end.

So let's do 43 x 58 via 43 x 48:

$$43 \xrightarrow{x2} 86 \xrightarrow{x2} 172 \xrightarrow{x2} 344 \xrightarrow{x2} 688 \xrightarrow{x3} 2,064 \xrightarrow{+[430]} 2,494 ✓$$

$$(x 2) \qquad (x 4) \qquad (x 8) \qquad (x 16) \qquad (x 48)$$

Step 2

43 x 58

The closest quarter or eighth to 43 is 50, which is ½ (of 100). One-half of 58 is 29. Therefore, 50 x 58 = 2,900. We need 43 x 58 which is 7 x 58 less. How do we multiply, mentally, 7 x 58? (7 x 50) → 350 → + (7 x 8) = 56 → 406. Therefore, 43 x 58 = 2,900 – 406 = <u>2,494</u> ✓

You can subtract 406 from 2,900 either by complement, adding 94: 2,994 - 500 = 2,494, or subtracting 400 from 2,900, which brings you to 2,500 and then subtracting 6, which also gives you the final result of <u>2,494</u> ✓

Step 3

43 x 58

The closest quarter or eighth to 58 is 62½ , but we have agreed that we shall avoid those eighths unless we are very close. So here, too, we'll work with 50 = ½ x 100.

One half of 43 is 21½ so 50 x 43 = 2,150. We need 43 x 58 which is 8 times 43 = 344 more. Therefore, 43 x 58 = 2,150 +344 = <u>2,494</u> ✓

So this was Level 4. I don't think it was too difficult. Don't you agree? And here are ten homework problems for you to solve by Level 4. Take the time and try to solve them also by the first three levels. You can use the practice. Finally, look at each problem to see whether, if you were not constrained by the level you are expected to be working in, you can find an easier solution to it.

1.	46 x 82
2.	34 x 87
3.	25 x 76
4.	51 x 83
5.	54 x 72
6.	28 x 57
7.	42 x 93
8.	67 x 78
9.	52 x 83
10.	24 x 56

LEVEL 5: *Flips*

2 Steps

This level has two steps – the second being the reverse of the first.

We multiply our two numbers by (in the first step) "flipping" the smaller number (A) and multiplying it with the number itself, then adding (or subtracting) the product of the "gap" (Δ) between the larger number (B) and the flip of the smaller number with the smaller number.

In the second step, we "flip" the larger number (B), multiplying it with the number itself then adding (or subtracting) the product of the "gap" (Δ) between the smaller number (A) and the flip of the larger with the larger number.

What is a flip?

It is a concept that we shall have much more to say about in future levels, especially in Levels 10 and 12. In this level, we are dealing with a "horizontal flip," by simply exchanging the tenner and the oner of a number. For instance, "flipping" 83, we get 38. Flipping 29, we get 92, etc. Flipping 33 or 77, still yields 33 or 77.

Here is the rule:

> *You multiple a number with its flip by multiplying the flipped full tenners*
>
> *and adding the sum of the squares of the (flipped) oners, multiplied by ten,*
>
> *and finally adding the product of the (flipped) oners.*

For instance, take 43.

Flipped it becomes 34.

Now, multiplying

43 x (flipped becomes) 34

1. Multiply the (flipped) full tenners: 40 x 30   →   1,200

2. The sum of the squares of the (flipped) oners x 10:

    $3^2 \times 4^2 = 9 + 16 \xrightarrow{\text{x10}}$ →   250

3. Product of the oners: 3 x 4   →   <u>12</u>

4. Add it all up: 43 x 34   →   <u>1,462</u> ✓

Another one:

73 x (flipped becomes) 37

1. Product of the (flipped) full tenners: 70 x 30   →   2,100

2. Sum of squares of the (flipped) oners x 10: (9 + 49) x 10   →   580

3. Product of the oners: 7 x 3   →   <u>21</u>

4. Add it all up: 73 x 37   →   <u>2,701</u> ✓

Naturally, you would be doing all of this in your head

One last one, and let's streamline it:

48 x (flipped becomes) 84

40 x 80 → 3,200 $\xrightarrow{+(16+64)\text{x}10=800}$ 4,000 $\xrightarrow{+8\text{x}4=32}$ →   <u>4,032</u> ✓

But these flips are only the first part of a problem.

Take the first example 43 and assume that the <u>real problem</u> was

43 x 76

We are committed (by Level 5) to first figure out what 43 x 34 is. We already have done that; it is $\boxed{1,462}$. But we need 43 x 76, which is 42 x 43 more. We are under no constraint as to how to solve that part and we'll use the easiest way to do it.

With what we've found so far, we can readily see that there are two easy and quick ways to solve 42 x 43.

1. We take the square of 42 (42 x 42) and add 1 x 42. So this is $(40^2 + 4 \times 40 + 2^2) = 1,764 + 42 = \boxed{1,806}$, or

2. We use the same-first-digit method, by which $42 \times 43 = 40^2 + (2 \times 3) \, 40 + (2 \times 3) = 1,600 + 200 + 6 = \boxed{1,806}$.

I am going into all this detail in order to alert you to always try to find a short cut or the easiest way of how to solve a problem.

But back to our real problem:

43 x 76

The answer is:

1.	43 x 34	$\rightarrow$	$\boxed{1,462}$
2.	43 x 42	$\rightarrow$	+1,806
3.	Add it up: 43 x 76	$\rightarrow$	3,268✓

That was Step 1.

For Step 2, we turn it around, which means that we flip 76 instead of 43. So we have…

43 x 76 becomes
76 x 67

148

So, as first click we have to flip 76 and multiply

76 x 67

Streamlining it (using Level 5) we get:

$$70 \times 60 \rightarrow 4{,}200 \xrightarrow{\ +(6^2+7^2)\times10=850\ } 5{,}050 \xrightarrow{\ +6\times7=42\ } \boxed{5{,}092}.$$

But we don't want 67 x 76. We want 43 x 76, which is 24 x 76 less than 5,092.

There are two easy ways to figure 24 x 76. Can you see them?

1. 24 + 76 = 100, which makes square-of-half-sum easy. One half of 100 is 50, and its square is 2,500. Δ (50 | 24) or (76 | 50) = 26. Its square (you know that, don't you?) is 676. Therefore, 24 x 76 = 2,500 – 676 = $\boxed{1{,}824}$.

2. 24 x 76 = (25 x 76) – (1 x 76). We learned in Level 4 how to quickly figure one-quarter (.25) of 76 (00). It's 76 (00) divided by 2 and again by 2, which is 1,900. We have to subtract 1 x 76 = 76; 1,900 – 76 = $\boxed{1{,}824}$.

We have to subtract $\boxed{1{,}824}$ from $\boxed{5{,}092}$, which brings us to the result: 43 x 76 = <u>3,268</u> ✓

(How do you, mentally, subtract 1,824 from 5,092? You don't have to cross a threshold and you therefore need not work with complements. You start, as we always do in such mental calculations, from the left: 50 – 18 = 32 $\rightarrow$ 3,200. 92 – 24: 92 – 20 – 4 $\rightarrow$ 72 $\rightarrow$ 68. Therefore, 5,096 – 1,824 = 3,268).

Note something: Δ_1 for Step 1 was 42; Δ_2 for Step 2 was 24. 24 is the flip of 42. Is that a coincidence? We'll come back to that in our algebra section.

Another example:

Step 1

**57 x 84 becomes
57 x 75**

We'll have to add 9 x 57 = $\boxed{513}$ at the end to get from 57 x 75 to 57 x 84.

Streamlining: 50 x 70 → 3,500 $\xrightarrow{+(5^2+7^2)\times10=740}$ 4,240 $\xrightarrow{+7\times5=35}$ 4,275 $\xrightarrow{+[513]}$ $\underline{4,788}$✓

Step 2

57 x 84 becomes
48 x 84

Well have to add 9 x 84 = $\boxed{756}$ at the end to get from 48 x 84 to 57 x 84.

Streamlining: 40 x 80 → 3,200 $\xrightarrow{(8^2+4^2)\times10=800}$ 4,000 $\xrightarrow{+8\times4=32}$ 4,032 $\xrightarrow{+[756]}$ $\underline{4,788}$✓

Let's look at these Δ's. Δ_1 is $(75 \mid 84) = 9$ and Δ_2 is $(48 \mid 57) = 9$. Are the two Δ's always the same?

Not quite. We'll have more to say about this later in this level and even more in our algebra section.

Let's do a couple more:

Step 1

31 x 49 becomes
31 x 13

Δ_1 is $(49 \mid 13) = 36$ so we'll need to add 31 x 36 = $\boxed{1,116}$ at the end to get from 31 x 13 to

31 x 49. Or, we can think of 49 as $(52 - 3)$. And, 52 is (4×13). So, in order to arrive at the

result, we quadruple 31 x 13 and subtract 3 x 31 = 93.

Let' do it.

1. 31 x 13

30 x 10 → 300 $\xrightarrow{+(3^2+1^2)\times10=100}$ 400 $\xrightarrow{+1\times3=3}$ $\boxed{403}$

2. 31 x 49

31 x 13 → $\boxed{403}$ $\xrightarrow{\text{x 4}}$ 1,612 $\xrightarrow{-3\times31=-93}$ 1,519 ✓

Step 2

31 x 49 becomes
94 x 49

Δ_2 is $(94\,|\,31) = 63$.

How do we get from 94 x 49 to 31 x 49? The best way is to subtract 1 x 49 = 49 from our intermediate result of 94 x 49, which brings us to 93 x 49. We divide that by 3, which brings us to where we want to be: 31 x 49.

1. 94 x 49

90 x 40 → 3,600 $\xrightarrow{+(9^2+4^2)\times10=970}$ 4,570 $\xrightarrow{+4\times9=36}$ $\boxed{4,606}$

2. 31 x 49

94 x 49 → 4,606 $\xrightarrow{-1\times49=-49}$ 4,557 $\xrightarrow{/3}$ 1,519 ✓

What were the Δ's? Δ_1 $(49\,|\,13) = 36$ in Step 1, and Δ_2 $(94\,|\,31) = 63$ in Step 2, the flip of each other.

And, one more:

Step 1

69 x 82 becomes
69 x 96

Δ_1 is $(96\,|\,82) = 14$. We'll have to subtract 69 x 14 = $\boxed{966}$ at the end to get to 69 x 82.

How do you figure 69 x 14? Easy: 70 x 14 = 980. In order to get to 69 x 14 subtract

$$1 \times 14 = 14 \rightarrow 966.$$

Let's streamline the whole problem without stopping at 69 x 96.

$$60 \times 90 \rightarrow 5,400 \xrightarrow{+(9^2+6^2)\times10=1,170} 6,570 \xrightarrow{+9\times6=54} 6,624 \xrightarrow{-[966]} \underline{5,658} \checkmark$$

And, of course: to subtract 966 from 6,624, you add 34 and subtract 1,000. $6,624 + 34 - 100 = \underline{5,658}$ ✓

And now for

Step 2

69 x 82 becomes
28 x 82

Δ_2 is $(69 \mid 28) = 41$. Again, it is the flip of Δ_1 which was 14.

How do we get from 28 x 82 to where we need to be, to 69 x 82? We realize that $28 = 2 \times 14$ and that 70 (which is 1 away from 69) is 5 x 14. Therefore, the easy way is to divide the result of 28 x 82 by 2 (bringing us to 14 x 82) then multiply it by 5, (which brings us to 70 x 82), and finally subtracting 1 x 82 = 82 from the result.

Here we go:

$$20 \times 80 \rightarrow 1,600 \xrightarrow{+(8^2+2^2)\times10=680} 2,280 \xrightarrow{+2\times8=16} 2,296 \xrightarrow{/2} 1,148 \xrightarrow{\times5}$$

$$5,740 \xrightarrow{-82} \underline{5,658} \checkmark$$

And one final one:

Step 1

29 x 68 becomes
29 x 92

Once we have arrived at 29 x 92, which we shall do in a minute, we'll have to figure how to get from there (29 x 92) to where we really want to be, namely 29 x 68.

29 x 68 is 29 x 24 less than 29 x 92. So 29 x 24 is what we have to subtract.

There are several ways to multiply 29 x 24, of course. The easy ways are:

1. Same first-digit method: $20^2 \rightarrow 400 \xrightarrow{+20(9+4)=260} 660 \xrightarrow{+9 \times 4=36}$ $\boxed{696}$, or

2. $29 \times 24 = (30 \times 24) - (1 \times 24) = 720 - 24 = \boxed{696}$

Take your choice.

Now let's figure 29 x 68, by first arriving at 29 x 92 and then subtracting $\boxed{696}$.

1.	20 x 90	$\rightarrow$	1,800
2.	$(9^2 + 2^2) \times 10 = (81 + 4) \times 10 = 850$	$\rightarrow$	2,650
3.	9 x 2 $\quad = 18$	$\rightarrow$	2,668
4.	Subtract $\boxed{696}$	$\rightarrow$	<u>1,972</u> ✓

How do you subtract 696 from 2,668? Easy as pie, of course: Add complement of 4 to bring it to 700. Therefore, $2,668 - 696 = 2,672 - 700 = 1,972$ ✓

Step 2

29 x 68 becomes
86 x 68

Once we've figured 86 x 68, how do we get to 29 x 68? Here is the easy way, and once you are a little further down the road, you'll see that right away. 87 is 3 x 29, and it's just 1 away from 86. So, once we've figured 86 x 68, all we have to do is add 1 x 68 = 68 and divide by 3.

Let's do it.

86 x 68

$80 \times 60 \rightarrow 4{,}800 \xrightarrow{\ +(6^2+8^2)\times10=1{,}000\ } 5{,}800 \xrightarrow{\ +6\times8=48\ } 5{,}848 \xrightarrow{\ +1\times68=68\ } 5{,}916$

$\xrightarrow{\ /3\ } \underline{1{,}972}\ \checkmark$

(How do we mentally divide 5,916 by 3? We have learned how, but let's repeat it here.

- You divide the number into two parts: 59 (00) and 16.

- We find that 59 is not divisible by 3. The closest lower number divisible by 3 is 57: 5,700 divided by 3 is 1,900.

- That leaves 216. Maybe you can see right away (and if you cannot, you will very soon) that 216 divided by 3 is 72. If you can't see it right away, split 216 into 210 and 6 and it will become clear that it is 70 + 2 = 72.

- Therefore, 5916 divided by 3 is 1,972.)

Δ_1 in Step 1 was 24; Δ_2 in Step 2 it was 57. How come? We've come to believe that Δ_2 will always be the flip of Δ_1 if Δ is a 2-digit number or the same if Δ is a 1 digit number. Is that not always the case? No, not really. Most of the time (with random numbers, five times out of nine or 56% of the time) they will be flips. But four times out of nine of the cases (44% of the time), they will not be flips. We'll talk about that in Section IV on algebra.

So this is it for Level 5. To work with flips is great exercise, so practice this level at home, just as you have practiced previous levels, until you are really anchored in it. You will get to use "flipping" more thoroughly in Level 10 and in Level 12.

154

As usual, I am going to give you a little homework. Work each of the examples by the Level 5 method. In each case, after you have established the Δ for each of the two steps, find the easiest way of how to get from the flipped multiplier to the multiplier you really need, as posed by the problem.

Then, go back over the exercise problems and also work each one of them by the previous four levels that you have learned. And finally, look at them and ask yourself if this were "real life", how you could most easily solve each problem without the constraints of the levels. Usually, you'll find that it will be by the Level 1 method, but give it thought and you might find other approaches.

Here are your exercise problems.

1.	38 x 67
2.	59 x 84
3.	21 x 92
4.	46 x 79
5.	35 x 72
6.	28 x 59
7.	47 x 67
8.	52 x 63
9.	24 x 81
10.	34 x 59

LEVEL 6: *Complements to 100*
2 Steps

This level also has only two steps. You will find it a little easier than Level 5.[1]

In Step 1, we multiply the lower number by 100 (hang on two zeros), then subtract from it that number times the complement (to 100) of the higher number. In Step 2, we do the opposite: We multiply the higher number by 100 (hang on two zeros), and subtract from it that number times the complement (to 100) of the lower number.

It's easiest to learn by example.

Let's take our old friend

37 x 82

In Step 1, we take the lower number (37) and multiply it by 100, which yields 3,700. We then take the complement of the higher number (82), which is 18. We multiply 37 x 18, which is 666.[2] We subtract that from 3,700 and get 3,034.[3]

You know, of course, how to subtract 5,166 from 8,200, but let's go through it together anyway: $8,200 \xrightarrow{-5,000} 3,200 \xrightarrow{-100} 3,100 \xrightarrow{-66} \underline{3,034} \checkmark$

---

(1) There's also a third step, a "bonus step." Turn to page 454 for it.

(2) Remember the special case of 37? 3 x 37 = 111; 6 x 37 = 222, etc. Since 18 = 6 x 3, 37 x 18 = 666.

(3) How to subtract (mentally) 666 from 3,700: $\xrightarrow{3,700-600} 3,100 \xrightarrow{-60} 3,040 \xrightarrow{-6} \underline{3,034}\checkmark$, or 3,700 + 34 (complement) = 3,734. 3,734 − 700 = $\underline{3,034}$ $\checkmark$

156

In Step 2, we turn it around. We multiply 82 x 100 which yields 8,200. We then take the complement of the lower number (37), which is 63. We multiply 82 x 63[1], which is 5,166. We subtract 5,166 from 8,700 and get 3,034.

Let's put it in the form of a rule.

> *To multiply two 2-digit numbers with each other, multiply either number by*
>
> *100 and subtract the product of that number and the complement (to 100) of*
>
> *the other number.*

Let's take a few examples.

39 x 52

Step 1

39 x 52
(100 x 39) – 39 (100 – 52)

Click 1:	100 x 39			→	3,900
Click 2:	100 – 52	→	48		
Click 3:	-48 x 39			→	-1,872
Click 4:	39 x 52			→	2,028✓

---

(1) The easiest way to multiply 82 x 63 is by Level 1 method, as follows: 80 x 60 → 4,800
$\xrightarrow{+80\times3=240}$ 5,040 $\xrightarrow{+2\times63=126}$ 5,166 ✓

Step 2

39 x 52
(100 x 52) – 52 (100 - 39)

Click 1:   100 x 52   →   5,200

Click 2:   100 – 39   →   61

Click 3:   -61 x 52   →   <u>-3,172</u>

Click 4:   39 x 52   =   →   <u>2,028</u> ✓

Here's another one. Let's see if we can streamline it.

48 x 69

Step 1

48 x 69
(100 x 48) – 48 (100 - 69)

$$4,800 \xrightarrow{-31 \times 48 = -1,488} \underline{3,312} \checkmark$$

(Subtract 1,488 from 4,800 by complement: 4,812 – 1,500 = 3,312)

Step 2

48 x 69
(100 x 69) – 69 (100 – 48)

$$6,900 \xrightarrow{-52 \times 69 = -3,588} \underline{3,312} \checkmark$$

158

Another one, again, streamlining:

62 x 79

Step 1

62 x 79
(100 x 62) – 62 (100-79)

$$6{,}200 \xrightarrow{\quad -62\times21=-1{,}302^{(1)(2)}\quad} \underline{4898} \checkmark$$

Step 2

62 x 79
(100 x 79) – 79 (100 – 62)

$$7{,}900 \xrightarrow{\quad -79\times38=-3{,}002^{(3)}\quad} \underline{4{,}898} \checkmark$$

Another one.

Step 1

53 x 94
(100 x 53) – 53 x (100 – 94)

$$5{,}300 \xrightarrow{\quad -53\times6=-318\quad} \underline{4{,}982} \checkmark$$

By the way, this is the way you would also solve this problem in "real life." It is the easiest way.

_____

(1) $62 \times 21 = (62 \times 20) + (62 \times 1) = 1{,}240 + 62 = \underline{1{,}302} \checkmark$

(2) $6{,}200 - 1{,}302$ (easiest): $6{,}200 - 1{,}300 = 4{,}900$. $4{,}900 - 2 = \underline{4{,}898} \checkmark$

(3) $79 \times 38 = (80 \times 38) - 38 = 3{,}040 - 38 = \underline{3{,}002} \checkmark$

Step 2

$$53 \times 94$$
$$(100 - 94) - 94 \ (100 - 53)$$

$$9{,}400 \xrightarrow{\ -94 \times 47 = -4{,}418^{(1)}\ } \underline{4{,}982} \ \checkmark$$

And one last one:

$$27 \times 84$$

Step 1

$$27 \times 84$$
$$(100 \times 27) - 27 \ (100 - 84)$$

$$2{,}700 \xrightarrow{\ -27 \times 16 = -432\ } \underline{2{,}268} \ \checkmark$$

Step 2

$$27 \times 84$$
$$(100 \times 84) - 84 \ (100 - 27)$$

$$8{,}400 \xrightarrow{\ -84 \times 73 = -6{,}132^{(2)}\ } \underline{2{,}268} \ \checkmark$$

---

(1) 94×47: Either $(100 \times 47) - (6 \times 47) = 4{,}700 - 288 = \underline{4{,}418}$ ✓, or
$\quad\quad\quad\quad\quad (50 \times 94) \ - (3 \times 94) = 4{,}700 - 282 = \underline{4{,}418}$ ✓

(2) There are several easy ways to multiply 84×73. Do you see them? The easiest perhaps is to figure 84×75 and then subtract $2 \times 84 = 168$. $25 \times 84 = 2{,}100$ (¼ of $8{,}400$). Therefore 75×84 is three times as much $= 6{,}300$. Subtract 168 and you get $6{,}132$.

We are at the end of Level 6. As usual, I am going to give you ten homework examples.

Do each one of them by the two steps of Level 6. Then, go back and do each one of them by

previous levels. It will be good practice for you.

Just as before, see which "real life" method is the fastest and easiest way which you could

solve each problem, if you were not constrained by the requirement of Level 6.

And finally, make up your own problems and practice with them.

Here is your homework.

1.   23 x 68

2.   38 x 54

3.   57 x 72

4.   45 x 83

5.   73 x 92

6.   62 x 86

7.   47 x 74

8.   68 x 92

9.   53 x 67

10.   27 x 44

Please turn to page 454 for an interesting "bonus" step for this level

(and also some other good stuff).

LEVEL 7: *Complement Squares 2 Steps*

This level, too, has only two steps, the second being the mirror image of the first. So you'll really have to learn only one thing.

In this level (Step 1) we take the square of the first (lower) number. We ascertain the gap (difference) between the lower and the higher number, and then multiply the lower number by that gap (Δ) and add it to the square.

In Step 2 we do the opposite.

Let's put it into the form of a rule.

The product of two numbers is the square of one of the numbers, plus (if the number that is being squared is the lower of the two) or minus (if the number being squared is the higher of the two) the product of the gap between the two numbers and that number.

Let's do a first example with our old friend

$$37 \times 82$$
$$37^2 + 37(82 - 37)$$

In Step 1, the first click would be to find the square of 37. You know how to do that, but let me refresh your memory:

$$37 \times 37: \xrightarrow{40 \times 40 = 1600} 1{,}600 \xrightarrow{-6 \times 40 = -240} 1{,}360 \xrightarrow{+3^2 = 9} \boxed{1{,}369} \checkmark$$

The second click is to ascertain the "gap" (Δ) between 37 and 82. I don't have to show you how to do that. You know right away that it's 45.

Our third click is to multiply 37 x 45. There are several easy ways of doing that, including keeping in mind the special case of 37 (remember that?). But, the easiest way to multiply anything by 45 is to think of the multiplier as (50-5).

You will know right away that 37 x 5 = 185 (30 x 5) + (7 x 5) and therefore that 50 x 37 = 1,850. 45 x 37, therefore, is 1,850 –185. And you get that, of course, by the complement method, by which you add 15 to both 1,850 and to 185 making it 1,865 – 200 = 1,665.

The final click is to add 1,665 to $\boxed{1,369}$. You do that by starting from the left (in your head): 1,600 + 1,300 = 2,900. 60 + 60 = 120 → 3,020. 9 + 5 = 14 → 3,034 ✓

I kind of took you by the hand on this one, step by step. Once you get a little practice, of course, you'll be able to do this sort of thing in one smooth mental movement, in (I assure you!) less than 15 seconds. You'll have to practice, but it will come.

Let's do Step 2, which is the reverse, a little faster.

$$\textbf{37 x 82}$$
$$\textbf{82}^2 - \textbf{(82} - \textbf{37)}$$

Click 1: 82^2: $\xrightarrow{\ +80^2\ }$ 6,400 $\xrightarrow{+4 \times 80 = 320}$ 6,720 $\xrightarrow{\ +2^2 = 4\ }$ 6,724

Click 2:   82 – 37   =   45

Click 3:   – (45 x 82): $\xrightarrow{-50 \times 82}$ -4,100 $\xrightarrow{+5 \times 82 = +410}$ =   -3,690

Click 4:   Add it up: 37 x 82   =   3,034 ✓

Let me tell you one more time how to subtract 3,690 from 6,724. By complement, of course! You add 10 to both 6,724 (which brings it to 6,734) and to 3,690 (which brings it to 3,700). Then you have 6,734 – 3,700, which is 3,034.

Let's try a few more examples.

$$34 \times 78$$

We'll streamline this now, because that's what I expect you eventually to do also.

Step 1

$$34 \times 78$$
$$34^2 + 34\,(78 - 34)$$

The problem boils down, of course, to $34^2 + (44 \times 34)$.

Click 1: $34^2 \xrightarrow{\;900+240+16\;}$ 1,156

Click 2:   44 x 34. Let's do it by the same-last-digit method:

    $44 \times 34 \xrightarrow{\;1,200+(4\times70)+16\;}$ <u>1,496</u>

Click 3:   Add it up: 34 x 78   =   <u>2,652</u> ✓

Step 2

$$34 \times 78$$
$$78^2 - (44 \times 78)$$

Click 1: $78^2: \xrightarrow{\;6,400-320+4\;}$ 6,084

Click 2: $-(44 \times 78)$. Several easy ways: Let's do it by

    $-[(40 \times 78) + (4 \times 78)] = -(3,120 + 312)$ →   <u>-3,432</u>

Click 3:   Therefore, 34 x 78   =   <u>2,652</u> ✓

(You know how, but let me tell you once again how to do that subtraction.) Since you don't cross a "threshold" you don't have to work with complements:

$$6,000 - 3,400 \rightarrow 2,600 \xrightarrow{+80-30=50} 2,650 \xrightarrow{+4-2=2} \underline{2,652} \checkmark$$

Here's another one.

Step 1

47 x 96

$47^2 + (49 \times 47)$

Hold just a minute. Our only "contract" on Level 7 is to start out with the square of one of the numbers, in this case the lower number (47). After that we are on our own.

We know, of course by now, how quickly to get the square of 47, namely $50^2 - 6 \times 50 + 3^2$ or $2,500 - 300 + 9 = \boxed{2,209}$

How about 49 x 47? There are two quick ways and I want you to see both.

1. $49 \times 47 = (50 \times 47) - 47 = 2,350 = 47 = \boxed{2,303}$, or

2. $49 \times 47 = 47^2 + (2 \times 47)$. We already know what 47^2 is, namely 2,209.

    So all we have to do is add $(2 \times 47) = 94$ and get $\boxed{2,303}$.

3. $49 \times 47 = 48^2 - 1^2 = 2,304 - 1 = \boxed{2,303}$.

Take your pick.

In any case, 47 x 96 is 2,209 + 2,303 $\qquad = \qquad \underline{4,512}\checkmark$

Step 2

47 x 96

$96^2 - (49 \times 96)$

Click 1:	$96^2 = 100^2 - (8 \times 100) + 4^2 = 10,000 - 800 + 16$	$\rightarrow$	9,216
Click 2:	$-(49 \times 96) = -(50 \times 96) + 96 = -4,800 + 96$	$\rightarrow$	$\underline{-4,704}$
Click 3:	Add it up: 47 x 96	$=$	$\underline{4,512}\checkmark$

Another one:

$$32 \times 57$$

Step 1

$$32 \times 57$$
$$32^2 + (25 \times 32)$$

This is an easy one. 32^2 is one of the series of powers of 2, which you should know by heart up to the 10th power.

It goes like this:

2, 4, 8, 16, 32, 64, 128, 256, 512, 1,024, 2,048, 4,096...

You see that 32 is 2 to the 5th power. Therefore, 32^2 has to be 2 to the 10th power, which is 1,024.

But, of course, you can also get it the old fashioned way:

$$32^2 = 30^2 + (4 \times 30) + 2^2 = 900 + 120 + 4 = \underline{1,024} \checkmark$$

The second part is also easy. To get 32 x 25, all we have to do is divide 32 by 4 and then hang on two zeros. So, 32 x 25 = 800.

Therefore, 32 x 57 = 1,024 + 800 = $\underline{1,824}$ ✓

As I do often, I show you these things in detail and fully expect that eventually, but certainly by the time you finish this book, you will recognize them yourself.

166

Step 2

$$32 \times 57$$
$$57^2 - (57 \times 25)$$

Click 1: $57^2 = 3{,}600 - 360 + 9$ →   3,249

Click 2: $- (57 \times 25)$ →   -1,425

Click 3:   Add it up: 32×57 =   1,824 ✓

(How do we multiply 57 x 25? Same old thing: 57 divided by 2 is 28½ . 28½ divided by

2 is 14¼ or 14.25. Multiply by 100 and you get 1,425.)

One final one:

Step 1

$$53 \times 84$$
$$53^2 + (53 \times 31)$$

Click 1: $53^2 = 2{,}500 + 300 + 9$ →   2,809

Click 2: $53 \times 31 = 50 \times 31 \ (1{,}550) + 3 \times 31 \ (93)$ →   1,643

Click 3:   Add it up: 53×84 =   4,452 ✓

Step 2

$$53 \times 84$$
$$84^2 - (84 \times 31)$$

Click 1: $84^2 = 6{,}400 + 640 + 16$ →   7,056

Click 2: $-(84 \times 31) = -(80 \times 31) - (4 \times 31) = -2{,}480 - 124$ →   -2,604

Click 3:   Therefore, 53×84 =   4,452 ✓

This was probably the easiest level so far and I hope that you enjoyed it. Remember, your "commitment" on this level is only to start out with the square of either of the numbers and then arrive at the "gap" (Δ), the product of Δ with that number and add it to (or subtract it from) that number. How you do that is entirely up to you. I expect you to find the best way.

Here, as usual, is your homework, ten examples on which to practice Level 7. And, as before, I shall expect you to solve all of these problems also by previous levels that we have learned and also decide which would be the easiest way (the "real life" way) to solve each problem if you didn't have the constraint of the respective level.

And, when you get through with these problems, make up some of your own and keep practicing.

So here we go:

1. 283 x 72

2. 45 x 67

3. 82 x 93

4. 54 x 73

5. 34 x 67

6. 29 x 81

7. 57 x 74

8. 38 x 56

9. 42 x 86

10. 27 x49

LEVEL 8: *Halves, Common Denominators, Halves and Doubles*
4 Steps

This level is a little of a hodgepodge. Step 1 and Step 2 have no relationship to each other, nor to Step 3 and 4 with them. Steps 3 and 4, as you will see, are reversals of each other.

In Step 1, we multiply one-half of each of the factors with each other and then multiply the result by 4. That will bring us to the result of the original multiplication if we had not divided the factors.

For instance, if our problem is 24 x 56 which, by now we can quickly figure out (by various methods) to be 1,346, we would, in Step 1 of Level 8, divide both factors by 2 and get 12 x 28. We quickly arrive at 336. Multiplying that by 4, (4 x 300 + 4 x 30 + 4 x 6 = 1,200 + 120 + 24) we get 1,344. We did it right.

Some problems, of course are a little more complicated than this. For example, the "complication" arises if one or both factors are odd numbers. If only one of the factors is odd and therefore only one-half of the factors after having been divided by 2 ends in one-half we should have no problem.

For instance, if our problem is 39 x 52, dividing both by 2 we get 19½ x 26. We can do that in our head by several means, easiest perhaps is as follows:

39 x 52

Divide both factors by 2, we get

19½ x 26

We can do this in our head by several means, the easiest perhaps as follows:

$$20 \times 26 \rightarrow 520 \xrightarrow{-(\frac{1}{2} \times 26) = -13} \rightarrow 507$$

We now multiply 507 x 4 and get 2,028, which is the result of 39 x 52.

If both factors are odd, both factors will end in ½ after we divide them by 2.

In this case proceed as follows:

Click 1: Multiply the halves with each other, disregarding the ½ at the end of each factor.

Click 2: Add the two halves and divide by 2. This may result in an integer (a number without fractions) or a number ending in ½.

Click 3: Disregard any dangling ½ in (2), add (2) to (1).

Click 4: Multiply the result by 4.

Click 5: If you had no dangling ½ in (3), add 1 to the result. If you did have a dangling ½ in (3), add 3 to the result.

Let's see, with a few examples, how that works. We've already seen how easy it is if both original factors are even, or if only one is odd. Now let's look at the possibility if both factors are odd.

CASE 1

37 x 85
½: 18½ x 42½

Click 1:	18 x 42: 40 x 18 = 720 $\xrightarrow{+2 \times 18 = 36}$		756
Click 2:	(18 + 42)/2	=	<u>30</u>
Click 3:	Add the above	=	786
Click 4:	(Multiply (3) by 4 and add 1.		
	(4 x 786) + 1 = 3,144 + 1. 37 x 85	=	<u>3,145</u> ✓

Note, there was no dangling ½ in Click 3, therefore, you only add 1 at the end.

170

CASE 2

49 x 95
½: 24½ x 47½

Click 1: 24 x 47: 20 x 40 → 800 $\xrightarrow{+20x7=140}$ 940 $\xrightarrow{+4x47=188}$ = 1,128

Click 2: (24 + 47)/2 = 35(½)

Click 3: Add the above (disregard the ½) = 1,163

Click 4: Multiple (3) by 4 and add 3. 4,652 + 3. 49 x 95 = 4,655 ✓

Note, that we had a dangling ½ in Click 2 and, therefore, had to add 3 at the end.

Let's do one more:

28 x 73
½: 14 x 36½

Click 1: 14 x 36 (by square of half sum) is $25^2 - 11^2 = 625 - 121$ = 504

Click 2: Add 14 x ½ = 7

Click 3: 14 x 36½ = 511

Click 4: Multiply (3) by 4: 28 x 73 = 511 x 4 = 2,044 ✓

All of this was Step 1 of this level.

In Step 2, we look for the largest common denominator of the two factors. If we can't hit it right on the head, we take something that's close by. If we can't find anything that will fit at all, we fudge by working with the closest tenner. You'll see.

Let's take the same examples that we used for Step 1 of this level.

CASE 1

24 x 56

The common denominator is 8. We can therefore express this as (8 x 3) x (8 x 7) or 8^2 x

21 = 64 x 21 = 1,344 ✓

64 x 21: 60 x 20 → 1,200 $\xrightarrow{+60 \times 1 = 60}$ 1,260 $\xrightarrow{+4 \times 21 = 84}$ =   1,344 ✓

CASE 2

39 x 52

The common denominator is 13. We can therefore express it as

(3 x 13) x (4 x 13) or 13^2 x 12 = 169 x 12 = 2,028 ✓

(You can think of 169 x 12 as (170 x 12) – (1 x 12), as follows:

17 x 12 = 204 $\xrightarrow{\text{x10}}$ 2,040 $\xrightarrow{-12}$ = 2,028 ✓)

CASE 3

37 x 85

There is no common denominator. But, we can approach it by first getting 34 x 85 and

then adding 3 x 85. 34 is 2 x 17 and 85 is 5 x 17. Therefore, 34 x 85 = (17 x 2) (17 x 5) = 17^2 x

10 = 289 x 10 = 2,890. We have to add 3 x 85 = 255 and get 2,890 + 255 = 37 x 85 = 3,145 ✓

CASE 4

49 x 95

Again, there is no common denominator, but we get close by first getting 49 x 98, which is

49^2 x 2. 49^2 is of course 50^2 – 99 = 2,401. We multiply that by 2 and get 4,802. But, we need

49 x 95, and not 49 x 98; therefore, we must subtract 3 x 49 = 147. 4,802 – 147 (complement by adding 53 and you get 4,855 – 200) = <u>4,655</u> ✓

CASE 5

28 x 73

The "close" common denominator is 14. 28 is 2 x 14, and 70 (somewhat removed from 73) is 5 x 14. Therefore, 28 x 70 = 14^2 x 10 = 1,960. But that is 28 x 70.

We need 28 x 73, which is 28 x 3 = 84 more.

Therefore, 28 x 73 = 1,960 + 84 = <u>2,044</u> ✓

All those went fairly neatly. We either hit the complement numbers right on the head, as in our first and second case, or got pretty close and were able to adjust the gap as in the last three cases.

But sometimes, especially if two primes are involved or if the two factors are close together, no reasonably common denominator can be found. In such case, (fortunately, not too frequent) you are allowed to fudge by working with the nearest tenners, a variation perhaps on both steps of Level 2.

For instance:

53 x 62

There is no reasonable common denominator. So, we "fudge" by saying:

Click 1:	50 x 60	→	3,000		
Click 2:	50 x 2	→	100	→	3,100

Click 3:	60 x 3	→	180	→	3,280
Click 4:	3 x 2	→	6	→	3,286
Click 5:	Therefore, 53 x 62			=	3,286 ✓

Or

29 x 43

Click 1:	30 x 40	→	1,200		
Click 2:	30 x 3	→	90	→	1,290
Click 3:	- 1 x 43	→	-43	→	1,247
Click 4:	Therefore, 29 x 43			=	1,247 ✓

But, to repeat, that shouldn't happen too often. Most of the time you will be able to find a common denominator or at least something close to it.

We now come to Steps 3 and 4 of this level. As I told you at the beginning, Step 4 is the reverse of Step 3.

In Step 3, we <u>double the first factor</u> and <u>halve the second</u>. Naturally, multiplying them with each other, we come to the original result. In Step 4, we <u>halve the first factor</u> and <u>double the second</u>. And again, we come to the same result.

Let's take the five examples of this level and run them through Steps 3 and 4.

EXAMPLE 1

24 x 56

Step 3

24 x 56
becomes 48 x 28

$50 \times 28 \rightarrow 1,400 \xrightarrow{-2 \times 28 = -56} \qquad\qquad \rightarrow \quad \underline{1,344} \checkmark$

or, by same-last-digit method:

$48 \times 28 \rightarrow 40 \times 20 \rightarrow 800 \rightarrow \xrightarrow{+(40+20) \times 8 = 480} 1,280 \xrightarrow{+8^2 = 64} \quad \underline{1,344} \checkmark$

Step 4

24 x 56
becomes 12 x 112

$12 \times 100 \rightarrow 1,200 \xrightarrow{+12^2 = 144} \qquad\qquad \rightarrow \quad \underline{1,344} \checkmark$

EXAMPLE 2

39 x 52

Step 3

39 x 52
becomes 78 x 26

78 x 25 (divide 78 by 2 and again by 2 $\rightarrow$ 39 $\rightarrow$ 19.5 $\rightarrow$ 1,950 $\rightarrow$ +78 $\quad \rightarrow \quad \underline{2,028} \checkmark$

or: $78 \times 26 = (80 \times 26) - (2 \times 26) = 2,080 - 52 \qquad \rightarrow \quad \underline{2,028} \checkmark$

Step 4

39 x 52
becomes 19½ x 104

$19½ \times 104: \ 20 \times 100 \rightarrow 2,000 \xrightarrow{+20 \times 4 = 80} 2,080 \xrightarrow{-½ \times 104 = -52} \quad \underline{2,028} \checkmark$

EXAMPLE 3

37 x 85

Step 3

37 x 85
becomes 74 x 42½

74 x 42½: 70 x 40 → 2,800 $\xrightarrow{+70 \times 2\frac{1}{2}=175}$ 2,975 $\xrightarrow{+4 \times 42\frac{1}{2}=170}$ → 3,145 ✓

Step 4

37 x 85
becomes 18½ x 170

Think of it as (17 x 170) + (1½ x 170)

17½ x 170: 17^2 → 289 $\xrightarrow{\times 10}$ 2,890 $\xrightarrow{+1\frac{1}{2}\times 170=255}$ 3,145 ✓

EXAMPLE 4

49 x 95

Step 3

49 x 95
becomes 98 x 47½

Think of it as (100 x 47½) - (2 x 47½)

100 x 47½ → 4,750 $\xrightarrow{-2 \times 47\frac{1}{2}=-95}$ = 4,655 ✓

Step 4

49 x 95
becomes 24½ x 190

Think of it as (25 x 190) – (½ x190). To get 25 x 190, divide 190 twice

by 2 (190 → 95 → 47.5) and multiply by 100 → 4,750.

Now subtract ½ x 190 = 95 → 4,655 ✓

176

EXAMPLE 5

28 x 73

Step 3

28 x 73
becomes 56 x 36½

Solve 56 x 36 by same-last-digit-method and add ½ x 56 = 28.

56 x 36½: 50 x 30 → 1,500 $\xrightarrow{+6(50+30)=480}$ 1,980 $\xrightarrow{+6^2=36}$ 2,016 $\xrightarrow{+\frac{1}{2}\times56=28}$ 2,044 ✓

Step 4

28 x 73

becomes 14 x 146

Think of it as (14 x 140) + (6 x 14).

14 x 146: 14^2 → 196 $\xrightarrow{x10}$ 1,960 $\xrightarrow{+6\times14=84}$ 2,044 ✓

You see how easy it is. Once you are freed from the constraints of the level, you may quickly find how to solve any problem in the easiest manner. All of the ones that we just did can be solved literally in seconds. The discipline of the levels of the paradigm gives you the tools with which to do that, how to quickly find the easiest way, the best shortcut, and how to solve most quickly any problem of multiplication of two 2-digit numbers and beyond.

Here is your homework for this level. I expect you to do every one of these problems through all four steps of this level. After you have done that, solve all of them by the methods of the previous levels that we have learned, and, of course, for best practice, make up your own problems after you have solved these.

So here we go:

1. 49 x 67

2. 38 x 86

3. 51 x 79

4. 28 x 87

5. 43 x 59

6. 37 x 66

7. 45 x 82

8. 39 x 72

9. 24 x 37

10. 53 x 91

LEVEL 9: *Plus and Minus 10*

4 Steps

In this level we add or subtract 10 from all of the factors, which gives us four combinations – four steps.

Step 1

Subtract 10 from the lower factor and add 10 to the higher factor.

Step 2

Add 10 to the lower factor and subtract 10 from the higher factor.

Step 3

Subtract 10 from each, the lower and the higher factors.

Step 4

Add 10 to each, the lower and the higher factors.

Here is the rule, or rather the rules:

---

1. *If, in multiplication of any two 2-digit numbers, the lower number is decreased by 10 and the higher number is increased by 10, the result will be less by 10 times the difference between the two numbers, minus 100.*

2. *If, in multiplication of any two 2-digit numbers, the lower number is increased by 10 and the higher number is decreased by 10, the result will be more by 10 times the difference between the two numbers, minus 100.*

3. *If, in multiplication of any two 2-digit numbers, both numbers are decreased by 10, the result will be less by 10 times the sum of the two numbers, plus 100.*

4. *If, in multiplication of any two 2-digit numbers, both numbers are increased by 10, the result will be more by 10 times the sum of the two numbers, plus 100.*

Let's try trusty 37 x 82 as an example.

We know from prior steps that it is 3,034.

Step 1

We decrease the lower factor by 10 and increase the higher factor by 10.

37 x 82 (3,034)
becomes 27 x 92

27 x 92: 30 x 90 → 2,700 $\xrightarrow{+30 \times 2 = 60}$ 2,760 $\xrightarrow{-3 \times 92 = -276}$ 2,484 ✓

Is that right? Is that in accordance with Rule (1)? The difference (Δ) between 37 and 82 is 45; so, our result (after decreasing the lower factor by 10 and increasing the higher factor by 10) should be $\boxed{3,034}$ – (10 x 45) – 100 = 3,034 – 450 – 100, and of course it is → <u>2,484</u> ✓

Step 2

37 x 82 (3,034)
becomes 47 x 72

We have increased the lower factor by 10 and decreased the upper factor by 10.

47 x 72: 50 x 72 → 3,600 $\xrightarrow{-3 \times 72 = -216}$ → <u>3,384</u> ✓

Is that right? Let's see. It should be:

$\boxed{3,034}$ + (10 x 45) + 100 = 3,034 + 450 – 100 → <u>3,384</u> ✓

Step 3

37 x 82 (3,034)
27 x 72

having decreased both the higher and the lower factor by 10.

We just learned how to do 27 x 72 – it's a flip. So it's

27 x 72: 20 x 70 → 1,400 $\xrightarrow{+10(7^2+2^2)=530}$ 1,930 $\xrightarrow{+2 \times 7 = 14}$ = <u>1,944</u> ✓

Is it right? The sum of 37 and 82 is 119.

Therefore, the result should be (37 x 82) – (10 x 119) + 100 =

$\boxed{3,034}$ - 1,190 + 100 = <u>1,944</u> ✓

(You know, of course, how to subtract 1,190 from 3,034. Add 10, which is the complement to 1,200, and you have 3,044 – 1,200 = 1,844. Add 100 and you have your correct result: 1,944.)

And finally,

Step 4

$$37 \times 82 \ (3,034)$$
$$\text{becomes } 47 \times 92$$

having added 10 to both the lower and the higher factor.

In figuring 47 x 92, keep in mind that you are not constrained by any method or by any level – you can solve your problem whichever way is easiest for you. You could figure for instance,

1. 47×92: $(50 \times 92) - (3 \times 92) = 4,600 - 276$ $\qquad = \qquad$ <u>4,324</u>

2. 47×92: (Since 92 is $(2 \times 47) - 2$):

   $2 \times 47^2 - (2 \times 47) = (2 \times 2,209) - 94$ $\qquad = \qquad$ <u>4,324</u>✓

(You know, of course: $47^2 = 50^2 - (6 \times 50) + 3^2 = 2,500 - 300 + 9 = 2,209$.)

Let's see how it works out with Rule 4. It should be:

$\boxed{3,034} + (10 \times 119) + 100 = 3,034 + 1,190 + 100$ $\qquad = \qquad$ <u>4,324</u>✓

So we had it right.

Let's try a few more.

54 x 68

The first thing we have to do is to solve the underlying problem, which is 54 x 68. You can do it by whichever way is easiest for you.

I think it would be 50 x 68 = 3,400 + (4 x 68) = 272   →   3,672 ✓

Or, by the square of half sum.

$61^2 - 7^2 = 3,721 - 49$ =   3,672 ✓

Δ (difference, the gap): 68 | 54 = 14, Δ/2 = 7.

Σ (The sum. It's pronounced "sigma" and is the Greek letter for S) is 68 | 54 = 122, Σ/2 = 61.

Step 1

54 x 68 (3,672)
becomes 44 x 78

Easy: 44 x 75 = 3,300. 44 x 3 = 132; 44 x 78 = 3,300 + 132   =   3,432 ✓

Check for correctness: 3,672 – (10 x 14) – 100 = 3,672 – 240   =   3,432 ✓

Step 2

54 x 68 (3,672)
becomes 64 x 58

64 x 58: 60 x 50 → 3,000 $\xrightarrow{+60 \times 8 - 480}$ 3,480 $\xrightarrow{+4 \times 58 = 232}$ 3,712 ✓

Check for correctness: 3,672 + (10 x 14) – 100 = 3,672 + 40   =   3,712 ✓

Step 3

54 x 68 (3,672)
becomes 44 x 58

Easiest: 40 x 58 → 2,320, 4 x 58 = 232. 2,320 + 232   →   2,552 ✓

(Note: You will of course first figure 4 x 58 = 232 and then, hanging on a zero to get 40 x 58 = 2,320.)

Is it correct? Remember, Σ is 122.

3,672 – (10 x 122) + 100 = 3,672 – 1,220 + 100 = 3,672 – 1,120   =   2,552 ✓

Finally,

Step 4

54 x 68 (3,672)
becomes 64 x 78

Easiest: 64 x 25 = 1,600; 64 x 75 (is 3 times as much) = 4,800; 64 x 78 is

      3 x 64 = 192 more   →   4,992 ✓

Let's check it: $\boxed{3{,}672}$ + (10 x 122) + 100 = 3,672 + 1,320   =   4,992 ✓

Let's do a few more.

48 x 79
$\Delta = 31; \Sigma = 127$

Easiest: (50 x 79) − (2 x 79) = 3,950 − 158   = $\boxed{3{,}792}$✓

Step 1

48 x 79 (3,792)
becomes 38 x 89

Easiest: 3,800 − (11 x 38) = 3,800 − 418   =   3,382 ✓

Note: 11 x 38 = 380 + 38 = 418; 3,800 − 418 = 3,882; 3,882 − 500   =   3,382 ✓

3,382 s/b*:

$\boxed{3{,}792}$ − (10 x 31) − 100 = $\boxed{3{,}792}$ − 310 − 100   =   3,382 ✓

----

*s/b stands for "should be"

Step 2

48 x 79 (3,792)
becomes 58 x 69

Easiest: 58 x 70: 7 x 58 $\rightarrow$ 406 $\xrightarrow{\text{x10}}$ 4,060 $\xrightarrow{-1 \times 58 = -58}$,   4,002 ✓

s/b $\boxed{3{,}792}$ + (10 x 31) − 100 = 3,792 + 210   =   4,002 ✓

Step 3

48 x 79 (3,792)
becomes 38 x 69

Easiest: 70 x 30 $\rightarrow$ 2,100 $\xrightarrow{+70 \times 8 = 560}$ 2,660 $\xrightarrow{-1 \times 38 = -38}$,   2,622 ✓

s/b $\boxed{3{,}792}$ − (10 x 127) + 100 = 3,792 − 1,170 $\rightarrow$ 2,622 ✓

Step 4

48 x 79
becomes 58 x 89

Easiest: 5,800 − (11 x 58) = 5,800 − 638   =   5,162 ✓

s/b $\boxed{3{,}792}$ + (10 x 127) + 100 = 3,792 + 1,370   =   5,162 ✓

Another one:

73 x 92
$\Delta = 19$; $\Sigma = 165$

We can solve 73 x 92 in either of two simple ways:

1.   73 x 92: 25 x 92 → 2,300 $\xrightarrow{\text{x3}}$ 6,900 $\xrightarrow{-2 \times 92 = -184}$ $\boxed{6,716}$ ✓

or

2.   73 x 92: 100 x 73 → 7,300 $\xrightarrow{-8 \times 70 = -560}$ 6,740 $\xrightarrow{-8 \times 3 = -24}$ $\boxed{6,716}$ ✓

$\boxed{\text{Step 1}}$

73 x 92 (6,716)
becomes 63 x 102

Easiest: $(100 \times 63) + (2 \times 63) = 6,300 + 126$ →   6,426 ✓

s/b $\boxed{6,716}$ - (10 x 19) – 100 = 6,716 – 290   →   6,426 ✓

$\boxed{\text{Step 2}}$

73 x 92 (6,716)
becomes 83 x 82

Easiest: $83 \times 82 = 82^2 + 82 = 6,400 + 320 + 4 + 82$ =   6,806 ✓

s/b $\boxed{6,716}$ + (10 x 19) – 100 = 6,716 + 90   =   6,806 ✓

$\boxed{\text{Step 3}}$

73 x 92 (6,716)
becomes 63 x 82

Let's try this by the same-last-digit method, keeping in mind that 63 x 82 is (62 x 82) + 82.

60 x 80 → 4,800 $\xrightarrow{+2 \times 140 = 280}$ 5,080 $\xrightarrow{+2^2 = 4}$ 5,084 → $\xrightarrow{+82}$ 5,166 ✓

s/b $\boxed{6,716}$ - (10 x 165) + 100 = 6,716 – 1,550   =   5,166 ✓

186

Step 4

73 x 92 (6,716)
becomes 83 x 102

Easiest: $(83 \times 100) + (83 \times 2) = 8,300 + 166$ $\qquad = \quad \underline{8,466}$ ✓

s/b $\boxed{6,716} + (10 \times 165) + 100 = 6,716 + 1,750$ $\qquad = \quad \underline{8,466}$ ✓

And one final one:

29 x 54
$\Delta = 25$; $\Sigma = 83$

Easiest: $29 \times 54 = (30 \times 54) - (1 \times 54) = 1,620 - 54$ $\qquad = \quad \boxed{1,566}$ ✓

Step 1

29 x 54 (1,566)
becomes 19 x 64

Easiest: $19 \times 64 = (20 \times 64) - 64 = 1,280 - 64$ $\qquad = \quad \underline{1,216}$ ✓

s/b $\boxed{1,566} - (10 \times 25) - 100 = 1,566 - 350$ $\qquad \rightarrow \quad \underline{1,216}$ ✓

Step 2

29 x 54 (1,566)
becomes 39 x 44

Easiest: $39 \times 44 = (40 \times 44) - 44 = 1,760 - 44$ $\qquad = \quad \underline{1,716}$ ✓

s/b $\boxed{1,566} + (10 \times 25) - 100 = 1,566 + 150$ $\qquad = \quad \underline{1,716}$ ✓

Step 3

29 x 54 (1,566)
becomes 19 x 44

Easiest: $19 \times 44 = (20 \times 44) - 44 = 880 - 44$ $=$ <u>836</u> ✓

s/b $\boxed{1,566}$ $- (10 \times 83) + 100 = 1,566 - 730$ $=$ <u>836</u> ✓

Step 4

29 x 54 (1,566)
becomes 39 x 64

Easiest: $39 \times 64 = (40 \times 64) - 64 = 2560 - 64$ $=$ <u>2,496</u> ✓

s/b $\boxed{1,566}$ $+ (10 \times 83) + 100 = 1,566 + 930$ $=$ <u>2,496</u> ✓

So this is it for Level 9. That was pretty easy wasn't it? And, it was kind of fun.

Perhaps I shouldn't tell you that, but I am really just warming you up with this easy level. As you will see, our next level, Level 10, is going to be very tough. It has seven steps and is the longest and most demanding of the entire Paradigm. We'll introduce some new concepts, which you may not find entirely easy to come to terms with at first. It is the level (I regret to say) in which a good number of my students have given up. But do not let that happen to you! Climb up that next mountain from which, with the possible exception of Level 12, it will be pretty easy coasting all the way to the end, to Level 16.

But don't let's worry about that right now. Let's wind up this Level 9 with the homework exercises that follow. And remember, as always, do the problems also by the previous levels, check your answers by the two methods that you have learned (last digit and sum of digits) and

make up your own problems besides those that I give you now.

1.   42 x 73

2.   23 x 67

3.   34 x 89

4.   48 x 74

5.   56 x 83

6.   71 x 85

7.   23 x 58

8.   42 x 63

9.   31 x 52

10.   62 x 77

LEVEL 10: *Flips and Diagonals* (Part 1)
7 Steps

I warned you at the end of Level 9 that this is going to be a tough one. And indeed, it will be. It has seven steps, all of them a little difficult perhaps. Also, we're going to introduce some new concepts.

But get over this level and you have it made. Level 11 is easy (compared to Level 10). Level 12 will again be difficult. It's similar to Level 10, but has only five steps and is to some degree a "replay" of Level 10. After that it's all coasting home to the end at Level 16.

You may recall that I told you that in all levels, except Level 10 (this one) and Level 12, you should visualize your problems as being side by side, like this

37 x 82

In this level, and in Level 12, you will have to visualize the problem as being "stacked" like this

37
x 82

Step 1 of this level will be to multiply the stacked factors.

Here are some new concepts:

❖   We'll call the tenner line 3(0) and 8(0), the "first vertical."

❖   We'll call the oner line, 7 and 2, the "second vertical."

❖   We'll call the Southwest-Northeast diagonal 8 and 7, the "first diagonal."

❖   We'll call the Northwest-Southeast diagonal 3 and 2, the "second diagonal."

With these definitions, this is the first rule of Step 1 in this level.

To multiply two stacked 2-digit numbers, multiply the digits of the first vertical with each other and multiple the result by 10. Multiply the digits of the first diagonal with each other and of the second diagonal with each other and add the sum of their products to the previous total. Multiply that total by 10. Add the product of the digits in the second vertical for the final total.

This is not nearly as bad as it sounds. Let me show you.

$$37$$
$$\times\ 82$$

Step 1

Original original:

Click 1: $3 \times 8 = 24 \xrightarrow{\ \times 10\ }$ 240

Click 2: $240 \xrightarrow{\ +7\times8=56\ } 296 \xrightarrow{\ +2\times3=6\ } 302 \xrightarrow{\ \times 10\ }$ 3,020

Click 3: $3{,}020 \xrightarrow{\ +7\times2=14\ }$ 3,034 ✓

Step 2

Vertical Flip, new original:

We make a vertical flip (new concept) of the second vertical, which means that we exchange oners. Instead of

$$
\begin{array}{r}
37 \\
\times\ \underline{82},
\end{array}
$$

we'll have

$$
\begin{array}{r}
32 \\
\times\ \underline{87}
\end{array}
$$

The Δ of the oners (gap between 7 and 2) is 5. Δ of the full tenners (gap between 80 and 30) is 50. The rule is:

> *The result of multiplication of two stacked 2-digit numbers that have been*
> *vertically flipped is larger or smaller than the pre-flipped result by the product*
> *of the Δ of the oners by the Δ of the full tenners. It is smaller than the original*
> *if the oner of the original first factor is greater than the oner of the original*
> *second factor and smaller if the reverse is the case.*

Wow, this again is one of those things that sounds very complicated when one puts it into a rule, but is really not too bad.

Let's try it on our example of

$$
\begin{array}{r}
37 \\
\times\ \underline{82}
\end{array}
$$

1.   The difference (Δ) between 7 and 2 is 5. 7 is greater than 5. Therefore, after we vertically flip it (32 x 87, instead of 37 x 82), the flipped result will be smaller.

2.   The difference between 80 and 30 is 50.

3.   5 x 50 = 250. Therefore, the flipped result will be smaller by 250 than the pre-flipped result.

Let's see whether it is. We still have to work within the constraints of Level 10. We therefore have to use the same method as in Step 1 on

$$32$$
$$\times \underline{87}$$

Click 1: $3 \times 8 = 24 \xrightarrow{\ +\times 10\ }$ 240

Click 2: $240 \xrightarrow{\ +(2\times 8)+(7\times 3)=37\ } 277 \xrightarrow{\ \times 10\ }$ 2,770

Click 3: $2,770 \xrightarrow{\ +(2\times 7)\ }$ 2,784 ✓

Click 4: Is it correct? $3,034 - 250 \rightarrow$ 2,784 ✓

So it checked out. The vertical flipped result is 250 less than the pre-flipped result.

Step 3

Horizontal Derivative:

In this step we horizontally flip both factors of the previous problem which was already vertically flipped from the original problem. Instead of

$$32$$
$$\times \underline{87}$$

we have

$$23$$
$$\times \underline{78}$$

For lack of a better term, we call this (23 x 78) the "horizontal derivative" of 32 x 87.

The product of the (original) oners (2 x 7) is 14. The product of the (original) tenners (3 x 8) is 24.

Here is the rule:

> *The horizontal derivative of two stacked 2-digit numbers is 99 times the gap*
>
> *(Δ) between the product of the oners and the product of the tenners. The*
>
> *result will be greater if the product of the oners is greater than the product*
>
> *of the tenners and smaller if the reverse is the case.*

This being so, it is clear that if the product of the oners and the tenners are the same, the horizontal derivative has to be the same as the original product. Take for instance

$$\begin{array}{r} 86 \\ \times\ \underline{34} \end{array}$$

The product of the oners (6 x 4) is 24, and the product of the tenners (8 x 3) is also 24. Therefore,

$$\begin{array}{r} 68 \\ \times\ \underline{43} \end{array}$$

should be the same as

$$\begin{array}{r} 86 \\ \times\ \underline{34} \end{array}$$

Is it? Let's see:

One easy way to solve 86 x 34 is by the square-of-half-sum method. 86 + 34 = 120, half sum is 60, and the square is 3,600. Δ (86|20) is 26 and its square is 676. Therefore, 86 x 34 = 3,600 – 676 = 2,924. ✓

How about the horizontal flip, the "horizontal derivative", 68 x 43?

70 x 43 = 2,800 + 210 = 3,010. Subtract 2 x 43 = 86 and you get 2,924 ✓ which is the same as the result of 86 x 34. Interesting, isn't it?

Here again, the rule sounds complicated, but it really isn't all that bad.

Let's do it:

$$\begin{array}{r} 23 \\ \times\ \underline{78} \end{array}$$

We are now free of the constraints of Level 10 and can solve this any way we want to.

Trust me, the easy way to do this is 25 x 78, which is 1,950. Divide 78 by 2 then again by

2, then multiply by 100, then subtract 2 x 78 = 156 → 1,950 – 156 = $\boxed{1,794}$ ✓

What is the product of the oners? It's 2 x 7 = 14.

What is the product of the tenners? It's 3 x 8 = 24.

Thus, Δ (24 |14) = 10. The product of the oners is smaller; therefore, the "horizontal

derivative" is smaller. By how much? By 99 x 10.

99 x 10 is of course very easy – it's 990. But it could have been more difficult. Δ could

have been say 43, which would give rise to a more complicated calculation, 99 x 43.

But there's a wonderful shortcut available to multiplying anything by 99. You probably

have found it already. Latch on to it. It's 99 = 100 – 1.

In our case (Δ being 10), 99 x 10 is 100 x 10 (1,000) – 1 x 10 (10). We know that it's 990,

but if we didn't know how to figure it out, we would just subtract 1,000 and add 10. (In the case

of 43 x 99, we would have subtracted (or added) 4,300 and then added (or subtracted) 43.

We have already figured out that

$$\begin{array}{r} 32 \\ \text{x } \underline{87} = 2,784 \end{array}$$

And we have also figured out that

$$\begin{array}{r} 23 \\ \text{x } \underline{78} = 1,794 \end{array}$$

Does that conform to the rule? The difference should be (–1,000 + 10). Let's see.

$$2,784 - 1,000 = 1,784$$

$$1,784 + 10 = \underline{1,794} ✓$$

Therefore, 1,794 is the horizontal derivative of 32 x 87.

In Steps 4 through 7 of this level, we'll introduce a new concept: the "diagonal flip."

There are two diagonal flips: 1. The Southwest-Northeast flip, and 2. The Northwest-Southeast flip.

Have a look at this diagram. It will make it clear.

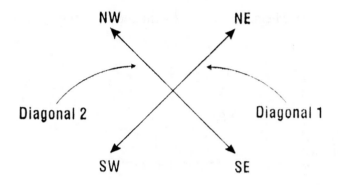

$$\Delta_1 = NE \mid SW$$

$$\Delta_2 = NW \mid SE$$

We take our (vertically flipped) example

$$
\begin{array}{r}
32 \\
\times\ \underline{87}
\end{array}
$$

which we know to be 2,784.

The flip of diagonal (1) affecting the SW-NE axis, changes

$$
\begin{array}{r}
32 \\
\times\ \underline{87}
\end{array}
$$

to

$$
\begin{array}{r}
38 \\
\times\ \underline{27}
\end{array}
$$

The flip of diagonal 2, affecting the NW-SE axis, changes

$$
\begin{array}{r}
32 \\
\times\ \underline{87}
\end{array}
$$

to

$$72$$
$$\times \underline{83}$$

How do the results of the diagonally flipped products differ from the result of the original problem (the "original" problem in this case being the vertically flipped from the "original, original"),

$$32$$
$$\times \underline{87}$$

and from the horizontal derivative

$$23$$
$$\times \underline{78}$$

Here is the rule:

The product of a diagonally flipped stacked multiplication of two 2-digit numbers will be the pre-flipped product plus/minus the Δ of that diagonal times 100 the tenner of the other diagonal minus/plus that Δ times the oner of the other diagonal.

The result will be larger if the product of the flipped tenners is larger than the pre-flipped product of the tenners and smaller if the reverse is the case.

Again, it seems rather complicated and difficult, but it isn't that bad.

Steps 4 and 5 relate to our flipping diagonal (1).

Steps 6 and 7 relate to our flipping diagonal (2).

Step 4

Diagonal 1 Flipped
Compared to Original:

$$32$$
$$\text{x } \underline{87} = 2{,}784 \text{ (the original, original, vertically flipped)}$$

$$23$$
$$\text{x } \underline{78} = 1{,}794 \text{ (the horizontal derivative)}$$

$$27$$
$$\text{x } \underline{38} \text{ (diagonal (1) flip)}$$

This is easy to solve by various means:

1. $(40 \times 27) - (2 \times 27) = 1{,}080 - 54$ $= \quad 1{,}026 \checkmark$

2. $38 \times 3 \rightarrow 114 \xrightarrow{\text{x3}} 342 \xrightarrow{\text{x3}}$ $1{,}026 \checkmark$

3. $37 \times 27 \text{ (remember 37?)} + (1 \times 27) = 999 + 27$ $= \quad 1{,}026 \checkmark$

4. $(25 \times 38) + (2 \times 38) = 950 + 76$ $= \quad 1{,}026 \checkmark$

I give you these several "reliable" ways of how to solve a problem and expect you to always be on the lookout for such opportunities and shortcuts.

In any case, we know that the result of the first diagonal flip is 1,026; we'll now have to check whether it confirms to the Rule --- how it compares to 2784 (the result of the original, vertically flipped) and 1,794, its horizontal derivative.

The tenner in the other diagonal (second diagonal) is 3 and the oner is 7. Δ_1 is 8|2 = 6. Therefore, the adjustment (to get from 1,026 to 2,784) is +(6 x 300) = +1,800 and - (6 x 7) = -42.

$$1{,}026 \xrightarrow{\;+1{,}800\;} 2{,}826 \xrightarrow{\;-42\;} \underline{2{,}784} \checkmark$$

It works!

As to the horizontal derivative, we'll look at it immediately.

Step 5

Diagonal 1 Flipped
Compared to Horizontal Derivative:

For Steps 5 and 7 (which both relate to the horizontal derivative), we need a new rule:

The product of a diagonally flipped stacked multiplication of two 2-digit

numbers will be the horizontal derivative, plus/minus 100 times the oner of

the diagonal times the Δ of the other diagonal, minus/plus the tenner of the

diagonal times the Δ of the other diagonal.

The result will be larger if the product of the tenners of the flipped product

is larger than the product of the tenners of the horizontal derivative, and

smaller if the reverse is the case.

We know that 2,784 is the product of the original (vertically flipped)

$$\begin{array}{r} 32 \\ + \underline{87} \end{array}$$

and that 1,794 is the horizontal derivative

$$\begin{array}{r} 23 \\ + \underline{78} \end{array}$$

and that 1,026 is the result of diagonal (1) flipped

$$38$$
$$+ \underline{27}$$

Δ_2 is $7|3 = 4$.

The oner of diagonal (1) is 2 and the tenner is 8.

$\therefore 1{,}026 + (400 \times 2) - (4 \times 8) = 1{,}026 + 800 - 32 = \boxed{1{,}794} \checkmark$

Which, as we expected from the rule, is the horizontal derivative.

Step 6

Diagonal 2 Flipped
Compared to Original:

$$32$$
$$\times \underline{87} = 2{,}784 \text{ (the original, vertically flipped)}$$

$$72$$
$$\times \underline{83} = 5{,}976 \text{ (diagonal (2) flipped)}$$

How do we get $72 \times 83 = 5{,}976$?

One easy way would be to use the same last digit method (72×82) and then add 72. $72 \times 82 = 5{,}600 + (2 \times 150) + 4 = 5{,}904$; we add 72 and get $5{,}976 \checkmark$.

There are other ways of doing this, of course, but this may be the easiest.

In this step, we have to get from 5,976 to 2,784, which is the (vertically flipped) original.

$\Delta \ 7|3 = 4$. The tenner of other diagonal is 8, and the oner of the other diagonal is 2. Therefore,

$5{,}976 - (4 \times 800) + (4 \times 2) = 5{,}976 - 3{,}200 + 8 + \underline{2{,}784} \checkmark$

Step 7

Diagonal 2 Flipped
Compared to Horizontal Derivative:

200

In this step, just as we did in Step 5, we relate the result of the diagonally flipped multiplication to the horizontal derivative.

The horizontal derivative is

$$\begin{array}{r} 23 \\ \times\ \underline{78} = 1{,}794 \end{array}$$

The diagonally flipped result (83 x 72) is 5,976.

The Δ of the other diagonal (Δ_1) is (8|2) = 6. Therefore, 5,976 – (600 x 7) + (6 x 3) = 5,976 – 4,200 + 18 = 1,794 ✓.

I realize that this was a little exhausting and, because I wanted to explain it in detail, a little lengthy. Let's now go through a few examples of Level 10, but we are going to streamline things.

The difference between Level 10, and as you will see, Level 12, is that in Level 10 we work with the vertically flipped version of the original problem whereas in Level 12 we shall be working with the original problem. As you will see, it will make things a little bit shorter and a little simpler.

Let's try this:

$$\begin{array}{r} 42 \\ \times\ \underline{61} \end{array}$$

Step 1

Original original:

$4 \times 6 \rightarrow 24 \xrightarrow{x10} 240 \xrightarrow{+2x6=12} 252 \xrightarrow{+1x4=4} 256 \xrightarrow{x10} 2{,,}560$

$\xrightarrow{+2x1=2} \boxed{2{,}562}$ ✓

Step 2

Vertical Flip, new original:

$$42$$
$$\times \underline{61}$$

becomes

$$41$$
$$\times \underline{62}$$

s/b (1-2) = -1; (60 – 40) = 20. Therefore, the vertical flipped result should be 20 less:

$$2,562 - 20 = \boxed{2,542} \checkmark$$

Now let's actually figure it out:

$$4 \times 6 \rightarrow 24 \xrightarrow{\times 10} 240 \xrightarrow{+2 \times 4 = 8} 248 \xrightarrow{+6 \times 1 = 6} 254 \xrightarrow{\times 10}$$

$$2,540 \xrightarrow{+2 \times 1 = 2} \boxed{2,542} \checkmark$$

Step 3

Horizontal Derivative:

$$41$$
$$\times \underline{62}$$

becomes

$$14$$
$$\times \underline{26}$$

14 x 26 = 10 x 26 + (4 x 26) = 260 + 104   =   364 $\checkmark$

s/b 99 (24 – 2) = 99 x 22 less than 2,542

or

– (100 x22) + 22

2,542 – 2,200 + 22   =   364 $\checkmark$

Step 4

**Diagonal 1 Flipped
Compared to Original:**

$$41$$
$$\text{x } \underline{62}$$

becomes

$$46$$
$$\text{x } \underline{12}$$

$46 \times 12 = (40 \times 12) + (6 \times 12) = 480 + 72 = \boxed{552}$ ✓

$\Delta_1 = 6|1 = 5$

$\boxed{552} + (500 \times 4) - (5 + 2) = 552 + 2000 - 10$ $\qquad = \qquad \underline{2,542}$ ✓

Step 5

**Diagonal 1 Flipped
Compared to Horizontal Derivative:**

$$41$$
$$\text{x } \underline{62}$$

becomes

$$46$$
$$\text{x } \underline{12}$$

$\Delta_2 = 4|2 = 2$

$\boxed{552} \xrightarrow{-200\text{x}1=-200} 352 \xrightarrow{+2\text{x}6=12}$ $\qquad \underline{364}$ ✓

Step 6

**Diagonal 2 Flipped
Compared to Original:**

$$41$$
$$\times \underline{62}$$

becomes

$$21$$
$$\times \underline{64}$$

$21 \times 64 = (20 \times 64) + 64 = 1{,}280 + 64 = 1{,}344$ ✓

$\Delta_2 = 4|2 = 2$

$1{,}344 + (200 \times 6) - (2 \times 1) = 1{,}344 + 1{,}200 - 2$ $=$ <u>2,542</u> ✓

Step 7

**Diagonal 2 Flipped
Compared to Horizontal Derivative:**

$$41$$
$$\times \underline{62}$$

becomes

$$21$$
$$\times \underline{64}$$

$21 \times 64 = 1{,}344$ ✓

(I don't have to show you how to do that.)

$\Delta = 6|1 = 5$

$1{,}344 - (500 \times 2) + (5 \times 4) = 1{,}344 - 1{,}000 + 20$ $=$ <u>2,542</u> ✓

Another one:

$$45$$
$$\times \underline{87}$$

204

Step 1

Original original:

$$4 \times 8 = 32 \xrightarrow{\ \times 10\ } 320 \xrightarrow{\ +7 \times 4 = 28\ } 348 \xrightarrow{\ +8 \times 5 = 40\ } 388 \xrightarrow{\ \times 10\ }$$

$$3,880 \xrightarrow{\ +7 \times 5 = 35\ } \qquad \boxed{3,915}\checkmark$$

Step 2

Vertical Flip, new original:

becomes
$$\begin{array}{r} 45 \\ \times\ \underline{87} \end{array}$$

$$\begin{array}{r} 47 \\ \times\ \underline{85} \end{array}$$

s/b $2 \times 40 = 80$ more than $\boxed{3,915} \rightarrow \boxed{3,995}\ \checkmark$

$$4 \times 8 = 32 \xrightarrow{\ \times 10\ } 320 \xrightarrow{\ +(7 \times 8)+(5 \times 4)=76\ } 396 \xrightarrow{\ \times 10\ } 3,960$$

$$\xrightarrow{\ +(7 \times 5)=35\ } \qquad \boxed{3,995}\checkmark$$

Step 3

Horizontal Derivative:

becomes
$$\begin{array}{r} 47 \\ \times\ \underline{85} \end{array}$$

$$\begin{array}{r} 74 \\ \times\ \underline{58} \end{array}$$

$$25 \times 58 = 1,450 \xrightarrow{\ \times 3\ } 4,350 \xrightarrow{\ -58\ } \qquad \rightarrow \boxed{4,292}\checkmark$$

s/b: $[(5 \times 7) - (4 \times 8)] = 3 \times 99$ more than $3,995$. $3,995 + 300 - 3 \qquad = \boxed{4,292}\checkmark$

Step 4

Diagonal 1 Flipped
Compared to Original:

$$47$$
$$\text{x } \underline{85}$$

becomes

$$48$$
$$\text{x } \underline{75}$$

48 x 75 = 3,600 (Note: It's ¾ of 48 x 100)

$\Delta_1 = 8|7 \qquad = 1$

3,600 + (1 x 400) − (1 x 5) = 3,600 + 400 - 5   = $\boxed{3,995}$ ✓

Step 5

Diagonal 1 Flipped
Compared to Horizontal Derivative:

$$47$$
$$\text{x } \underline{85}$$

becomes

$$48$$
$$\text{x } \underline{75}$$

48 x 75 = 3,600

$\Delta_2 = 5 | 4 = 1$

3,600 + (1 x 700) − (1 x 8) = 3,600 + 700 − 8   = $\boxed{4,292}$ ✓

Step 6

Diagonal 2 Flipped
Compared to Original:

$$47$$
$$\text{x } \underline{85}$$

becomes

$$57$$
$$\text{x } \underline{84}$$

$50 \times 84 = 4,200 \xrightarrow{+7 \times 80 = 560} 4,760 \xrightarrow{+7 \times 4 = 28} \qquad 4,788 \checkmark$

$\Delta_2 = 5|4 = 1$

$4,788 - (1 \times 800) + (1 \times 7) \qquad\qquad = \boxed{3,995} \checkmark$

Step 7

Diagonal 2 Flipped
Compared to Horizontal Derivative:

becomes

$$\begin{array}{r} 47 \\ \times\, \underline{85} \end{array}$$

$$\begin{array}{r} 57 \\ \times\, \underline{84} \end{array}$$

$57 \times 84 = 4,788$ (easiest: $(60 \times 84) - (3 \times 84) = 5,040 - 252$)

$\Delta_1 = 8|7 = 1$

$4,788 - (1 \times 500) + (1 \times 4) = 4,788 - 500 + 4 \qquad\qquad = \boxed{4,292} \checkmark$

Another one:

$$\begin{array}{r} 35 \\ \times\, \underline{73} \end{array}$$

Here is something new, because two of the digits (3) are in common to the two factors. As you will see, that will make things a little easier.

Step 1

Original original:

$$\begin{array}{r} 35 \\ \times\, \underline{73} \end{array}$$

$3 \times 7 \times 10 = 210 \xrightarrow{+3 \times 3 = 9} 219 \xrightarrow{+7 \times 5 = 35} 254 \xrightarrow{\times 10} 2,540 \xrightarrow{+5 \times 3 = 15} \boxed{2,555} \checkmark$

Step 2

Vertical Flip (New Original):

$$\begin{array}{r} 35 \\ \times\ \underline{73} \end{array}$$

becomes

$$\begin{array}{r} 33 \\ \times\ \underline{75} \end{array}$$

$$3 \times 7 \times 10 = 210 \xrightarrow{+5\times3=15} 225 \xrightarrow{+7\times3=21} 246 \xrightarrow{\times10} 2{,}460 \xrightarrow{+3\times5=15} \boxed{2{,}475}\ \checkmark$$

Is that right? Is that what it should be? Let's see:

Δ oners $3\,|\,5 = 1$; Δ tenners: $70\,|\,30 = 40$.

$\therefore$ (This symbol means "therefore". Please remember it.)

$\therefore$ it s/b $(2 \times 40) = 80$ less than 2,555. $2{,}555 - 80 = \boxed{2{,}475}\ \checkmark$

Step 3

Horizontal Derivative:

Remember, in Level 10, the vertically flipped result (2,475 in this case) is the basis (the new original) for this and all future steps in this level.

$$\begin{array}{r} 33 \\ \times\ \underline{75} \end{array}$$

becomes

$$\begin{array}{r} 33 \\ \times\ \underline{57} \end{array}$$

$$33 \times 57:\ 3 \times 50 \rightarrow 150 \xrightarrow{+3\times7=21} 171 \xrightarrow{+\times10} 1{,}710 \xrightarrow{+3\times57=171} 1{,}881\ \checkmark$$

Let me stop here for a minute. I'd like to show you something that should become second nature to you, namely how to quickly check your work.

33 x 57 should

- be between 30 x 50 = 1,500 and 40 x 60 = 2,400. 1,881 ✓

- end in 1, because 3 x 7 = 21. 1,881 ✓

- be divisible by 9, because 33 and 57 are both divisible by 3. Sum of digits should be 9. 1,881 ✓

- Finally, (since 33 is divisible by 11) the difference of the sums of alternate digits should be zero or divisible by 11; and of course it is, because the sums of the alternate digits of 1,881 (1 + 8 and 8 + 1) are the same. Naturally, the result would also have been divisible by 11 if the difference of the sums of the alternate digits were not the same but were 11 or multiple of 11, as we learned earlier in this book.

Having applied these four tests, you can in this case be 100% sure that your result is correct because a number fulfilling the last three requirements occurs only once in every 990 times. For instance, the next number lower to 1,881 that fulfills the requirements is 891 and the next number higher that fulfills this is 2,871. But, both of them fall outside the 1,500-2,400 bracket, which is our first condition. Therefore, no other number fulfills our requirements and we can be 100% sure that 1,881 is the correct answer.

Most frequently, however, you will not be able to be 100% sure that your answer is correct, after applying the tests. There are often two or more other numbers within the bracket that fulfill the requirements. I'll tell you more in Section IV (Algebra, ouch!) about what probability you have that your result is correct. You can be 100% sure however, that your result is not correct if it even fails one of these tests.

I hope you do not mind this digression too much. My purpose is to make you more and more knowledgeable about and familiar with numbers – to recognize patterns, to see the shortcuts and lightning quick to check your work. You should be able to perform the four tests I have just described above in literally seconds.

Now back to our problem. We determined in Step 3 that the horizontal derivative of 33 x 75, which is 33 x 57, is 1,881.

It should be smaller than the result of the pre-flipped problem (2,475) by [(3 x 7) – (3 x 5)] x 99 = 6 x 99 = 600 – 6.

Let's test it:

1,881 + 600 – 6 = 2,475 ✓

Step 4

Diagonal 1 Flipped
Compared to Original:

$$\begin{array}{r} 33 \\ \times \underline{75} \end{array}$$

Flipping the first diagonal, we get:

$$\begin{array}{r} 37 \\ \times \underline{35} \end{array}$$

Easy to solve by the rule of square of half sum: It's $36^2 - 1^2 = 1,295$

$\Delta_1\ 7|3 = 4$

$1,295 + (400 \times 3) - (4 \times 5) = 2,475$ ✓

Step 5

Diagonal 1 Flipped
Compared to Horizontal Derivative:

$$\begin{array}{r} 33 \\ \times \underline{75} \end{array}$$

becomes

$$\begin{array}{r} 37 \\ \times\ \underline{35} \end{array}$$

$37 \times 35 = 1,295$ ✓

$\Delta_2 = 5 | 3 = 2$

$1,295 + (200 \times 3) - (2 \times 7) = 1,295 + 600 - 14 = 1,881$ ✓

Step 6

Diagonal 2 Flipped
Compared to Original:

becomes

$$\begin{array}{r} 33 \\ \times\ \underline{75} \end{array}$$

$$\begin{array}{r} 53 \\ \times\ \underline{73} \end{array}$$

This, too, is easily solved by square of half sum.

The half sum is 63, and the square of 63 is $3,600 + (6 \times 60) + 3$	=	3,969
Δ is 10, and its square, which we subtract	=	$\underline{-100}$
$\therefore$ 53 x 73 =	=	$\boxed{3,869}$ ✓

Δ_2 is $5 | 3 = 2$

$\boxed{3,869} - (200 \times 7) + (2 \times 3) = 3,869 - 1,400 + 6$	=	$\underline{2,475}$ ✓

Step 7

Diagonal 2 Flipped
Compared to Horizontal Derivative:

becomes

$$\begin{array}{r} 33 \\ \times\ \underline{75} \end{array}$$

$$\begin{array}{r} 53 \\ \times\ \underline{73} \end{array}$$

We know that 53 x 73 $\qquad$ = 3,869 ✓

Δ_1 is 7|3 = 4

3,869 − (400 x 5) + (4 x 3) = 3,869 − 2,000 + 12 $\qquad$ = <u>1,881</u> ✓

And one final one:

$$52$$
$$\times \underline{96}$$

In this one, I'll just streamline through the steps, without giving any further explanations (or very few). You know by now how to do most of these steps, of course.

Step 1

Original original:

$$52$$
$$\times \underline{96}$$

5 x 9 x 10 → 450 $\xrightarrow{+6x5=30}$ 480 $\xrightarrow{+9x2=18}$ 498 $\xrightarrow{x10}$ 4,980 $\xrightarrow{+2x6=12}$ 4,992 ✓

Step 2

Vertical Flip, new original:

$$52$$
$$\times \underline{96}$$

becomes

$$56$$
$$\times \underline{92}$$

Easy way to figure 56 x 92: 56 x 100 (5,600) − 56 x 8 (448) $\qquad$ = 5,152 ✓

This should be greater than 4,992 by (6 − 2) (90 − 50) = 4 x 40 = 160

Let's see: 4,992 + 160 $\qquad$ = 5,152 ✓

Step 3

Horizontal Derivative:

$$56$$
$$\text{x } \underline{92}$$

becomes

$$65$$
$$\text{x } \underline{29}$$

$29 \times 65 = (30 \times 65) - (1 \times 65) = 1{,}950 - 65 = 1{,}885 \checkmark$

$(9 \times 5) = 45$ and $(2 \times 6) = 12$

∴ The horizontal derivative should be larger than the original by

$99 \, (45 - 12) = 99 \times 33$ or, $+ (100 \times 33) - 33 = 1{,}885 + 3{,}300 - 33 \quad = \quad \boxed{5{,}152} \checkmark$

Step 4

Diagonal 1 Flipped
Compared to Original:

$$56$$
$$\text{x } \underline{92}$$

becomes

$$59$$
$$\text{x } \underline{62}$$

59×62 is 60×62 $(3{,}720)$ minus 1×62 (62) $\qquad = \qquad 3{,}658 \checkmark$

Δ_1 is $9|6 = 3$

∴ The original should be $3{,}658 + (300 \times 5) - (3 \times 2) = 3{,}658 + 1{,}500 - 6 \quad = \quad \boxed{5{,}152} \checkmark$

Step 5

Diagonal 1 Flipped
Compared to Horizontal Derivative:

$$56$$
$$\text{x } \underline{92}$$

becomes

$$59$$
$$x\ \underline{62}$$

59 x 62 = 3,658 ✓

Δ_2 is 5|2 = 3

∴ Horizontal derivative should be: 3,658 − (300 x 6) + (3 x 9)   = $\boxed{1,885}$ ✓

Step 6

Diagonal 2 Flipped
Compared to Original:

$$56$$
$$x\ \underline{92}$$

becomes

$$26$$
$$x\ \underline{95}$$

26 x 95 = (26 x 100) − (26 x 5) = 2,600 − 130 = 2,470 ✓

Δ_2 = 5|2 = 3

∴ 2,470 + (300 x 9) − (3 x 6)   = $\boxed{5,152}$ ✓

Step 7

Diagonal 2 Flipped
Compared to Horizontal Derivative:

$$56$$
$$x\ \underline{92}$$

becomes

$$26$$
$$x\ \underline{95}$$

We know that 26 x 95   =   2,470 ✓

Δ_1 is 9|6 = 3

∴ Horizontal derivative should be 2,470 − (300 x 2) + (3 x 5)   = $\boxed{1,885}$ ✓

Wow!! That was some effort wasn't it? I hope that you hung in there all the way and that you understood, and have the knowledge of what we have been doing.

This is by far the longest and most difficult of the levels of this whole Paradigm. Level 12, which is only five steps, plows the same ground, so should not be too difficult for you. Everything else, from here on out, is really quite easy and you should have no trouble with it.

Stick with me! In only six levels more, you will have completed the entire Paradigm and by then (providing that you won't rest on your laurels and keep practicing) will be well on your way to developing that razor-sharp mind and that steel trap memory.

But since this was such a long level and such a complicated one, with all those new concepts and flips, let's summarize the seven steps.

Step 1

Regular Stacked

- ❖ Multiply tenners and multiply the result by ten.

- ❖ Add sum of criss-crossed results of multiplication of oners and tenners.

- ❖ Multiply result by 10.

- ❖ Add product of oners.

Step 2

Vertical Flip (new original for this Level)

- ❖ The product will differ from the "original, original" in Step 1, by the product of the difference of the oners and the difference of the full tenners.

❖   *Note*: The product of this step, the Vertical Flip, will be the "new original" for the steps that follow.

Step 3

Horizontal Flip

❖   The product will differ from that of the (new) original by 99 times the difference of the products of the oners and tenners.

Step 4 & Step 6

Flipped Diagonal Compared to Original

❖   The result of the problem, after the diagonal has been flipped, will be greater/smaller than the original by the Δ of the flipped diagonal times 100 the tenner of the other diagonal, minus/plus the Δ of the flipped original times the oner of the other diagonal.

Step 5 & Step 7

Flipped Diagonal Compared to Horizontal Derivative

❖   The result after the diagonal has been flipped will be greater/smaller than the horizontal derivative by the Δ of the other diagonal times 100 the oner of the flipped diagonal minus/plus the Δ of other diagonal times the tenner of the flipped diagonal.

And, here is your homework for Level 10. As in all previous levels:

- Check your results by the tests that we have learned.

- After you go through the several steps of this level, determine in each case how you would solve the problem in "real life", i.e., the easiest way.

- Solve each problem also through the steps of the previous levels that we have learned.

And remember: You are "committed" to solve the problems by Level-10 methods only in Step 1 and Step 2. After that you are on your own and are at liberty to determine, in every case, what is for you the easiest way.

1. 48 x 91

2. 32 x 57

3. 28 x 42

4. 33 x 67

5. 29 x 78

6. 41 x 56

7. 35 x 65

8. 24 x 83

9. 43 x 68

10. 73 x 98

LEVEL 11: *Skewed*

2 Steps

This is a fairly easy level and will serve as a relief to you after just having undergone the rigors of Level 10.

Here is the rule for Step 1 of Level 11.

> *You multiply two 2-digit numbers with each other by multiplying their full tenners, then adding to it the product of the sum of the oners and the smaller of the two numbers, adding to that the product of the oner of the smaller number and the difference of the full tenners, and subtracting from that the square of the oner of the smaller number.*

Step 2 is the reverse of Step 1 and the rule for it is as follows:

> *You multiply two 2-digit numbers with each other by multiplying their full tenners, then adding to it the product of the sum of the oners and the larger of the two numbers, subtracting from that the product of the oner of the larger number and the difference of the full tenners and subtracting from that the square of the oner of the larger number.*

Let's try both steps with our favorite problem:

37 x 82

Step 1

Click 1:	30 x 80		=	2,400
Click 2:	+ (7 + 2) x 37 = 9 x 37	→ +333 →		2,733
Click 3:	+ (80 – 30) x 7 = 50 x 7	→ +350 →		3,083
Click 4:	- 7^2 =	→ -49 →		3,034 ✓

Step 2

37 x 82

Click 1:	30 x 80		=	2,400
Click 2:	+ (7 + 2) x 82 = 9 x 82	→ + 738 →		3,138
Click 3:	- (80 – 30) x 2 = - 50 x 2	→ -100 →		3,038
Click 4:	-2^2 =	→ -4 →		3,034 ✓

That was pretty easy, wasn't it? Let's try a few more.

48 x 69

Step 1

(streamlining)

$$40 \times 60 \rightarrow 2{,}400 \xrightarrow{17 \times 48 = 816} 3{,}216 \xrightarrow{+8 \times 20 = 160} 3{,}376 \xrightarrow{-8^2 = -64} \underline{3{,}312} \checkmark$$

Step 2

$$40 \times 60 \rightarrow 2{,}400 \xrightarrow{+17 \times 69 = 1{,}173} 3{,}573 \xrightarrow{-9 \times 20 = -180} 3{,}393 \xrightarrow{-9^2 = -81} \underline{3{,}312} \checkmark$$

A little review: How do we mentally multiply 1. 17 x 48 and 2. 17 x 69?

1.   17 x 48 = (17 x 50) – (17 x 2) = 850 – 34 = 816 ✓

2.   17 x 69 = (17 x 70) – (17 x 1) = 1,190 – 17 = 1,173 ✓

A few more.

26 x 84

This one is going to be even a little easier because $6 + 4 = 10$ and that, of course, is a very easy multiplier.

Step 1

$20 \times 80 \rightarrow 1,600 \xrightarrow{+10\times26=260} 1,860 \xrightarrow{+6\times60=360} 2,220 \xrightarrow{-6^2=-36} 2,184 \checkmark$

Step 2

$20 \times 80 \rightarrow 1,600 \xrightarrow{+10\times84 = 840} 2,440 \xrightarrow{-4\times60=-240} 2,200 \xrightarrow{-4^2=-16} 2,184 \checkmark$

How about:

52 x 93

Step 1

$50 \times 90 \rightarrow 4,500 \xrightarrow{+5\times52 = 260} 4,760 \xrightarrow{+2\times40=80} 4,840 \xrightarrow{-2^2=-4} 4,836 \checkmark$

Step 2

$50 \times 90 \rightarrow 4,500 \xrightarrow{+5\times93=465} 4,965 \xrightarrow{-3\times40=-120} 4,845 \xrightarrow{-3^2=-9} 4,836 \checkmark$

And one final one:

63 x 81

Step 1

$60 \times 80 \rightarrow 4,800 \xrightarrow{+4\times63 = 252} 5,052 \xrightarrow{+3\times20=60} 5,112 \xrightarrow{-3^2=9} 5,103 \checkmark$

Step 2

$$60 \times 80 \rightarrow 4{,}800 \xrightarrow{\ +4\times81=324\ } 5{,}124 \xrightarrow{\ -1\times20=-20\ } 5{,}104 \xrightarrow{\ -1^2=-1\ } 5{,}103 \checkmark$$

So this is it for Level 11. As I told you, it was going to be pretty easy, and indeed it was. But you deserve this respite, after what you have gone through in Level 10.

Level 12, I am afraid, is going to be another pretty tough one, almost identical to Level 10. But you know now how to handle that, and there will be only five steps, instead of seven; they are all the same as in Level 10. After that, it will be easy and smooth sailing – all the way through Level 16. And just imagine how smart you will be by then.

And here is your homework for this level – ten problems. As before, please address the problems also by the methods of the other levels that we have learned. Decide how you would solve them in "real life" and, of course, make up your own problems.

1. **28 x 39**

2. **62 x 98**

3. **33 x 49**

4. **23 x 68**

5. **31 x 58**

6. **42 x 79**

7. **27 x 55**

8. **38 x 91**

9. **56 x 62**

10. **45 x 73**

LEVEL 12: *Flips and Diagonals* (Part 2)
5 Steps

We had a pretty easy ride in Level 11. This level is going to be a little more difficult. In fact, as you will see, the five steps in Level 12 are exactly the same as the last five steps (3 to 7) of Level 10. The only difference is that, whereas in Level 10, Step 1 was to solve the problem by stacking the factors and Step 2 to do the same but, having vertically flipped the oners, we won't do that in Level 12. We already know the procedure of how to solve the standard problem and we know the result. In this level we don't work with the vertically flipped. We go right to the "horizontal derivative." That was Step 3 in Level 10; it will be Step 1 in this level.

Again, as in Level 10, we have to stack the problem --- one factor on top of the other, instead of having them side by side. That's how we need to visualize, (mentally project) them when we work on these two, and only on these two, levels --- Level 10 and Level 12.

Since Levels 10 and 12 are essentially the same, we work with the same rules in this level as we did in Level 10.

The first example in Level 12 (just as in most of the other levels) is:

$$37$$
$$\text{x } \underline{82}$$

So let's go with that.

We know from Level 10 that the result is 3,034.

So let's go to –

Step 1

Horizontal Derivative:

Instead of 37 x 82, we now have

$$\begin{array}{r} 73 \\ \times\ \underline{28} \end{array}$$

You remember from Level 10 that the difference between the original and the horizontal derivative is 99x the difference between the products of the tenners and of the oners, or 100x - 1x that difference and that the horizontal derivative will be larger if the product of the oners in the original problem was larger than the product of the tenners and, smaller if the opposite were the case.

In our case: 7 x 2 = 14 (the product of oners) and 3 x 8 = 24 (the product of the tenners). The Δ (24 – 14) = 10. The product of the tenners is larger. Therefore, the horizontal derivative of

$$\begin{array}{r} 37 \\ \times\ \underline{82} \end{array} \quad \text{which is} \quad \begin{array}{r} 73 \\ \times\ \underline{28} \end{array}$$

is smaller than the original by 10 x 99 or less 10 x 100 plus 10 x 1 or less 1,000 plus 10. Thus, 73 x 28 should be $\boxed{3,034}$ – 1,000 + 10 = <u>2,044</u> ✓

Is it? What is the easy (the "real life") way of solving 73 x 28?

There are two easy ways. Can you see them?

1.   25 x 28 (1/4 of 28 x 100) = 700 $\xrightarrow{\times 3}$ 2,100 $\xrightarrow{-2\times 28=-56}$ 2,044 ✓

or

2.   30 x 73 = 2,100 + 90 → 2,190 $\xrightarrow{-2\times 73=-146}$ 2,044 ✓

Step 2

Diagonal 1 Flipped
Compared to Original:

This, the same as Step 4 in Level 10, is the diagonal (1) SW-NE flip.

$$37$$
$$\text{x } \underline{82}$$

becomes

$$38$$
$$\text{x } \underline{72}$$

I hope you remember from Level 10 how this works. The difference between the diagonal flip and the original is: plus/minus the Δ of the diagonal $(8\,|\,7) = 1$ times 100 the tenner of the other diagonal, minus/plus Δ times the oner of the other diagonal. Since the product of the original tenners (7 x 8) is larger than that of the diagonally flipped (3 x 7) the result will be less by

$$(-1 \times 300) + (1 \times 2) \text{ or } 3,034 - 300 + 2 \qquad = \qquad \boxed{2,736}\checkmark$$

Let's check it out. Two easy ways:

1.   38 x 72: 40 x 70 $\rightarrow$ 2,800 $\xrightarrow{+40\text{x}2=80}$ 2,880 $\xrightarrow{-2\text{x}72=-144}$ $\boxed{2,736}\checkmark$

2.   38 x 72: 38 + 72 $\rightarrow$ 110 $\xrightarrow{/2}$ 55 $\xrightarrow{squared}$ 3,025 $\xrightarrow{-17^2=-289}$ $\boxed{2,736}\checkmark$

Step 3

Diagonal 1 Flipped
Compared to Horizontal Derivative:

$$37$$
$$\text{x } \underline{82} = 3,034$$

becomes

$$\begin{array}{r} 38 \\ \times\ \underline{72} = 2{,}736 \end{array}$$

We compare that to the horizontal derivative, which is <u>2,044</u>.

Remember the rule?

Take the Δ of the other diagonal (3 – 2 = 1) times 100 times the oner of the

original of the flipped diagonal, less Δ times the tenner of the original

diagonal. Since the product of the tenners of the flipped problem (3 × 7 =

21) is less than the product of the tenners of the original problem (3 × 8 =

24) the result (the horizontal derivative) will be less by that amount.

Let's see. We know that 38 × 72 = $\boxed{2{,}736}$. We have just figured it out. 2,736 – (100 × 7) + (1 × 8) = 2,736 – 700 + 8 = $\boxed{2{,}044}$ ✓ which is indeed the horizontal derivative.

Steps 4 and 5 are exactly the same as Steps 2 and 3, except that we work with the SE-NW diagonal (2), instead of the SW-NE (1) diagonal.

Here we go:

$$\begin{array}{r} 37 \\ \times\ \underline{82} \end{array}$$

and diagonally flip to

$$\begin{array}{r} 27 \\ \times\ \underline{83} \end{array}$$

How much is that? You will see by now that there are several ways to solve this. You could do it by the square of half-sum ($55^2 - 28^2$ or $3{,}025 - 784 = 2{,}241$) or by (30×83) – (3×83), which is $2{,}490 - 249$. In either case, you will quickly get to the correct result of $\boxed{2{,}241}$.

Step 4

Diagonal 2 Flipped
Compared to Original:

$$37$$
$$\times\ \underline{82}$$

diagonally flip to

$$27$$
$$\times\ \underline{83} = 2{,}241$$

Δ_2: $3|2 = 1$. Therefore,

$$2{,}241 + (1 \times 800) - (1 \times 7) = 2{,}241 + 800 - 7 = \underline{3{,}034}\ \checkmark$$

Which, as we expected, is the original result, and

Step 5

Diagonal 2 Flipped
Compared to Horizontal Derivative:

Δ_1: $8|7 = 1$. Therefore,

$$2{,}241 - (100 \times 2) + (1 \times 3) = 2{,}441 - 200 + 3 = \underline{2{,}044}\ \checkmark$$

which, as we expected, is the horizontal derivative of this problem.

We will now do the other examples that we had in Level 10. In Level 10 I explained every click in full detail. Now, that you know what we are doing, especially the principles and the rules involved, we can move much faster and streamline the operations. That, of course, if essentially what you will be doing in your head – shorten the process as much as possible.

OK, here is the next example from Level 10.

$$\begin{array}{r} 42 \\ \times\ \underline{61} \end{array}$$

We know from Level 10 this to be $\boxed{2,562}$, but we could quickly recalculate that, or course.

Step 1

Horizontal Derivative:

becomes

$$\begin{array}{r} 42 \\ \times\ \underline{61} \end{array}$$

$$\begin{array}{r} 24 \\ \times\ \underline{16} \end{array}$$

Just by looking at it we know that it has to be $\boxed{384}$, because

$25 \times 16 = 16/4 \times 100$ less $1 \times 16 = 400 - 16 = 384$

or, by square of half sum --

$20^2 - 4^2 = 400 - 16 = 384$

How does $24 \times 16 = 384$ (the horizontal derivative) relate to the original $42 \times 61 = 2,562$?

The product of the tenners (4×6) is 24. The product of the oners (2×1) is 2. Therefore, Δ is $(24 - 2) = 22$. The difference should be $+ (100 \times 22) - (1 \times 22)$ and since the product of the oners is smaller, the derivative should be smaller by that amount.

$384 + (100 \times 22) - (1 \times 22) = 384 + 2,200 - 22 \qquad = \qquad \boxed{2,562}\checkmark$

Steps 2 & 3

Diagonal 1 Flipped
Compared to Original and to Horizontal Derivative:

$$42$$
$$\times \underline{61}$$

diagonally flip to

$$46$$
$$\times \underline{21}$$

46 x 21? Easy:

$$20 \times 46 = 920 \xrightarrow{\ +1x46=+46\ } 966 \checkmark$$

Δ_4: $(6 \mid 2) = 4$. $\therefore$ Original s/b: $966 + (400 \times 4) - (4 \times 1) = 966 + 1{,}600 - 4 =$ $\boxed{2{,}562}\checkmark$

Δ_2: $(4 \mid 1) = 3$. $\therefore$ Horizontal derivative (HD) s/b:

$$966 - (300 \times 2) - (3 \times 6) = 966 - 600 + 18 \qquad = \qquad \boxed{384}\checkmark$$

Steps 4 & 5

Diagonal 2 Flipped
Compared to Original and to Horizontal Derivative:

$$42$$
$$\times \underline{61}$$

diagonally flip to

$$12$$
$$\times \underline{64}$$

12 x 64 = $\boxed{768}$. I am sure I don't have to show you how to do this. It's, of course, 10 x 64 + 2 x 64.

Δ_2: $(4\,|\,1) = 3$. $\therefore$ Original s/b: $\boxed{768}$ + (300 x 6) – (3 x 2) = 768 + 1,800 – 6 = $\boxed{2,562}$ ✓

Δ_1: $(6\,|\,2) = 4$. $\therefore$ HD s/b: $\boxed{768}$ – (400 x 1) + (4 x 4) = 768 – 400 + 16 = $\boxed{384}$ ✓

Next example, also from Level 10:

$$\begin{array}{r} 45 \\ \times\ \underline{87} \end{array}$$

Step 1

Horizontal Derivative:

$$\begin{array}{r} 45 \\ \times\ \underline{87} \end{array}$$

We know from Level 10 that it is $\boxed{3,915}$. Flip horizontally and it becomes

$$\begin{array}{r} 54 \\ \times\ \underline{78} \end{array}$$

Here is how.

$$5 \times 7 \rightarrow 35 \xrightarrow{\times 10} 350 \xrightarrow{+(5\times8)+(4\times7)=68} 418 \xrightarrow{\times 10} 4180 \xrightarrow{+4\times8=32} \boxed{4,212}\ ✓$$

Does it check out? Let's see.

The product of the oners is 32 and that of the tenners is 35. Therefore, the horizontal derivative should be (3 x 100) – (3 x 1) larger than the original. Is it?

Steps 2 & 3

Diagonal 1 Flipped
Compared to Original and to Horizontal Derivative:

$$45$$
$$\text{x } \underline{87}$$

flip diagonally to

$$48$$
$$\text{x } \underline{57}$$

Easy way: 50 x 57 minus 2 x 57 = 2,850 – 116   = $\boxed{2,736}$✓

Δ_1: (8 | 5) = 3. ∴ Original s/b: $\boxed{2,736}$ + (300 x 4) – (3 x 7) = 2,736 +

1,200 - 21   = $\boxed{3,915}$✓

Δ_2: (7 | 4) = 3. ∴ HD s/b: $\boxed{2,736}$ + (300 x 5) – (3 x 8) = 2,736 + 1,500 – 24= $\boxed{4,212}$✓

Steps 4 & 5

Diagonal 2 Flipped
Compared to Original and to Horizontal Derivative:

$$45$$
$$\text{x } \underline{87}$$

Flip diagonally to

$$75$$
$$\text{x } \underline{84}$$

You know how to do this in seconds, of course:

25 x 84 (1/4 of 84 x 100) is 2,100; ∴ 75 x 84 is 3 times as much   = $\boxed{6,300}$✓

Δ_2: $(7\,|\,4) = 3$. $\therefore$ Original s/b: $\boxed{6,300} - (300 \times 8) + (3 \times 5) = 6,300$

$$-\,2,400 + 15 \qquad\qquad\qquad = \qquad \boxed{3,915}\checkmark$$

Δ_1: $(8\,|\,5) = 3$. $\therefore$ HD s/b: $\boxed{6,300} - (300 \times 7) + (3 + 4) = 6,300 - 2,100 + 12 = \boxed{4,212}\checkmark$

Another one, also from Level 10.

$$\mathbf{35}$$
$$\mathbf{x\ \underline{73}}$$

We know from Level 10 (although we could easily figure it out again) that

$$35 \times 73 \qquad\qquad\qquad\qquad = \qquad \boxed{2,555}\checkmark$$

This is how you figure:

$$35 \times 73 = (35 \times 75) - (2 \times 35) = 2,625 - 70 \qquad\qquad = \qquad \boxed{2,555}\checkmark$$

Step 1

Horizontal Derivative:

$$\mathbf{35}$$
$$\mathbf{x\ \underline{73}}$$

flip horizontally to

$$\mathbf{53}$$
$$\mathbf{x\ \underline{37}}$$

How much is that? Two easy ways:

1. $50 \times 37 = 1,500 + 350 = 1,850$. Add $3 \times 37 = 111$ and we get $\qquad = \qquad \boxed{1,961}\checkmark$

or

2. $53 + 37 = 90$. Half sum $= 45$. $45^2 = 2,025$. $8^2 = 64$. $2,025 - 64 \qquad = \qquad \boxed{1,961}\checkmark$

It should be smaller than the original (2,555) by 99 x (21 – 15) = 99 x 6

$$\boxed{2,555} - (100 \times 6) + (1 \times 6) = 2,555 - 600 + 6 \qquad\qquad = \qquad \boxed{1,961}\checkmark$$

Steps 2 & 3

Diagonal 1 Flipped
Compared to Original and to Horizontal Derivative:

$$\begin{array}{r} 35 \\ \times\ \underline{73} \end{array}$$

flip to

$$\begin{array}{r} 37 \\ \times\ \underline{53} \end{array}$$

Do you notice something? This is the same as the HD. The reason, of course, is that the two factors (35 and 73) have a common digit, namely 3. Therefore, we know that the result of the first diagonal flip is 1,961 ✓

Let's see how it works.

Δ_1: $(7\,|\,5) = 2$. ∴ Original s/b: $1,961 + (200 \times 3) - (2 \times 3) = 1,961 + 600 - 6 \qquad = \qquad \boxed{2,552}\checkmark$

Δ_2: $(3\,|\,3) = 0$. ∴ HD s/b: $1,961 + (0 \times 500) - (0 \times 7) \qquad\qquad = \qquad \boxed{1,961}\checkmark$

(Of course!)

Steps 4 & 5

Diagonal 2 Flipped
Compared to Original and to Horizontal Derivative:

$$35$$
$$\times \underline{73}$$

flip to

$$35$$
$$\times \underline{73}$$

You see, not too surprisingly that, again, because of that common digit (3), the second diagonal flip is the same as the original. So, we don't really have to go through the process. Let's do it anyway, just for the sake of practice.

Δ_2: $(3 \mid 3) = 0$. $\therefore$ Original s/b: $2,555 + (0 \times 500) - (0 \times 7)$ $=$ $\boxed{2,255}$ ✓

Δ_1: $(7 \mid 5) = 2$. $\therefore$ HD s/b: $= 2,555 - (200 \times 3) + (2 \times 3)$ $=$ $\boxed{1,961}$ ✓

And one final one, also as in Level 10.

$$52$$
$$\times \underline{96}$$

We know from Level 10 that this is $\boxed{4,992}$, but we don't' really have to look or remember. We could easily figure:

1. $50 \times 96 = 4,800 + (2 \times 96)$ $\rightarrow$ $\boxed{4,992}$ ✓

or

2. $100 \times 52 = 5,200 \xrightarrow{\;-4\times52=-208\;}$ $\boxed{4,992}$ ✓

Step 1

Horizontal Derivative:

$$\begin{array}{r} 52 \\ \times \underline{96} \end{array}$$

flip to

$$\begin{array}{r} 25 \\ \times \underline{69} \end{array}$$

You can figure 25 x 69 two easy ways.

1. Divide 69 by 4 (same as multiplying by 25), which you can do

    by dividing by 2 twice → 34.5 → 17.25 → $\boxed{1,725}$✓

or

2. 70 x 25 = 1,750; less 1 x 25 = 25 = $\boxed{1,725}$✓

What should the horizontal derivative be?

The product of the oners is (2 x 6) = 12 and the product of the tenners is (5 x 9) = 45. The difference is (45 – 12) = 33. Therefore, the resultant derivative should be smaller by (33 x 100) + 33 than the original. Is it? Let's check it:

$\boxed{4,992}$ – 3,300 + 33 = 1,692 + 33 = $\boxed{1,725}$✓

234

Steps 2 & 3

Diagonal 1 Flipped
Compared to Original and to Horizontal Derivative:

$$52$$
$$\text{x } \underline{96}$$

flip to

$$59$$
$$\text{x } \underline{26}$$

How much is that?

59 x 26: 60 x 20 $\rightarrow$ 1,200 $\xrightarrow{+60\text{x}6=360}$ 1,560 $\xrightarrow{-1\text{x}26=-26}$ $\rightarrow$ $\boxed{1,534}$✓

Δ_1: $(9 \mid 2) = 7$. $\therefore$ Original s/b: $1,534 + (700 \times 5) - (7 \times 6) = 1,534 +$

3,500 – 42   = $\boxed{4,992}$✓

Δ_2: $(6 \mid 5) = 1$. $\therefore$ HD s/b: $1,534 + (100 \times 2) - (1 \times 9) = 1,534 + 200 - 9$ = $\boxed{1,725}$✓

Steps 4 and 5

Diagonal 2 Flipped
Compared to Original and to Horizontal Derivative:

$$52$$
$$\text{x } \underline{96}$$

flip to

$$62$$
$$\text{x } \underline{95}$$

How much is 62 x 95? It is, of course, 62 x 100 (6,200) minus 62 x 5 (310) = $\boxed{5,890}$ ✓

Δ_2: $(6 \mid 5) = 1$. ∴ Original s/b: $5,890 - (100 \times 9) + (1 \times 2) = 5,890 - 900 + 2$ = $\boxed{4,992}$ ✓

Δ_1: $(9 \mid 2) = 7$. ∴ HD s/b: $= 5,890 - (700 \times 6) + (7 \times 5) = 5,890 - 4,200 + 35$ = $\boxed{1,725}$ ✓

So that is it for Level 12. It wasn't really that bad after all, particularly after we went through in Level 10 and after we learned to streamline it, was it?

As I promised you, this level (Level 12) was really the last difficult one that you will have to handle. From now on out, its going to be pretty much downhill, quite easy, all the way to Level 16, with its last two steps.

I am going to give you the same problems for this level as I gave you for Level 10 since, in reality, Level 12 is a continuation of Level 10.

Here they are.

1. 48 x 91

2. 32 x 57

3. 28 x 42

4. 33 x 67

5. 29 x 78

6. 41 x 56

7. 35 x 65

8. 24 x 83

9. 43 x 68

10. 73 x 98

LEVEL 13: *Square of Half-Sum and Centered on 50*

I promised you that it would be all downhill, pretty easy, from here on out, after the rigors of Level 10 and, to somewhat lesser degree, of Level 12. You will not be disappointed. Level 13 is not really too difficult.

There are three steps. The first one is our old friend the square of half-sum method. Steps 2 and 3, which are the reverse of each other, center the problem on 50. You'll see.

Let's start out with our trusty friend

$$37 \times 82$$

The sum of the factors is 119, and the half sum is $59\frac{1}{2}$. Δ, the difference between the half sum and either of the factors, is $22\frac{1}{2}$. Therefore, 37×82 will be

$$59\frac{1}{2}^2 - 22\frac{1}{2}^2$$

You remember, of course, that the square of a number ending in $\frac{1}{2}$ is the square of the integer immediately below it plus that integer, or the square of the integer immediately above it minus that integer. In either case, the square actually ends in .25 after that number. We have decided, however, that we can disregard that .25 for our purposes, because we shall in each case subtract the square of another number also ending in $\frac{1}{2}$ so that those two .25's will cancel each other.

Step 1

So, $59\frac{1}{2}^2$ is $60^2 - 60 = 3,600 - 60 = \boxed{3,540}$

(That is the, of course, the easy way to do it. We also could have said that $59\frac{1}{2}^2 = 59^2 + 59$. 59^2 is $60^2 - (60 + 59) = 60^2 - 119 = 3,600 - 119 = 3,481$. Adding 59 to that brings us, of course, also to 3,540. But it's clear that it is more difficult. You are encouraged always to see and to take the easiest road -- unless you are under the "constraints" of a level.)

How much is $22\frac{1}{2}$? We know (I hope you remember, if not, please go back to Section 1 and review squares) that --

$$22^2 = 20^2 + (4 \text{ x } 20) + 2^2 \qquad\qquad = \qquad 484$$

and that

$$22\frac{1}{2}^2 \text{ is 22 more or } 484 + 22 \qquad\qquad = \qquad 506$$

$$37 \text{ x } 82 = 59\frac{1}{2}^2 - 22\frac{1}{2}^2 = \boxed{3,540} - 506 \qquad\qquad = \qquad \underline{3,034} \checkmark$$

The rule for Step 2 and Step 3 is:

> ***The product of two 2-digit number is 2,500 less the square of Δ between one of the numbers and 50 plus (if the sum of the two numbers is greater than 100) or minus (if the sum of the two numbers is less than 100) the product of the number and the Δ between the sum of the two numbers and 100.***

Step 2

Let's try this with the following:

37 x 82

Click 1:		$\rightarrow$	2,500
Click 2:	$50 - 37 - 13$		
Click 3:	$-13^2 \rightarrow -169$	$\rightarrow$	2,331

238

Click 4: $37 \times 82 = 119$; $\Delta = 19$

Click 5: $37 \times 19 = 703$ →   3,034

Click 6: 37×82 →   3,034 ✓

(You know how to figure that, but let me show you again: $2,500 - 169 = 2,531 - 200 = 2,331$. $2,331 + 703 = 3,034$. ✓)

Step 3

37 x 82

Click 1:   →   2,500

Click 2: $82 - 50 = 32$

Click 3: -32^2 → $-1,024$ →   1,476

Click 4: $37 + 82 = 119$; $\Delta = 19$

Click 5: $82 \times 19^{(1)}$ → $1,558$ →   3,034

Click 6 37×82 =   3,034 ✓

---

(1) $82 \times 19 = (82 \times 20) - 82$. $1,640 - 82 = 1,658 - 100 = \underline{1,558}$ ✓

Another one:

62 x 93

Step 1

- $62 + 93 = 155$

- Half sum = $77\frac{1}{2}$

- $\Delta = 77\frac{1}{2} - 62 = 15\frac{1}{2}$

$62 \times 93 = 77\frac{1}{2}^2 - 15\frac{1}{2}^2$

$77\frac{1}{2}^2 = 80^2 - (5 \times 80) + 2\frac{1}{2}^2 = 6{,}400 - 400 + 6$ →   6,006

$-15\frac{1}{2}^2 = -225 - 15 = -240$ →   5,766

62×93 =   <u>5,766</u> ✓

62 x 93

Step 2

- $62 - 50 - 12$

- $12^2 = \boxed{144}$

- $\Sigma = 155$, $\Delta = 55$

- $62 \times 55 = 3{,}100 + 310 = \boxed{3{,}410}$

- $62 \times 93 = 2{,}500 - \boxed{144} + \boxed{3{,}410}$

  $= 5{,}910 - 144 = 5{,}966 - 200$ =   <u>5,766</u>✓

62 x 93

Step 3

- $93 - 50 = 43$

- $43^2 = 40^2 + (6 \times 40) + 3^2 - 1{,}600 + 240 + 9 = \boxed{1{,}849}$

- $\Sigma = 155$; $\Delta = 55$

- $93 \times 55 = 100 \times 55 \,(5{,}500) - 7 \times 55 \,(385) = \boxed{5{,}115}$

- $62 \times 93 = 2{,}500 - \boxed{1{,}849} + \boxed{5{,}115} = 7{,}615 - 1{,}849 = 7{,}666 -$

  $1{,}900 = \underline{5{,}766}$ ✓

Another one:

42 x 86

Step 1

- $42 + 86 = 128$. Half sum $= 64$

- $64 - 42 = 22$ (Δ)

- $42 \times 86 = 64^2 - 22^2 = 4{,}096 - 484 = \underline{3{,}612}$ ✓

(You realize, of course that 64^2 is 2^6; therefore, 64^2 is $2^{6 \times 2} = 2^{12}$. And, you can quickly determine what that is by doubling 64 six times, as follows: $2^7 = 128$, $2^8 = 256$, $2^9 = 512$, $2^{10} = 1{,}024$, $2^{11} = 2{,}048$, $2^{12} = 64^2 = 4{,}096$.

Or you could have figured it by the same last digit method: $64 \times 64 - 3{,}600 + (4 \times 120) + 4^2 = 4{,}096$; or by $64^2 = 65^2 - (65 + 64) = 4{,}225 - 129 = 4{,}096$ ✓.

Always look for the best way!)

42 x 86

Step 2

- $50 - 42 = 8$

- $8^2 = \boxed{64}$

- $\Sigma = 128$; $\Delta = 28$

- $42 \times 28 = \boxed{1{,}176}$ [1]

- $42 \times 86 = 2{,}500 - \boxed{64} + \boxed{1{,}176} = \underline{3{,}612}$ ✓

42 x 86

Step 3

- $86 - 50 = 36$

- $36^2 = \boxed{1{,}296}$

- $\Sigma = 128;\ \Delta\ 28$

- $86 \times 28 = \boxed{2{,}408}$ [2]

- $42 \times 86 = 2{,}500 - \boxed{1{,}296} + \boxed{2{,}408} = 4{,}908 - 1{,}296 = \underline{3{,}612}$ ✓

---

(1) $(42 \times 30) - (42 \times 2) = 1{,}260 - 84 = 1{,}176$ ✓ or $42 \times 28 = 35^2 - 7^2 = 1{,}225 - 49 = 1{,}176$ ✓

(2) One of several easy ways for 86×28: $100 \times 28 = 2{,}800$. Subtract 28×14, which is $2 \times 14^2 = 2 \times 196 = 392$. Therefore $86 \times 28 = 2{,}800 - 392 = 2{,}408$. Also: $30 \times 86 = 2{,}580 - (2 \times 86) = 172 \rightarrow 2{,}408$ ✓

Let's do one where both factors are greater than 50.

58 x 73

Step 1

- $58 \times 73 = 131$. Half sum $= 65\frac{1}{2}$

- $65\frac{1}{2} - 58 = 7\frac{1}{2}\ (\Delta)$

- $58 \times 73 = 65\frac{1}{2}^2 - 7\frac{1}{2}^2 = (4{,}225 + 65)$

  $- (49 + 7) = 4{,}290 - 56 = \underline{4{,}234}$ ✓

Step 2

- $58 - 50 = 8$

- $8^2 = \boxed{64}$

- $\Sigma = 58 + 73 = 131$; $\Delta = 31$

- $58 \times 31 = \boxed{1,798}$

- $58 \times 73 = 2,500 - 64 + \boxed{1,798} = \underline{4,234}$ ✓

Step 3

- $73 - 50 = 23$

- $23^2 = \boxed{529}$

- $\Sigma = 131$; Δ 31

- $73 \times 31 = \boxed{2,263}$

- $58 \times 73 = 2,500 - \boxed{529} + \boxed{2,263} = 4,763 - 529 = \underline{4,234}$ ✓

Let's do one final one, in which Σ (sum of the factors) is less then 100. Let's see if the rule will hold. (It will!)

23 x 39

Step 1

- $23 + 39 = 62$. Half sum = 31

- $31 - 23 = 8$ (Δ)

- $23 \times 39 = 31^2 - 8^2 = 961 - 64 = \underline{897}$ ✓

23 x 39

Step 2

- $50 - 23 = 27$

- $27^2 = \boxed{729}$

- $\Sigma = 23 + 39 = 62; \; \Delta \; 62 - 100 = -38$

- $23 \times (-38) = \boxed{-874}$

- $23 \times 39 = 2{,}500 - \boxed{729} - \boxed{874} = 2{,}500 - 1{,}603 = \underline{897} \; \checkmark$

23 x 39

Step 3

- $50 - 39 = 11$

- $11^2 = \boxed{121}$

- $\Sigma = 62; \; \Delta = \boxed{-38}$

- $39 \times (-38)^{(1)} = \boxed{-1{,}482}$

- $23 \times 39 = 2{,}500 - \boxed{121} - \boxed{1{,}482} = 2{,}500 - 1{,}603 = \underline{897} \; \checkmark$

So, that's it for Level 13. I told you that it was going to be an easy on, and it was, wasn't it?

Please re-read this Level fully, familiarizing yourself with it. You should by now be able to do this in your sleep. (Well, not just yet, but give yourself some time and practice and you'll get there soon enough.)

Here are ten problems, your homework, which you will please solve by the three steps of Level 13. And, as before, run all of them through the previous levels. It will be excellent practice for you.

In any case, check your results by the tests that we have learned. In each case, determine

---

(1) Solve 38×39 either by $40 \times 38 \; (1{,}520) - 38 = 1{,}482\checkmark$, or by $38^2 + 38 = 40^2 - (4 \times 40) + 2^2 + 38 = 1{,}600 - 160 + 4 + 38 = 1{,}482\checkmark$

what would be the easiest, the "real life" way to solve each of these problems if you were not committed to the restraints of Level 13.

1. 52 x83

2. 41 x 67

3. 25 x 58

4. 37 x 92

5. 57 x 74

6. 32 x 59

7. 67 x 87

8. 43 x 52

9. 48 x 78

10. 23 x 38

LEVEL 14: *Complement to 10*

2 Steps

This level is, as I promised you, is another easy one. It only has two steps – one being the mirror image of the other.

In this level we must "equalize" the oners so that they add up to 10 (if they don't already). Then, after we have performed the operation, we must, of course, add or subtract for the adjustment that we have to make.

Suppose our problem is (our old friend)

37 x 82

For Step 1, we would keep 37, but change 82 to 83, which would make the oners add up to 10. In Step 2, we would keep the 82 and change the 37 to 38, again so as to make the oners add up to 10. In the former case, we would have to subtract 1 x 37 from our product at the end, because we would have figured 37 x 83, and what we wanted was 37 x 82. In the second case, we would have to subtract 1 x 82 = 82 from our product, because we would have figured 38 x 82 and of course what we wanted was 37 x 83.

Here's the rule:

> *To multiple two 2-digit numbers whose oners add up to 10, multiply the lower full tenner with the upper full tenner plus 10, add the product of the lower oner and the difference between the upper full tenner plus 10 and the lower full tenner, and subtract the square of the lower oner.*

Again, WOW! But really, it just sounds complicated; it's really quite easy.

Let's try it with good old

$$37 \times 82$$

$$37 \times 82$$

becomes

$$37 \times 83$$

We'll have to subtract $1 \times 37 = \boxed{37}$ at the end.

Click 1:	$30 \times (80 + 10) = 30 \times 90$		→	2,700
Click 2:	$7 \times (90 - 30) = 7 \times 60$	→+420	→	3,120
Click 3:	$-7^2 =$	→ -49	→	3,071
Click 4:	Subtract $\boxed{37}$		→	3,034
	37×82		=	<u>3,034</u> ✓

$$37 \times 82$$

becomes

$$38 \times 82$$

We'll have to subtract $\boxed{82}$ at the end.

Click 1:	$30 \times (80 + 10) = 30 \times 90$		→	2,700
Click 2:	$8 \times (90 - 30) = 8 \times 60$	→ 480	→	3,180
Click 3:	-8^2	→ -64	→	3,116
Click 4:	Subtract $\boxed{82}$		→	3,034
	37×82		=	<u>3,304</u> ✓

Let's do a few more, but we are going to streamline them.

$$59 \times 76$$

Step 1

becomes

$$59 \times 76$$

$$59 \times 71$$

We'll have to add 5 x 59 = $\boxed{295}$ at the end.

$$50 \times 80 \rightarrow 4{,}000 \xrightarrow{+9\times30=270} 4{,}270 \xrightarrow{-9^2=-81} 4{,}189 \xrightarrow{+[295]} \qquad \underline{4{,}484} \checkmark$$

Step 2

becomes

$$59 \times 76$$

$$54 \times 76$$

We'll have to add 5 x 76 = $\boxed{380}$ at the end.

$$50 \times 80 \rightarrow 4{,}000 \xrightarrow{+4\times30=120} 4{,}120 \xrightarrow{-4^2=-16} 4{,}104 \xrightarrow{+[380]} \qquad \underline{4{,}484} \checkmark$$

How about –

$$38 \times 56$$

Step 1

becomes

$$38 \times 56$$

$$38 \times 52$$

We'll have to add 4 x 38 = $\boxed{152}$ at the end.

$$30 \times 60 \rightarrow 1{,}800 \xrightarrow{+8\times30=240} 2{,}040 \xrightarrow{-8^2=-64} 1{,}976 \xrightarrow{+[152]} \qquad \underline{2{,}128} \checkmark$$

248

Step 2

38 x 56

becomes

34 x 56

We'll have to add 4 x 56 = 224 at the end.

$30 \times 60 \rightarrow 1{,}800 \xrightarrow{+4 \times 30 = 120} 1{,}920 \xrightarrow{-4^2 = -16} 1{,}904 \xrightarrow{+[224]} \underline{2{,}128} \checkmark$

Let do two more:

29 x 69

Step 1

29 x 69

becomes

29 x 61

We'll have to add 8 x 29 = 232 at the end.

$20 \times 70 \rightarrow 1{,}400 \xrightarrow{+9 \times 50 = 450} 1{,}850 \xrightarrow{-9^2 = -81} 1{,}769 \xrightarrow{+[232]} \underline{2{,}001} \checkmark$

Step 2

29 x 69

becomes

21 x 69

We'll have to add 8 x 69 = 552 at the end.

$20 \times 70 \rightarrow 1{,}400 \xrightarrow{+1 \times 50 = 50} 1{,}450 \xrightarrow{-1^2 = -1} 1{,}449 \xrightarrow{+[552]} \underline{2{,}001} \checkmark$

And a final one:

48 x 72

What do you know? The oners of this problem add up to ten. There's going to be only one step and no adjustment will be required.

$40 \times 80 \rightarrow 3{,}200 \xrightarrow{\ +8 \times 40 = 320\ } 3{,}520 \xrightarrow{\ -8^2 = -64\ }$ $\quad\quad\quad$ <u>3,456</u> ✓

So that was Level 14, a really easy one, wasn't it?

And here is your homework. I know I am beginning to sound like a Dutch Uncle, but:

❖   Do all problems also by previous levels.

❖   Look at all problems carefully and critically and decide the best way how you would solve it in "real life," if you were not constrained by the level.

❖   Check you answers by the tests that you have learned.

❖   Make up your own problems – and practice, practice, practice!

1.   **42 x 79**

2.   **31 x 86**

3.   **29 x 74**

4.   **83 x 92 (90 + 10 = 100, of course)**

5.   **24 x 57**

6.   **36 x 84**

7.   **22 x 75**

8.   **34 x 62**

9.   **51 x 93**

10.   **27 x 82**

LEVEL 15: *Equal Oners and Tenners*

4 Steps

This is the one before the last – the 15th out of 16 levels. You are almost there. And this is another easy one.

There are four steps, but it's really only two because the first two are the reverse of each other and the last two are the reverse of each other.

In Steps 1 and 2 of this level, we equalize the oners; in Steps 3 and 4, we equalize the tenners, provided of course that they are not already the same. And we are dealing with rules that we already learned in Section I of this book (*Review of Arithmetic*) under the headings "Multiplying Numbers that End in the Same Digit" and "Multiplying Numbers that have the Same Initial Digit(s)".

To save you the bother of having to look it up, I repeat the two rules here:

The product of two 2-digit numbers[*] ending in the same digit is the product of the full tenners of those numbers, plus the sum of those full tenners times the common last digit, plus the square of that common last digit.

The product of two 2-digit numbers* that have the same tenners is the square of those common full tenners, plus that full tenner multiplied by the sum of the last digits, plus the product of those last digits.

---

[*] The same principle would of course apply also to numbers with more than two digits. But since we are dealing here only with 2-digit numbers, we shall confine the rules to that.

Let's try it with good old reliable

37 x 82

In Step 1, we equalize the oners so as to conform with the oner of the first (lower) number.

37 x 82

becomes

37 x 87

We'll have to subtract 5 x 37 = $\boxed{185}$ at the end.

Let's do it.

Click 1:	30 x 80	→	2,400
Click 2:	(30 + 80) x 7 = 110 x 7	→ 770 →	3,170
Click 3:	7^2	→ 49 →	3,219
Click 4:	- $\boxed{185}$	→-185 →	3,034
Click 5:	∴ 37 x 82	=	3,034 ✓

Step 2

In this step, we equalize the oners so as to confirm with the oner of the second (higher) number.

37 x 82

becomes

32 x 82

We'll have to add 5 x 82 = $\boxed{410}$ at the end.

Click 1:	30 x 80	=	2,400

Click 2:	$(30 + 80)$ x $2 = 110$ x 2	→	+220	→	2,620
Click 3:	2^2	→	+4	→	2,624
Click 4:	+ 410	→	+410	→	3,034
Click 5:	$\therefore$ 37 x 82		=		3,034 ✓

Step 3

In this step we equalize the tenners so as to conform with the tenner of the first (lower) number.

37 x 82

becomes

37 x 32

We'll have to add 50 x 37 = 1,850 at the end.

Click 1:	30^2		→		900
Click 2:	$(2 + 7)$ x $30 = 9$ x 30	→	+270	→	1,170
Click 3:	7 x 2	→	+14	→	1,184
Click 4:	+ 1,850	→	+ 1,850	→	3,034
Click 5:	$\therefore$ 37 x 82		=		3,034 ✓

Step 4

In this step we equalize the tenners so as to conform with the tenners of the second (higher) number.

37 x 82

becomes

$$\textbf{87 x 82}$$

We'll have to subtract 50 x 82 = $\boxed{4{,}100}$ at the end.

Click 1:	80^2	$\rightarrow$	$6{,}400 =$	$6{,}400$
Click 2:	$(7 + 2) \times 80 = 9 \times 80 =$	$\rightarrow$	$+720 \rightarrow$	$7{,}120$
Click 3:	7×2	$\rightarrow$	$+14 \rightarrow$	$7{,}134$
Click 4:	$- \boxed{4{,}100}$	$\rightarrow$	$- 4{,}100 =$	$3{,}034$
Click 5:	$\therefore 37 \times 82$		$=$	$\underline{3{,}034}\ \checkmark$

That wasn't too bad, was it?

Let's try a few more.

$$\textbf{23 x 59}$$

Step 1

$$\textbf{23 x 59}$$

becomes

$$\textbf{23 x 53}$$

We'll have to add 6 x 23 = $\boxed{138}$ at the end.

Let's streamline it.

$20 \times 50 \rightarrow 1{,}000 \xrightarrow{+3(20+50)=210} 1{,}210 \xrightarrow{+3^2=9} 1{,}219 \xrightarrow{+[138]} \underline{1{,}357}\ \checkmark$

Step 2

$$\textbf{23 x 59}$$

becomes

29 x 59

We'll have to subtract 6 x 59 = $\boxed{354}$ at the end.

$$20 \times 50 \to 1{,}000 \xrightarrow{\;+9(20+50)=630\;} 1{,}630 \xrightarrow{\;+9^2=81\;} 1{,}711 \xrightarrow{\;-[354]\;} \qquad \underline{1{,}357}\ \checkmark$$

Step 3

23 x 59

becomes

23 x 29

We'll have to add 30 x 23 = $\boxed{690}$ at the end.

$$20^2 \to 400 \xrightarrow{\;+(3+9)\times20=240\;} 640 \xrightarrow{\;+3\times9=27\;} 667 \xrightarrow{\;+[690]\;} \qquad \underline{1{,}357}\ \checkmark$$

Step 4

23 x 59

becomes

53 x 59

We'll have to subtract 30 x 59 = $\boxed{1{,}770}$ at the end.

$$50^2 \to 2{,}500 \xrightarrow{\;+(3+9)\times50=600\;} 3{,}100 \xrightarrow{\;+3\times9=27\;} 3{,}127 \xrightarrow{\;-[1{,}770]\;} \qquad \underline{1{,}357}\ \checkmark$$

How about:

62 x 92

We find that the last digit of the two numbers are the same, namely 2, so we have only one step in the first half of this level.

Let's do it:

Steps 1 & 2

62 x 92

$60 \times 90 \rightarrow 5{,}400 \xrightarrow{+2(60+90)=300} 5{,}700 \xrightarrow{+2^2=4} \underline{5{,}704}$ ✓

Step 3

62 x 92

becomes

62 x 62

We'll have to add $30 \times 62 = \boxed{1{,}860}$ at the end.

$60^2 \rightarrow 3{,}600 \xrightarrow{+60(2+2)=240} 3{,}840 \xrightarrow{2^2=4} 3{,}844 \xrightarrow{+[1{,}860]} \underline{5{,}704}$ ✓

Step 4

62 x 92

becomes

92 x 92

We'll have to subtract $30 \times 92 = \boxed{2{,}760}$ at the end.

$90^2 \rightarrow 8{,}100 \xrightarrow{+90(2+2)=360} 8{,}460 \xrightarrow{2^2=4} 8{,}464 \xrightarrow{-[2{,}760]} \underline{5{,}704}$ ✓

And another one:

58 x 74

becomes

58 x 78

We'll have to subtract 4 x 58 = $\boxed{232}$ at the end.

Step 1

$50 \times 70 \rightarrow 3{,}500 \xrightarrow{8(50+70)=960} 4{,}460 \xrightarrow{+8^2=64} 4{,}524 \xrightarrow{-[232]} \qquad \underline{4{,}292} \checkmark$

Step 2

58 x 74

becomes

54 x 74

We'll have to add 4 x 74 = $\boxed{296}$ at the end.

$50 \times 70 \rightarrow 3{,}500 \xrightarrow{+4(50+70)=480} 3{,}980 \xrightarrow{+4^2=16} 3{,}996 \xrightarrow{+[296]} \qquad \underline{4{,}292} \checkmark$

Step 3

58 x 74

becomes

58 x 54

We'll have to add 20 x 58 = $\boxed{1{,}160}$ at the end.

$50^2 \rightarrow 2{,}500 \xrightarrow{+(8+4)\times50=600} 3{,}100 \xrightarrow{+4\times8=32} 3{,}132 \xrightarrow{+[1{,}160]} \qquad \underline{4{,}292} \checkmark$

Step 4

58 x 74

becomes

78 x 74

We'll have to subtract 20 x 74 = $\boxed{1,480}$ at the end.

$70^2 \to 4,900 \xrightarrow{+(8+4)\times70=840} 5,740 \xrightarrow{+8\times4=32} 5,772 \xrightarrow{-[1,480]} \underline{4,292}$ ✓

And, one final one.

49 x 66

Step 1

49 x 66

becomes

49 x 69

We'll have to subtract 3 x 49 = $\boxed{147}$ at the end.

$40 \times 60 \to 2,400 \xrightarrow{+9(40+60)=900} 3,300 \xrightarrow{+9^2=81} 3,381 \xrightarrow{-[147]} \underline{3,234}$ ✓

Step 2

49 x 66

becomes

46 x 66

We'll have to add 3 x 66 = $\boxed{198}$ at the end.

$40 \times 60 \to 2,400 \xrightarrow{+6(40+60)=600} 3,000 \xrightarrow{+6^2=36} 3,036 \xrightarrow{+[198]} \underline{3,234}$ ✓

Step 3

49 x 66

becomes

49 x 46

We'll have to add 20 x 49 = $\boxed{980}$ at the end.

$40^2 \rightarrow 1,600 \xrightarrow{+(9+6)\text{x}40=600} 2,200 \xrightarrow{+9\text{x}6=54} 2,254 \xrightarrow{+[980]} \qquad \underline{3,234} \checkmark$

Step 4

49 x 66

becomes

69 x 66

We'll have to subtract 20 x 66 = $\boxed{1,320}$ at the end.

$60^2 \rightarrow 3,600 \xrightarrow{+(9+6)\text{x}60=900} 4,500 \xrightarrow{+9\text{x}6=54} 4,554 \xrightarrow{-[1,320]} \qquad \underline{3,234} \checkmark$

How did you like Level 15? It was really easy, wasn't it? We applied what we had already learned.

There is only one level left – Level 16. It is pretty much of a powder puff, with only two steps. So, you just about have it made, as far as the Paradigm is concerned.

Before we go into this last level, let's give you some homework. As before, work all the examples also by the methods of all the previous levels that we have learned; in every case, also determine how you would solve the problem in "real life" (the easiest way, unrestrained by the demands of the level) and also check out each of your answers by applying the tests that we have learned.

1. 39 x 87

2. 54 x 68

3. 27 x 54

4. 38 x 53

5. 46 x 77

6. 31 x 82

7. 45 x 79

8. 28 x 94

9. 63 x 67 (Only one click for Steps 3 and 4)

10. 51 x 84

LEVEL 16: *Strip the Tenners*

2 Steps

We are coming to the end of this road – Level 16, the last level of the Paradigm and it's kind of an anticlimax because there are only two steps, and they are pretty easy ones.

On this level we "eliminate," we "strip," the tenners – in Step 1, the tenner of the lower number and in Step 2, the tenner of the higher number.

For instance, in our favorite example

37 x 82
becomes 7 x 52

having taken away 30 from both the lower and the higher number.

Step 2, in which we eliminate the tenner of the higher number is a little tricky because it causes the lower number to become negative. In our case

37 x 82

we eliminate (we "strip") 80 (the tenner of the higher number) and

37 x 82
becomes (37 – 80) x (82 – 80)
– 43   x   2

And, here's the rule:

> *If, in multiplying two 2-digit numbers with each other, the tenner of either number has been eliminated ("stripped") and the other number has been reduced by the same amount, the result of the original problem is obtained as follows: Take the square of the eliminated full tenner; add the product of the eliminated full tenner and the sum of the reduced factors; add the product of the reduced factors.*

Sounds a little complicated?

Yes, it does, but it's really quite simple.

Let's go back to

37 x 82

Step 1

37 x 82
becomes 7 x 52

Click 1:	Eliminate the full tenner = 30. 30^2		→	900
Click 2:	30 (7 + 52) = 30 x 59	→ +1,770	→	2,670
Click 3:	7 x 52	→ +364	→	3,034
Click 4:	∴ 37 x 82		=	3,034 ✓

Quick and easy, wasn't it!

Step 2

37 x 82
becomes -43 x 2, because 37 – 80 = -43

Click 1:	80^2		→	6,400
Click 2:	80 (-43 +2) = 80 x -41	→	-3,280 →	3,120
Click 3:	-43 x 2	→	-86 →	3,034
Click 4:	∴ 37 x 82		=	3,034 ✓

Another one:

62 x 93

Step 1

62 x 93
becomes 2 x 33

Streamlining it:

$$60^2 = 3,600 \xrightarrow{+60(2+33)=2,100} 5,700 \xrightarrow{+2x33=66} \qquad \underline{5,766} \checkmark$$

Step 2

62 x 93
becomes -28 x 3

$90^2 = 8,100$ $\xrightarrow{90(-28+3)=-2,250}$ $5,850$ $\xrightarrow{-28x3=-84}$ $\underline{5,766}$ ✓

And another one:

48 x 77

Step 1

48 x 77
becomes 8 x 37

$40^2 \rightarrow 1,600$ $\xrightarrow{+40(8+37)=1,800}$ $3,400$ $\xrightarrow{+(8x37)=296}$ $\underline{3,696}$ ✓

Step 2

48 x 77
becomes -22 x 7

$70^2 = 4,900$ $\xrightarrow{70(-22+7)=-1,050}$ $3,850$ $\xrightarrow{-22x7=-154}$ $\underline{3,696}$ ✓

And one more:

52 x 87

Step 1

52 x 87
becomes 2 x 37

$50^2 \rightarrow 2,500$ $\xrightarrow{+50(2+37)=1,950}$ $4,450$ $\xrightarrow{+(2x37)=74}$ $\underline{4,524}$ ✓

Step 2

52 x 87
becomes -28 x 7

$80^2 = 6,400$ $\xrightarrow{\;80(-28+7)=-1,680\;}$ $4,720$ $\xrightarrow{\;-28\text{x}7=-196\;}$ $\underline{4,524}$ ✓

And a last one:

78 x 99

Step 1

78 x 99
becomes 8 x 29

$70^2 \rightarrow 4,900$ $\xrightarrow{\;+70(8+29)=2,590\;}$ $7,490$ $\xrightarrow{\;+8\text{x}29=232\;}$ $\underline{7,722}$ ✓

Step 2

78 x 99
becomes – 12 x 9

$90^2 = 8,100$ $\xrightarrow{\;90(-12+9)=-270\;}$ $7,830$ $\xrightarrow{\;-12\text{x}9=-108\;}$ $\underline{7,722}$ ✓

Let's check this last one by the following four tests as to whether it's right.

❖ It should be between 70 x 90 (6,300) and 80 x 100 (8,000). It is. ✓

❖ It should end in 2, because 8 x 9 = 72. It does. ✓

❖ It should be divisible by 9, because 99 is, of course, is divisible by 9. Sum of digits of 7,722 is 18 → 9. Yes, it is. ✓

❖ It should be divisible by 11 because 99 is divisible by 11. The sum of the first and third digits of 7,722 is 9, and the sum of the second and fourth digits is 9; they are the same, so 7,722 is divisible by 11. Yes, it is. ✓

Can you be 100% sure that this is the right answer? No you can't, but you can be reasonable sure. There is one other number that fulfills the four requirements, namely 6,732, but that's all. We'll have some more to say about this in our section about algebra. But as we learned before, you can be 100% sure that your result is wrong if it fails even only one of these tests.

So we have come to the end of this section and to the end of the 16-level Paradigm. If, as I know you have, have stuck with me through to this level, your mind should by now be very much sharper than it was before and your memory should be much enhanced. But, you will not get the full benefit until after we'll have done the next section together, in which I take you step-by-step and level by level --- the full 16-level Paradigm --- through a number of examples.

But in the meantime, please do the ten examples that follow by the Level 16 method. And, as always, solve the same examples with the methods of all the other fifteen levels, make up your own examples and check your results by the methods we have learned.

Good luck, and we'll meet again in Section III of this book.

1.   23 x 86

2.   43 x 72

3.   58 x 83

4.   42 x 77

5.   53 x 92

6.   27 x 44

7.   36 x 94

8.   52 x 88

9.   42 x 73

10.   51 x 84

Section III

A FEW FULL TRIPS THROUGH THE 16-LEVEL PARADIGM

In Section II, we went through and (I hope) learned the individual levels of the 16-Level Paradigm. In this section, we are putting it all together. We shall go together through six complete paradigms. It is what I shall want you to do eventually by yourself, of course. Once you get through with this book, I expect you always to have one problem, one paradigm, going. You should be working on it while you shower, while you jog, while you swim your laps, while you drive to and from work, and – believe it or not – while in bed, before you go to sleep. It will do wonders for you. But we will talk about this some more later.

At the end of this section, after we have done those problems together, I shall give you ten more problems to work on. In each case, I shall give you hints and shortcuts on how to solve these problems in the easiest, the "real life" way. Because, remember, you are only committed to the constraints of each level on the initial, main operation. For all intermediate calculations, you are on your own and may do the best you can.

So, let's start with our first problem.

Problem #1

38 x 54

LEVEL 1 (THE EASIEST) .... *2 STEPS*

Step 1   **38 x 54**

- $(30 \times 54) + (8 \times 54)$

- $30 \times 54 \ = \ (30 \times 50) + (30 \times 4) \ = \ 1,500 + 120 \ \rightarrow \ \ 1,620$

- $8 \times 54 \ \ = \ (8 \times 50) + (8 \times 4) \ \ = \ 400 + 32 \ \ \ \rightarrow \underline{\ \ \ \ 432}$

∴ **38 x 54** $= \ \ \mathbf{2,052} \ \checkmark$

Step 2   **38 x 54**

- $(50 \times 38) + (4 \times 38)$

- $50 \times 38 \ \ = \ (50 \times 30) + (50 \times 8) \ = \ 1,500 + 400 \ \rightarrow \ \ 1,900$

- $4 \times 38 \ \ \ = \ (4 \times 30) + (4 \times 8) \ \ \ = \ 120 + 32 \ \ \ \ \rightarrow \underline{\ \ \ \ 152}$

∴ **38 x 54** $= \ \ \mathbf{2,052} \checkmark$

LEVEL 2 (THE CLASSIC) .... *2 STEPS*

Step 1   **38 x 54**

- $(30 \times 50) + (8 \times 50) + (4 \times 30) + (8 \times 4)$

- $1,500 \xrightarrow{+8 \times 50 = +400} 1,900 \xrightarrow{+4 \times 30 = +120} 2,020 \xrightarrow{+8 \times 4 = +32} 2,052 \ \checkmark$

Step 2   **38 x 54**

                                                (40-2) x (60-6)

- $(40 \times 60) - (2 \times 60) - (6 \times 40) + (2 \times 6)$

• $2,400 \xrightarrow{\;-2\times60=-120\;} 2,280 \xrightarrow{\;-6\times40=-240\;} 2,040 \xrightarrow{\;+2\times6=+12\;} 2,052 \checkmark$

LEVEL 3 (CENTERED AROUND 5) .... *5 STEPS*

Step 1   **38 x 54**

• 35 x 55[*]   → 1,925

• For 38 x 55, add 3 x 55   → +165 → 2,090

• For 38 x 54, subtract 1 x 38   → -38 → 2,052 $\checkmark$

    Δ   → +127 $\checkmark$

Step 2   **38 x 54**
                                                38 x 52

We will have to add 2 x 38 = $\boxed{+76}$ at the end.

• 50-30 = 20

• 8-5   =   3

• 3 x 20   →   +60

• -3^2 →   -9

• Add: → $\boxed{+76}$

    Δ   → +127 $\checkmark$

Step 3   **38 x 54**
                                                36 x 54

We will have to add 2 x 54 = $\boxed{+108}$ at the end.

• 50-30 = 20

• 6-5   =   1

---

[*] If you have forgotten how to multiply two numbers that end in 5, turn back to Section I for a refresher.

- 1 x 20   →   +20

- -1^2 →   -1

- Add: → $\boxed{+108}$

     Δ →   +127 ✓

Step 4   **38 x 54**

                           38 x 58

We will have to subtract 4 x 38 = $\boxed{-152}$ at the end.

- 30+50+10 = 90

- 8-5   =   3

- 3 x 90   →   +270

- $+3^2$ →   +9

- Subtract: → $\boxed{-152}$

     Δ →   +127 ✓

Step 5   **38 x 54**

                           34 x 54

We will have to add 4 x 54 = $\boxed{+216}$ at the end.

- 30+50+10 = 90

- 4-5   =   -1

- -1 x 90   →   -90

- $+(-1^2)$ →   +1

- Add: → $\boxed{+216}$

     Δ →   +127 ✓

LEVEL 4 (POWERS OF 2 OR 3, QUARTERS OR EIGHTHS)...............*3 STEPS*

Step 1 38 x 54

32 x 54

We will have to add 6 x 54 = $\boxed{324}$ at the end.

- 108 → 216 → 432 → 864 → 1,728 $\xrightarrow{\boxed{+324}}$ 2,052 ✓
  (x2) (x4) (x8) (x16) (x32)

Step 2 38 x 54

37½ x 54 (⅜ x 54 x 100)

We will have to add ½ x 54 = $\boxed{27}$ at the end.

- 54/8 = 6¾ $\xrightarrow{\text{x 3}}$ 18¾ → 20¼ $\xrightarrow{\text{x100}}$ 2,025 $\xrightarrow{\boxed{+27}}$ 2,052 ✓

Step 3 38 x 54

38 x 50

We will have to add 4 x 38 = $\boxed{+152}$ at the end.

- 50 x 38 → 1,900 $\xrightarrow{\boxed{+152}}$ 2,052 ✓

LEVEL 5 (FLIPS) ....*2 STEPS*

Step 1 38 x 54

38 x 83

After we have arrived at 38 x 83, we have to bring it back to 38 x 54. There are two ways of doing it:

1) Subtract 29 x 38.

2) Subtract 2 x 38 = $\boxed{76}$, which brings you to 38 x 81; divide that by three, which brings you to 38 x 27; multiply that by 2, which brings you to 38 x 54.

But first, we have to solve 38 x 83:

- 38 x 83 → 30 x 80 → 2,400 $\xrightarrow{+10(8^2+3^2)=+730}$ 3,130 $\xrightarrow{+8\times3=+24}$ 3,154

270

1) Subtract 29 x 38:

- 29 x 38 → 30 x 38 = 1,140 − 38 = 1,102.

- 3,154 − 1,102 = 2,052✓

2) Subtract 2 x 38 = $\boxed{76}$ from the result. Then divide the result by three and multiply it by 2:

- $3{,}154 \xrightarrow{-2\text{x}38=\boxed{-76}} 3{,}078 \xrightarrow{/3} 1{,}026 \xrightarrow{\text{x}2} 2{,}052$✓

Step 2   **38 x 54**

45 x 54

We will have to subtract 7 x 54 = $\boxed{378}$ at the end.

- $45 \times 54 \to 40 \times 50 \to 2{,}000 \xrightarrow{+10(5^2+4^2)=+410} 2{,}410 \xrightarrow{+5\text{x}4=+20} 2{,}430 \xrightarrow{\boxed{-378}} 2{,}052$✓
(Remember: 2,430 − 378 → 2,430 + 22 − 400 = 2,452 − 400 = 2,052.)

LEVEL 6 (COMPLEMENTS TO 100) .... *2 STEPS*

Step 1   **38 x 54**

3,800 − (46 x 38)

- Solve 46 x 38 by half-sum: $42^2 - 4^2 = 1{,}764 - 16 = 1{,}748$.

- 3,800 − 1,748 = 2,052✓

Step 2   **38 x 54**

5,400 − (62 x 54)

- 62×54: $50 \times 60 \to 3{,}000 \xrightarrow{+50\text{ x }2 = +100} 3{,}100 \xrightarrow{+4\text{ x }62 = +248} 3{,}348$

- 5,400 − 3,348 = 2,052✓

LEVEL 7 (COMPLEMENT SQUARES).. *2 STEPS*

Step 1   **38 x 54**

$\Delta = 16$

- $38^2 + (16 \times 38) = 1{,}444 + 608 = 2{,}052$✓

Note:

- $(38^2 = 40^2 - 4 \times 40 + 2^2 = 1{,}600 - 160 + 4 = 1{,}444)$

- $(16 \times 38 = 16 \times 40 - 2 \times 16 = 640 - 32 = 608)$

Step 2   **38 x 54**

$\Delta = 16$

- $54^2 - (16 \times 54) = 2{,}916 - 864 = 2{,}052\checkmark$

LEVEL 8 (HALVES, COMMON DENOMINATORS, HALVES AND DOUBLES)...*4 STEPS*

Step 1   **38 x 54**

19 x 27 (x 4)

- 19×27: $20 \times 27 \rightarrow 540 \xrightarrow{-27} 513 \xrightarrow{\times 4} 2{,}052\checkmark$

Step 2   **38 x 54**

Closest common denominator is 18 or 19. Let's take 19.

38 x 54

38 x 57

We will have to subtract $3 \times 38 = \boxed{114}$ at the end.

- $38 = 2 \times 19; 57 = 3 \times 19$

- $38 \times 54 = 19^2 \times 6 - \boxed{114} = (361 \times 6) - 114 = 2{,}166 - 114 \rightarrow 2{,}052\checkmark$

Step 3   **38 x 54**

76 x 27

- $76 \times 27 = (76 \times 30) - (76 \times 3) = 2{,}280 - 228 = 2{,}052\checkmark$

Step 4   **38 x 54**

19 x 108

- $19 \times 108 = (19 \times 100) + (19 \times 8) = 1{,}900 + 152 = 2{,}052\checkmark$

LEVEL 9 (PLUS AND MINUS 10)...*4 STEPS*

Step 1   **38 x 54**

                                              28 x 64

$\Delta = 54 \mid 38 = 16$. Result should be $(10 \times 16) + 100 = \boxed{260}$ less.

- Should be $2,052 - \boxed{260} = 1,792$✓

- $28 \times 64 = (30 \times 64) - (2 \times 64) = 1,920 - 128 = 1,792$✓

Step 2   **38 x 54**

                                              48 x 44

- $\Delta = 54 \mid 38 = 16$. Result should be $(10 \times 16) - 100 = \boxed{60}$ more.

- Result should be $2,052 + \boxed{60} = 2,112$✓

- $48 \times 44 = 46^2 - 2^2 = 2,116 - 4 = 2,112$✓

(How do you get 46^2 mentally and quickly? You know that $45^2 = 2,025$ ($4^2 + 4$ and hang on 25).

46^2 is $45 + 46$ more than 45^2; therefore, $46^2 = 2,025 + 91 = 2,116$.)

Step 3   **38 x 54**

                                              28 x 44

$\sum = 92$. Result should be $(10 \times 92) - 100 = \boxed{820}$ less.

- Should be $2,052 - \boxed{820} = 1,232$✓

- $28 \times 44 = (30 \times 44) - (2 \times 44) = 1,320 - 88 = 1,232$✓

Step 4   **38 x 54**

                                              48 x 64

- $\sum = 92$. Result should be $(10 \times 92) + 100 = \boxed{1,020}$ more.

- Result should be $2,052 + \boxed{1,020} = 3,072$✓

- $48 \times 64 = (50 \times 64) - (2 \times 64) = 3,200 - 128 = 3,072$✓

LEVEL 10 (FLIPS AND DIAGONALS: PART I).................................... *7 STEPS*

Step 1

$$38$$
$$\times \underline{54}$$

- $3 \times 5 \rightarrow 15 \xrightarrow{\times 10} 150 \xrightarrow{+(8 \times 5) + (4 \times 3) = +52} 202 \xrightarrow{\times 10} 2{,}020 \xrightarrow{+8 \times 4 = +32} 2{,}052$ ✓

Step 2: Vertical Flip

$$38$$
$$\times \underline{54}$$

$$34$$
$$\times \underline{58}$$

Δ of oners is 4; Δ of tenners is 20.

Result should be $4 \times 20 = 80$ less than $2{,}052 \rightarrow 1{,}972$ ✓

- $3 \times 5 \rightarrow 15 \xrightarrow{\times 10} 150 \xrightarrow{+(4 \times 5) + (8 \times 3) = +44} 194 \xrightarrow{\times 10} 1{,}940 \xrightarrow{+4 \times 8 = +32} 1{,}972$ ✓

Step 3: Horizontal Derivative

$$34$$
$$\times \underline{58}$$

$$43$$
$$\times \underline{85}$$

- Product of oners is $4 \times 8 = 32$

- Product of tenners is $3 \times 5 = 15$.

- $\Delta = 32 \mid 15 = 17$.

- Therefore, the horizontal derivative should be 1,700 more and 17 less than 1,972.

- Result should be $1{,}972 + 1{,}700 - 17 = 3{,}655$ ✓

- $43 \times 85 = 40 \times 85 \rightarrow 3{,}400 \xrightarrow{+3 \times 85 = +255} 3{,}655$ ✓

274

Step 4: First Diagonal Flip (1)   34

                                                   x <u>58</u>

                                                   35

                                                   x <u>48</u>

- $35 \times 48 = (50 \times 35) - (2 \times 35) = 1{,}750 - 70 = 1{,}680$ ✓

$\Delta_1 = 5 \mid 4\ = 1$

Difference should be $+(100 \times 3) - (1 \times 8) = \boxed{+\,300 - 8}$.

- $1{,}680 + (100 \times 3) - (1 \times 8) = 1{,}680 \boxed{+\,300 - 8} = 1{,}972$ ✓

Step 5: First Diagonal Flip (2)   34

                                                   x <u>58</u>

                                                   35

                                                   x <u>48</u>

- $35 \times 48 = 1{,}680$ ✓

$\Delta_2 = 8 \mid 3 = 5$

Difference should be $+(500 \times 4) - (5 \times 5) = \boxed{+\,2{,}000 - 25}$

- $1{,}680 \boxed{+\,2{,}000 - 25} = 3{,}655$ ✓

Step 6: Second Diagonal Flip (1)   34

                                                   x <u>58</u>

                                                   84

                                                   x <u>53</u>

- $84 \times 53 = (50 \times 84) + (3 \times 84) = 4{,}200 + 252 = 4{,}452$ ✓

$\Delta_2 = 8 \mid 3\ = 5$

Difference should be $-(500 \times 5) + (5 \times 4) = \boxed{-\,2{,}500 + 20}$

- $4{,}452 \boxed{-\,2{,}500 + 20} = 1{,}972$ ✓

Step 7: Second Diagonal Flip (2)

$$34 \\ \times \underline{58}$$

$$84 \\ \times \underline{53}$$

- $84 \times 53 = 4{,}452$ ✓

$\Delta_1 = 5 \mid 4 = 1$

Difference should be $-(100 \times 8) + (1 \times 3) = \boxed{-\,800 + 3}$

- $4{,}452 \boxed{-\,800 + 3} = 3{,}655$ ✓

LEVEL 11 (SKEWED).. *2 STEPS*

Step 1 $\qquad\qquad\qquad 38 \times 54$

- $30 \times 50 \to 1{,}500 \xrightarrow{+(8+4) \times 38 = +456} 1{,}956 \xrightarrow{+8(50-30)=+160} 2{,}116 \xrightarrow{-8^2 = -64} 2{,}052$ ✓

Step 2 $\qquad\qquad\qquad 38 \times 54$

- $30 \times 50 \to 1{,}500 \xrightarrow{+(8+4) \times 54 = +648} 2{,}148 \xrightarrow{-4(50-30)=-80} 2{,}068 \xrightarrow{-4^2 = -16} 2{,}052$ ✓

LEVEL 12 (FLIPS AND DIAGONALS: PART II)................................. *5 STEPS*

Step 1: Horizontal Derivative

$$38 \\ \times \underline{54}$$

$$83 \\ \times \underline{45}$$

- Product of oners is $3 \times 5 = 15$.

- Product of tenners is $8 \times 4 = 32$.

- $\Delta = 32 \mid 15 = 17$.

- Therefore, the horizontal derivative should be 1,700 more and 17 less than 2,052.

- Result should be $2{,}052 + 1{,}700 - 17 = 3{,}735$ ✓

- $83 \times 45 = (80 \times 45) + (3 \times 45) = 3{,}600 + 135 = 3{,}735$ ✓

Step 2: First Diagonal Flip (1)
$$38$$
$$\text{x } \underline{54}$$

$$35$$
$$\text{x } \underline{84}$$

- $84 \times 35 = (80 \times 35) + (4 \times 35) = 2{,}800 + 140 = 2{,}940$ ✓

$\Delta_1 = 8 \mid 5 = 3$

Difference should be $+(300 \times 3) - (3 \times 4) = \boxed{+888}$

- $2{,}052 + \boxed{888} = 2{,}940$ ✓

Step 3: First Diagonal Flip (2)
$$38$$
$$\text{x } \underline{54}$$

$$35$$
$$\text{x } \underline{84}$$

- $35 \times 84 = 2{,}940$ ✓

$\Delta_2 = 4 \mid 3 = 1$

Difference should be $(100 \times 8) - (1 \times 5) = \boxed{+\ 800 - 5}$

- $2{,}940 \boxed{+\ 800 - 5} = 3{,}735$ ✓

Step 4: Second Diagonal Flip (1)
$$38$$
$$\text{x } \underline{54}$$

$$48$$
$$\text{x } \underline{53}$$

- $48 \times 53 = (50 \times 48) + (3 \times 48) = 2{,}400 + 144 = 2{,}544$ ✓

$\Delta_2 = 4 \mid 3 = 1$

Difference should be $-(100 \times 5) + (1 \times 8) = \boxed{-500 + 8}$

- $2{,}544 \boxed{-\ 500 + 8} = 2{,}052$ ✓

Step 5: Second Diagonal Flip (2)
$$38$$
$$\times \underline{54}$$

$$48$$
$$\times \underline{53}$$

- $48 \times 53 = 2{,}544$ ✓

$\Delta_1 = 8 \mid 5 = 3$

Difference should be $+(300 \times 4) - (3 \times 3) = \boxed{+1{,}200 - 9}$

- $2{,}544 \boxed{+1{,}200 - 9} = 3{,}735$ ✓

LEVEL 13 (SQUARE OF HALF-SUM AND CENTERED ON 50)..........*3 STEPS*

Step 1   **38 x 54**

- $\Sigma(38 + 54) = 92.$ $\Sigma/2 = 46.$

- $\Delta = 46 \mid 38 = 8.$

- $38 \times 54 = 46^2 - 8^2 = 2{,}116 - 64 = 2{,}052$ ✓

(Remember: $46^2 = 45^2 + 45 + 46 = 2{,}025 + 91 = 2{,}116.$)

Step 2   **38 x 54**

- $\Sigma(38 + 54) = 92.$

- $92 - 100 = -8.$

- $\Delta = 50 \mid 38 = 12.$

- $38 \times 54 = 2{,}500 - 12^2 - (8 \times 38) = 2{,}500 - 144 - 304 = 2{,}500 - 448 = 2{,}052$ ✓

Step 3   **38 x 54**

- $\Sigma(38 + 54) = 92.$

- $92 - 100 = -8.$

- $\Delta = 54 \mid 50 = 4.$

- $38 \times 54 = 2{,}500 - 4^2 - (8 \times 54) = 2{,}500 - 16 - 432 = 2{,}500 - 448 = 2{,}052$ ✓

LEVEL 14 (COMPLEMENT TO 10) .... *2 STEPS*

Step 1   **38 x 54**

38 x 52 (make oners add to 10)

Add 2 x 38 = $\boxed{76}$ at the end.

- $50 + 10 = 60$

- $60 - 30 = 30$

- $38 \times 54 = (60 \times 30) + (8 \times 30) - 8^2 \boxed{+ 76} = 1{,}800 + 240 \boxed{+ 76} - 64 = 2{,}116 - 64 = 2{,}052 \checkmark$

Step 2   **38 x 54**

36 x 54 (make oners add to 10)

Add 2 x 54 = $\boxed{108}$ at the end.

- $50 + 10 = 60$

- $60 - 30 = 30$

- $38 \times 54 = (60 \times 30) + (6 \times 30) - 6^2 \boxed{+ 108} = 1{,}800 + 180 - 36 \boxed{+ 108} = 2{,}088 - 36 = 2{,}052 \checkmark$

LEVEL 15 (EQUAL ONERS AND TENNERS) .... *4 STEPS*

Step 1   **38 x 54**

38 x 58 (to equalize oners)

Subtract 4 x 38 = $\boxed{152}$ at the end.

- $30 \times 50 \rightarrow 1{,}500 \xrightarrow{+(30+50)8=+640} 2{,}140 \xrightarrow{+8^2=+64} 2{,}204 \xrightarrow{\boxed{-152}} 2{,}052 \checkmark$

(Note: $2{,}204 - 152 = 2{,}252 - 200 = 2{,}052$)

Step 2   **38 x 54**

34 x 54 (to equalize oners)

Add 4 x 54 = $\boxed{216}$ at the end.

- $30 \times 50 \rightarrow 1{,}500 \xrightarrow{+(30+50)4=+320} 1{,}820 \xrightarrow{+4^2=+16} 1{,}836 \xrightarrow{\boxed{+216}} 2{,}052 \checkmark$

Step 3   **38 x 54**

                                               38 x 34 (to equalize tenners)

Add 20 x 38 = $\boxed{760}$ at the end.

- $30^2 \rightarrow 900 \xrightarrow{+30(8+4)=+360} 1{,}260 \xrightarrow{+4 \times 8=+32} 1{,}292 \xrightarrow{\boxed{+760}} 2{,}052 \checkmark$

Step 4   **38 x 54**

                                               58 x 54 (to equalize tenners)

Subtract 20 x 54 = $\boxed{1{,}080}$ at the end.

- $50^2 \rightarrow 2{,}500 \xrightarrow{+50(8+4)=+600} 3{,}100 \xrightarrow{+4 \times 8=+32} 3{,}132 \xrightarrow{\boxed{-1{,}080}} 2{,}052 \checkmark$

(Note: $3{,}132 - 1{,}080 = 3{,}152 - 1{,}100 = 2{,}052$.)

LEVEL 16 (STRIP THE TENNERS).. *2 STEPS*

Step 1   **38 x 54**

                                               8 x 24 (eliminating the first tenner)

- $38 \times 54 = 30^2 + 30(8+24) + (8 \times 24) = 900 + 960 + 192 = 2{,}052 \checkmark$

Step 2   **38 x 54**

                                               -12 x 4 (eliminating the second tenner)

- $38 \times 54 = 50^2 + 50(-12+4) + (-12 \times 4) = 2{,}500 - 400 - 48 = 2{,}052 \checkmark$

Now let's go on to Problem #2.

Problem #2

28 x 67

LEVEL 1 (THE EASIEST) .... *2 STEPS*

<u>Step 1</u>   28 x 67

- (20 x 67) + (8 x 67)

- 20 x 67   =   (20 x 60) + (20 x 7)   =   1,200 + 140   →   1,340

- 8 x 67   =   (8 x 60) + (8 x 7)   =   480 + 56   →   +536

$$\therefore \quad 28 \times 67 = \underline{1{,}876}\checkmark$$

<u>Step 2</u>   28 x 67

- (60 x 28) + (7 x 28)

- 60 x 28   =   (60 x 20) + (60 x 8)   =   1,200 + 480   →   1,680

- 7 x 28   =   (7 x 20) + (7 x 8)   =   140 + 56   →   +196

$$\therefore \quad 28 \times 67 = \underline{1{,}876}\checkmark$$

LEVEL 2 (THE CLASSIC) .... *2 STEPS*

<u>Step 1</u>   28 x 67

- (20 x 60) + (8 x 60) + (7 x 20) + (8 x 7)

- $1{,}200 \xrightarrow{+8x60=480} 1{,}680 \xrightarrow{+7x20=140} 1{,}820 \xrightarrow{+8x7=56} 1{,}876 \checkmark$

<u>Step 2</u>   28 x 67
                                                        (30 – 2) x (70 – 3)

- (30 x 70) - (2 x 70) – (3 x 30) + (2 x 3)

- $2{,}100 \xrightarrow{-2x70=-140} 1{,}960 \xrightarrow{-3x30=-90} 1{,}870 \xrightarrow{+2x3=6} 1{,}876 \checkmark$

LEVEL 3 (CENTERED AROUND 5) .... *5 STEPS*

Step 1   **28 x 67**

- 25 x 65 $\rightarrow$ 1,625

- For 28 x 65, add 3 x 65 $\rightarrow$ +195 $\rightarrow$ 1,820

- For 28 x 67, add 2 x 28 $\rightarrow$ <u>+56</u> $\rightarrow$ 1,876✓

    Δ $\rightarrow$ +251✓

Step 2   **28 x 67**
                                       28 x 62

We will have to add 5 x 28 = $\boxed{140}$ at the end.

- 60 – 20   =   40

- 8 – 5   =   3

- 3 x 40 $\rightarrow$ +120

- -3^2 $\rightarrow$ -9

- Add: $\rightarrow$ $\boxed{+140}$

    Δ $\rightarrow$ +251✓

Step 3   **28 x 67**
                                       23 x 67

We will have to add 5 x 67 = $\boxed{335}$ at the end.

- 60 – 20   =   40

- 3 – 5   =   -2

- -2 x 40   →   -80

- $-(-2^2)$ →   -4

- Add: → $\boxed{+335}$
                 ———

     Δ   →   +251✓

Step 4

28 x 67

28 x 68

We will have to subtract 1 x 28 = $\boxed{28}$ at the end.

- 20 + 60 + 10   = 90

- 8 – 5   =   3

- 3 x 90   →   +270

- $+3^2$ →   +9

- Subtract: → $\boxed{-28}$
                 ———

     Δ   →   +251✓

Step 5

28 x 67

27 x 67

We will have to add 1 x 67 = $\boxed{67}$ at the end.

- 20 + 60 + 10   = 90

- 7 – 5   =   2

- 2 x 90   →   180

- $+(2^2)$ →   +4

- Add: → $\boxed{+67}$
                 ———

     Δ   →   +251✓

LEVEL 4 (POWERS OF 2 OR 3, QUARTERS OR EIGHTHS) .... *3 STEPS*

Step 1   28 x 67

27 x 67

We will have to add 1 x 67 = $\boxed{67}$ at the end.

- 201 → 603 → 1,809 $\xrightarrow{\boxed{+67}}$ 1,876 ✓
  (x3)   (x9)   (x27)

Step 2   28 x 67

25 x 67

We will have to add 3 x 67 = $\boxed{201}$ at the end.

- 25 x 67: 67/2 → 33.5 $\xrightarrow{/2}$ 16.75 $\xrightarrow{x\,100}$ 1,675 $\xrightarrow{\boxed{+201}}$ 1,876 ✓

Step 3   28 x 67

28 x 75

We will have to subtract 8 x 28 = $\boxed{224}$ at the end.

- 28 x 75: 28 $\xrightarrow{/4}$ 7 $\xrightarrow{x3}$ 21 $\xrightarrow{x\,100}$ 2,100 $\xrightarrow{\boxed{-224}}$ 1,876 ✓

LEVEL 5 (FLIPS) .... *2 STEPS*

Step 1   28 x 67

28 x 82

After we have arrived at 28 x 82, we have to bring it back to 28 x 67. The easy way of doing this is to subtract 15 x 28 = $\boxed{420}$.

But first we have to solve 28 x 82:

- 28 x 82 → 20 x 80 → 1,600 $\xrightarrow{+10(2^2+8^2)=680}$ 2,280 $\xrightarrow{+8x2=16}$ 2,296

Now, to bring it back to 28 x 67, you must subtract 28 x 15:

- 28 x 15 → (28 x 10) + (28 x 5) = 280 + 140 = $\boxed{420}$

- $2,296 - \boxed{420} = 1,876 \checkmark$

Step 2

$$28 \times 67$$

$$76 \times 67$$

The easy way to get from 76 x 67 to 28 x 67 is to first divide by 2, which brings us to 38 x 67, and then to subtract 10 x 67 = $\boxed{670}$.

- $76 \times 67 \rightarrow 70 \times 60 \rightarrow 4,200 \xrightarrow{+10(7^2+6^2)=850} 5,050 \xrightarrow{+7 \times 6=42} 5,092$

Now, to bring it back to 28 x 67, you must divide by 2 and subtract 10 x 67:

- $5,092 \xrightarrow{/2} 2,546 \xrightarrow{\boxed{-670}} 1,876 \checkmark$

LEVEL 6 (COMPLEMENTS TO 100) .... *2 STEPS*

Step 1

$$28 \times 67$$

$$2,800 - (33 \times 28)$$

- $33 \times 28 \rightarrow 840 + 84 \rightarrow 924$
- $2,800 - 924 \rightarrow 2,800 + 76 - 1,000 = 1,876 \checkmark$

Step 2

$$28 \times 67$$

$$6,700 - (72 \times 67)$$

- Solve 72 x 67 by square of half-sum: $(69\frac{1}{2})^2 - (2\frac{1}{2})^2 = (4,900 - 70) - 6 = 4,830 - 6 = 4,824$
- $6,700 - 4,824 = 6,776 - 4,900$ or $6,876 - 5,000 = 1,876 \checkmark$

LEVEL 7 (COMPLEMENT SQUARES) .... *2 STEPS*

Step 1

$$28 \times 67$$

$$\Delta = 39$$

- $28^2 + (39 \times 28) = 784 + 1,092 = 1,876 \checkmark$

(Note: $28^2 = 30^2 - (4 \times 30) + 2^2 = 900 - 120 + 4 = 784.$

   $39 \times 28 = (40 \times 28) - 28 = 1,120 - 28 = 1,092.$)

Step 2   **28 x 67**

$$\Delta = 39$$

• $67^2 - (39 \times 67) = 4,489 - 2,613 = 1,876$ ✓

(Note: $67^2 = 70^2 - (6 \times 70) + 3^2 = 4,900 - 420 + 9 = 4,489$.

   $39 \times 67 = (40 \times 67) - 67 = 2,680 - 67 = 2,613$.

   $4,489 - 2,613 = 4,489 - 2,600 \rightarrow 1,889 - 13 \rightarrow 1,876$ ✓)

LEVEL 8 (HALVES, COMMON DENOMINATORS, HALVES AND DOUBLES) .... *4 STEPS*

Step 1   **28 x 67**

14 x 33½ (x 4)

• $14 \times 33\frac{1}{2}$: $30 \times 14 \rightarrow 420 \xrightarrow{+3 \times 14 = 42} 462 \xrightarrow{+\frac{1}{2} \times 14 = 7} 469 \xrightarrow{\times 4} 1,876$ ✓

(Note: $4 \times 469 = (4 \times 400) + (4 \times 60) + (4 \times 9) = 1,600 + 240 + 36 = 1,876$ ✓)

Step 2   **28 x 67**

Closest common denominator is 14.

28 x 67
28 x 70

We will have to subtract $3 \times 28 = \boxed{84}$ at the end.

• $28 = 2 \times 14$; $70 = 5 \times 14$

• $28 \times 67 = 14^2 \times 10 - \boxed{84} = (196 \times 10) - 84 = 1,960 - 84 \rightarrow 1,876$ ✓

Step 3   **28 x 67**

56 x 33½

• $56 \times 33\frac{1}{2} = (56 \times 30) + (56 \times 3) + (56 \times \frac{1}{2}) = 1,680 + 168 + 28 = 1,876$ ✓

Step 4   **28 x 67**
                                               14 x 134

Use same last digit method:

- $14 \times 134 = (10 \times 130) + (4 \times 140) + 4^2 = 1,300 + 560 + 16 = 1,876$ ✓

- $(14 \times 140) - (14 \times 6) = (14^2 \times 10) - 84 = 1,960 - 84 = 1,876$ ✓

LEVEL 9 (PLUS AND MINUS 10)... *4 STEPS*

Step 1   **28 x 67**
                                               18 x 77

$\Delta = 67 \mid 28 = 39$. Result should be $(10 \times 39) + 100 = \boxed{490}$ less.

- Should be $1,876 - \boxed{490} = 1,386$ ✓

- $18 \times 77 = (20 \times 77) - (2 \times 77) = 1,540 - 154 = 1,386$ ✓

Step 2   **28 x 67**
                                               38 x 57

- $\Delta = 67 \mid 28 = 39$. Result should be $(10 \times 39) - 100 = \boxed{290}$ more.

- Result should be $1,876 + \boxed{290} = 2,166$ ✓

- $38 \times 57 = (40 \times 57) - (2 \times 57) = 2,280 - 114 = 2,166$ ✓

Step 3   **28 x 67**
                                               18 x 57

$\Sigma = 28 + 67 = 95$. Result should be $(10 \times 95) - 100 = \boxed{850}$ less.

- Should be $1,876 - \boxed{850} = 1,026$ ✓

- $18 \times 57 = (20 \times 57) - (2 \times 57) = 1,140 - 114 = 1,026$ ✓

Step 4   **28 x 67**
                                               38 x 77

- $\Sigma = 28 + 67 = 95$. Result should be $(10 \times 95) + 100 = \boxed{1,050}$ more.

- Result should be $1,876 + \boxed{1,050} = 2,926$ ✓

- $38 \times 77 = (40 \times 77) - (2 \times 77) = 3,080 - 154 = 2,926$ ✓, or

- $38 \times 77 = (2 \times 38^2) + 38 = 2(1,444) + 38 = 2,888 + 38 = 2,926$ ✓

LEVEL 10 (FLIPS AND DIAGONALS: PART I) .... *7 STEPS*

Step 1
$$28$$
$$\times 67$$

- $2 \times 6 \rightarrow 12 \xrightarrow{\times 10} 120 \xrightarrow{+(8 \times 6)+(7 \times 2)=62} 182 \xrightarrow{\times 10} 1{,}820 \xrightarrow{+8 \times 7=56} 1{,}876\checkmark$

Step 2: Vertical Flip
$$28$$
$$\times 67$$

$$27$$
$$\times 68$$

Δ of oners is 1; Δ of tenners is 40.

Result should be $1 \times 40 = 40$ less than $1{,}876 \rightarrow 1{,}836\checkmark$

- $2 \times 6 \rightarrow 12 \xrightarrow{\times 10} 120 \xrightarrow{+(7 \times 6)+(8 \times 2)=58} 178 \xrightarrow{\times 10} 1{,}780 \xrightarrow{+7 \times 8=56} 1{,}836\checkmark$

Step 3: Horizontal Derivative
$$27$$
$$\times 68$$

$$72$$
$$\times 86$$

- Product of oners is $7 \times 8 = 56$

- Product of tenners is $2 \times 6 = 12$.

- $\Delta = 56 \mid 12 = 44$.

- Therefore, the horizontal derivative should be 4,400 more and 44 less than 1,836.

- Result should be $1{,}836 + 4{,}400 - 44 = 6{,}192\checkmark$

- $72 \times 86 = 79^2 - 7^2 \rightarrow 6{,}241 - 49 = 6{,}192\checkmark$

Step 4: First Diagonal Flip (1)

$$\begin{array}{r} 27 \\ \times\, \underline{68} \end{array}$$

$$\begin{array}{r} 26 \\ \times\, \underline{78} \end{array}$$

- $26 \times 78 = (25 \times 78) + 78 = 1{,}950 + 78 = 2{,}028$ ✓

$\Delta_1 = 7 \mid 6\ = 1$

Difference should be $-(100 \times 2) + (1 \times 8) = \boxed{-200 + 8}$.

- $2{,}028 - (100 \times 2) + (1 \times 8) = 2{,}028\ \boxed{-200 + 8} = 1{,}836$ ✓

Step 5: First Diagonal Flip (2)

$$\begin{array}{r} 27 \\ \times\, \underline{68} \end{array}$$

$$\begin{array}{r} 26 \\ \times\, \underline{78} \end{array}$$

- $26 \times 78 = (25 \times 78) + 78 = 1{,}950 + 78 = 2{,}028$ ✓

$\Delta_2 = 8 \mid 2 = 6$

Difference should be $+(600 \times 7) - (6 \times 6) = \boxed{+4{,}200 - 36}$

- $2{,}028\ \boxed{+4{,}200 - 36} = 6{,}192$ ✓

Step 6: Second Diagonal Flip (1)

$$\begin{array}{r} 27 \\ \times\, \underline{68} \end{array}$$

$$\begin{array}{r} 87 \\ \times\, \underline{62} \end{array}$$

- $87 \times 62 = 6{,}200 - (13 \times 62) = 6{,}200 - 806 = 5{,}394$ ✓, or

- $87 \times 62 = (80 \times 62) + (7 \times 62) = 4{,}960 + 434 = 5{,}394$ ✓

$\Delta_2 = 8 \mid 2\ = 6$

Difference should be $-(600 \times 6) + (6 \times 7) = \boxed{-3{,}600 + 42}$

- $5{,}394\ \boxed{-3{,}600 + 42} = 1{,}836$ ✓

Step 7: Second Diagonal Flip (2)

$$\begin{array}{r} 27 \\ \times 68 \end{array}$$

$$\begin{array}{r} 87 \\ \times 62 \end{array}$$

- 87 x 62 = 5,394✓ (see Step 6, above)

$\Delta_1 = 7 \mid 6 \ = 1$

Difference should be +(100 x 8) - (1 x 2) = $\boxed{+\ 800 - 2}$

- 5,394 $\boxed{+\ 800 - 2}$ = 6,192✓

LEVEL 11 (SKEWED)... *2 STEPS*

Step 1   **28 x 67**

- 20 x 60 → 1,200 $\xrightarrow{+(8+7)\times28=420}$ 1,620 $\xrightarrow{+8(60-20)=320}$ 1,940 $\xrightarrow{-8^2=-64}$ 1,876✓

Step 2   **28 x 67**

- 20 x 60 → 1,200 $\xrightarrow{+(8+7)\times67=1,005}$ 2,205 $\xrightarrow{-7(60-20)=-280}$ 1,925 $\xrightarrow{-7^2=-49}$ 1,876✓

LEVEL 12 (FLIPS AND DIAGONALS: PART II) .... *5 STEPS*

Step 1: Horizontal Derivative

$$\begin{array}{r} 28 \\ \times 67 \end{array}$$

$$\begin{array}{r} 82 \\ \times 76 \end{array}$$

- Product of oners is 8 x 7 = 56.

- Product of tenners is 2 x 6 = 12.

- $\Delta = 56 \mid 12 = 44.$

- Therefore, the horizontal derivative should be 4,400 more and 44 less than 1,876.

- Result should be $1{,}876 + 4{,}400 - 44 = 6{,}232$ ✓

- $82 \times 76 = 79^2 - 3^2 = 6{,}241 - 9 = 6{,}232$ ✓

Step 2: First Diagonal Flip (1)

$$\begin{array}{r} 28 \\ \times\ \underline{67} \end{array}$$

$$\begin{array}{r} 26 \\ \times\ \underline{87} \end{array}$$

- $26 \times 87 = (100 \times 26) - (13 \times 26) = (100 \times 26) - (13^2 \times 2) = 2{,}600 - 338 = 2{,}262$ ✓

$\Delta_1 = 8\ |\ 6 = 2$

Difference should be $+(200 \times 2) - (2 \times 7) = \boxed{+400 - 14}$

- $1{,}876 \boxed{+\ 400 - 14} = 2{,}262$ ✓

Step 3: First Diagonal Flip (2)

$$\begin{array}{r} 28 \\ \times\ \underline{67} \end{array}$$

$$\begin{array}{r} 26 \\ \times\ \underline{87} \end{array}$$

- $26 \times 87 = 2{,}262$ ✓ (see above)

$\Delta_2 = 7\ |\ 2 = 5$

Difference should be $+(500 \times 8) - (5 \times 6) = \boxed{+\ 4{,}000 - 30}$

- $2{,}262 \boxed{+\ 4{,}000 - 30} = 6{,}232$ ✓

Step 4: Second Diagonal Flip (1)

$$\begin{array}{r} 28 \\ \times\ \underline{67} \end{array}$$

$$\begin{array}{r} 78 \\ \times\ \underline{62} \end{array}$$

The easiest way to calculate 78×62 is by square of half sum:

- $78 \times 62 = 70^2 - 8^2 = 4{,}900 - 64 = 4{,}836$ ✓

$\Delta_2 = 7\ |\ 2 = 5$

Difference should be -(500 x 6) + (5 x 8) = $\boxed{-3,000 + 40}$

- $4,836 \boxed{-3,000 + 40} = 1,876$ ✓

Step 5: Second Diagonal Flip (2)

$$\begin{array}{r} 28 \\ \times\ \underline{67} \end{array}$$

$$\begin{array}{r} 78 \\ \times\ \underline{62} \end{array}$$

- $78 \times 62 = 4,836$ ✓ (see above)

$\Delta_1 = 8 \mid 6\ = 2$

Difference should be +(200 x 7) - (2 x 2) = $\boxed{+ 1,400 - 4}$

- $4,836 \boxed{+ 1,400 - 4} = 6,232$ ✓

LEVEL 13 (SQUARE OF HALF-SUM AND CENTERED ON 50)..........*3 STEPS*

Step 1   **28 x 67**

- $\Sigma(28 + 67) = 95$. $\Sigma/2 = 47\frac{1}{2}$

- $\Delta = 67 \mid 28 = 39$. $\Delta \mid 2 = 19\frac{1}{2}$

- $28 \times 67 = (47\frac{1}{2})^2 - (19\frac{1}{2})^2 = 2,256 - 380 = 1,876$ ✓

(Remember: $(47\frac{1}{2})^2 = 50^2 - (5 \times 50) + 2\frac{1}{2}^2 = 2,500 - 250 + 6(.25) = 2,256(.25)$

(Also: $(19\frac{1}{2})^2 = 20^2 - 20 + (\frac{1}{2})^2 = 400 - 20 + \frac{1}{4} = 380(.25)$

Step 2   **28 x 67**

- $\Sigma(28 + 67) = 95$.

- $95 - 100 = -5$.

- $\Delta = 50 \mid 28 = 22$

- $28 \times 67 = 2,500 - 22^2 - (28 \times 5) = 2,500 - 484 - 140 = 1,876$ ✓

Step 3   **28 x 67**

- $\Sigma(28 + 67) = 95$.

- $95 - 100 = -5$.

- $\Delta = 67 \mid 50 = 17$.

- $28 \times 67 = 2,500 - 17^2 - (5 \times 67) = 2,500 - 289 - 335 = 1,876\checkmark$

LEVEL 14 (COMPLEMENT TO 10).. *2 STEPS*

<u>**Step 1**</u>   **28 x 67**

28 x 62 (make oners add to 10)

Add $5 \times 28 = \boxed{140}$ at the end.

- $60 + 10 = 70$

- $70 - 20 = 50$

- $28 \times 67 = (70 \times 20) + (8 \times 50) - 8^2 + \boxed{140} = 1,400 + 400 - 64 + \boxed{140} = 1,876\checkmark$

<u>**Step 2**</u>   **28 x 67**

23 x 67 (make oners add to 10)

Add $5 \times 67 = \boxed{335}$ at the end.

- $60 + 10 = 70$

- $70 - 20 = 50$

- $28 \times 67 = (70 \times 20) + (3 \times 50) - 3^2 + \boxed{335} = 1,400 + 150 - 9 + \boxed{335} = 1,876\checkmark$

LEVEL 15 (EQUAL ONERS AND TENNERS) .... *4 STEPS*

<u>**Step 1**</u>   **28 x 67**

28 x 68 (to equalize oners)

Subtract $1 \times 28 = \boxed{28}$ at the end.

- $20 \times 60 \rightarrow 1,200 \xrightarrow{+8(20+60)=640} 1,840 \xrightarrow{+8^2=64} 1,904 \xrightarrow{\boxed{-28}} 1,876\checkmark$

Step 2   **28 x 67**

                                              27 x 67 (to equalize oners)

Add 1 x 67 = $\boxed{67}$ at the end.

- $20 \times 60 \rightarrow 1{,}200 \xrightarrow{+7(20+60)=560} 1{,}760 \xrightarrow{+7^2=49} 1{,}809 \xrightarrow{\boxed{+67}} 1{,}876\checkmark$

Step 3   **28 x 67**

                                              28 x 27 (to equalize tenners)

Add 40 x 28 = $\boxed{1{,}120}$ at the end.

- $20^2 \rightarrow 400 \xrightarrow{+20(7+8)=300} 700 \xrightarrow{+7 \times 8=56} 756 \xrightarrow{\boxed{+1{,}120}} 1{,}876\checkmark$

Step 4   **28 x 67**

                                              68 x 67 (to equalize tenners)

Subtract 40 x 67 = $\boxed{2{,}680}$ at the end.

- $60^2 \rightarrow 3{,}600 \xrightarrow{+60(8+7)=900} 4{,}500 \xrightarrow{+8 \times 7=56} 4{,}556 \xrightarrow{\boxed{-2{,}680}} 1{,}876\checkmark$

(Note: $4{,}556 - 2{,}680 = 4{,}576 - 2{,}700 = 1{,}876\checkmark$ or $4{,}556 - 2{,}680 = 4{,}876 - 3{,}000 = 1{,}876\checkmark$)

LEVEL 16 (STRIP THE TENNERS) .... *2 STEPS*

Step 1   **28 x 67**

                                              8 x 47 (eliminating the first tenner)

- $28 \times 67 = 20^2 + 20(8 + 47) + (8 \times 47) = 400 + 1{,}100 + 376 = 1{,}876\checkmark$

Step 2   **28 x 67**

                                              -32 x 7 (eliminating the second tenner)

$28 \times 67 = 60^2 + 60(-32 + 7) + (-32 \times 7) = 3{,}600 - 1{,}500 - 224 = 1{,}876\checkmark$

And on to Problem #3.

Problem #3

53 x 86

LEVEL 1 (THE EASIEST) .... *2 STEPS*

Step 1   53 x 86

- $(50 \times 86) + (3 \times 86)$

- $50 \times 86 \quad = \quad (50 \times 80) + (50 \times 6) = 4{,}000 + 300 \quad \rightarrow \quad 4{,}300$

- $3 \times 86 \quad = \quad (3 \times 80) + (3 \times 6) = 240 + 18 \quad\quad \rightarrow \quad \underline{\;\;258}$

$$\therefore 53 \times 86 \quad = \quad \underline{4{,}558}\checkmark$$

Step 2   53 x 86

- $(80 \times 53) + (6 \times 53)$

- $80 \times 53 \quad = \quad (80 \times 50) + (80 \times 3) = 4{,}000 + 240 \rightarrow \quad 4{,}240$

- $(6 \times 53) \quad = \quad (6 \times 50) + (6 \times 3) \quad = \quad 300 + 18 \rightarrow \quad \underline{\;\;318}$

$$\therefore 53 \times 86 \quad = \quad \underline{4{,}558}\checkmark$$

LEVEL 2 (THE CLASSIC) .... *2 STEPS*

Step 1   53 x 86

- $(50 \times 80) + (3 \times 80) + (6 \times 50) + (3 \times 6)$

- $4{,}000 \xrightarrow{+3 \times 80 = 240} 4{,}240 \xrightarrow{+6 \times 50 = 300} 4{,}540 \xrightarrow{+3 \times 6 = 18} 4{,}558 \checkmark$

Step 2   53 x 86

(60 − 7) x (90 − 4)

- $(60 - 90) - (7 \times 90) - (4 \times 60) + (4 \times 7)$

- $5,400 \xrightarrow{-7 \times 90 = -630} 4,770 \xrightarrow{-4 \times 60 = -240} 4,530 \xrightarrow{+4 \times 7 = 28} 4,558 \checkmark$

LEVEL 3 (CENTERED AROUND 5) .... *5 STEPS*

Step 1   53 x 86

- 55 x 85   →   4,675

- For 53 x 85, subtract 2 x 85   →   -170   →   4,505

- For 53 x 86, add 1 x 53   →   +53   →   4,558 $\checkmark$

     Δ →   -117 $\checkmark$

Step 2   53 x 86
                               53 x 87

We will have to subtract 1 x 53 = $\boxed{53}$ at the end.

- $80 - 50$ =   30

- $3 - 5$ =   -2

- -2 x 30   →   -60

- $- (-2^2)$ →   -4

- Subtract   →   - $\boxed{53}$

     Δ →   -117 $\checkmark$

Step 3   53 x 86
                               54 x 86

We will have to subtract 1 x 86 = $\boxed{86}$ at the end.

- $80 - 50$ =   30

- $4 - 5$ =   -1

296

- -1 x 30   →   -30

- $-(-1^2)$ →   -1

- Subtract: →   - $\boxed{86}$
  _____

    Δ   →   -117✓

Step 4   **53 x 86**

                 53 x 83

We will have to add 3 x 53 = $\boxed{159}$ at the end.

- 50 + 80 + 10   =140

- 3 – 5   = -2

- -2 x 140   →   -280

- $+(2^2)$ →   +4

- Add: →   + $\boxed{159}$
  _____

    Δ   →   -117✓

Step 5   **53 x 86**

                 56 x 86

We will have to subtract 3 x 86 = $\boxed{258}$ at the end.

- 50 + 40 + 10   =140

- 6 – 5   = 1

- 1 x 140   →   140

- $+(1^2)$ →   +1

- Subtract: →   - $\boxed{258}$
  _____

    Δ   →   -117✓

LEVEL 4 (POWERS OF 2 OR 3, QUARTERS OR EIGHTHS)............... *3 STEPS*

Step 1   **53 x 86**

53 x 81

We will have to add 5 x 53 = 265 at the end.

- $159 \rightarrow 477 \rightarrow 1{,}431 \rightarrow 4{,}293 + \xrightarrow{\boxed{+265}} 4{,}558$ ✓

    (x3)   (x9)   (x27)   (x81)

Step 2   **53 x 86**

50 x 86

We will have to add 3 x 86 = 258 at the end.

- $50 \times 86 \rightarrow 4{,}300 \xrightarrow{\boxed{+258}} 4{,}558$ ✓

Step 3   **53 x 86**

53 x 87½ (53 x ⅞ x 100)

We will have to subtract 1 ½ x 53 = 79½ at the end.

- $53/8 = 6^{5}/_{8}.\ 6^{5}/_{8} \times 7 = 42^{35}/_{8} = 46^{5}/_{8} \xrightarrow{+100} 4{,}637½ \xrightarrow{-79½} 4{,}558$ ✓

LEVEL 5 (FLIPS) .... *2 STEPS*

Step 1   **53 x 86**

53 x 35

After we have arrived at 53 x 35, we have to bring it back to 53 x 86. The easiest way to do that is to add 51 x 53.

And we solve that by either

1) $51^2 + (2 \times 51)$ = $2{,}601 + 102 = \boxed{2{,}703}$ ✓, or

2) $(50 \times 53) + (1 \times 53) =$ $2{,}650 + 53\ \ =\ \boxed{2{,}703}$ ✓

3) $52^2 - 1^2$ = $2{,}704 - 1\ \ =\ \boxed{2{,}703}$ ✓

But first we have to solve 53 x 35:

298

$\bullet\ 53 \times 35 \rightarrow 50 \times 30 \rightarrow 1,500 \xrightarrow{+10(5^2+2^2)=340} 1,840 \xrightarrow{+5\times3=15} 1,855 \xrightarrow{\boxed{2,703}} 4,558\checkmark$

Step 2

$$53 \times 86$$
$$68 \times 86$$

We'll have to subtract 15 x 86 = $\boxed{1,290}$ at the end.

$68 \times 86 \rightarrow 60 \times 80 \rightarrow 4,800 \xrightarrow{+10(6^2+8^2)=1,000} 5,800 \xrightarrow{+6\times8=48} 5,848 \xrightarrow{\boxed{-1,290}} 4,558\checkmark$

LEVEL 6 (COMPLEMENTS TO 100) .... *2 STEPS*

Step 1

$$53 \times 86$$

$$5,300 - (14 \times 53)$$

$\bullet\ 14 \times 53 = (50 \times 14) + (3 \times 14) = 700 + 42 = \boxed{742}$

$\bullet\ 53 \times 86 = 5,300 - \boxed{742} = 4,558\checkmark$

(Note: $5,300 - 742 = 5,300 + 58 - 800 = 5,358 - 800 = 4,558\checkmark$)

Step 2

$$53 \times 86$$

$$8,600 - (47 \times 86)$$

$\bullet\ 47 \times 86 = (50 \times 86) - (3 \times 86) = 4,300 - 258 = \boxed{4,042}$

$\bullet\ 8,600 - \boxed{4,042} = 4,558\checkmark$

LEVEL 7 (COMPLEMENT SQUARES) .... *2 STEPS*

Step 1

$$53 \times 86$$

$$\Delta = 33$$

$\bullet\ 53^2 + (33 \times 53) = 2,809 + 1,749 = 4,558\checkmark$

(Note: $53^2 = 50^2 + (6 \times 50) + 3^2 = 2,500 + 300 + 9 = 2,809$

33×53 (same last digit): $(30 \times 50) + (3 \times 80) + 3^2 = 1,500 + 240 + 9 = 1,749$)

Step 2   **53 x 86**

                                              $\Delta = 33$

• $86^2 - (33 \times 86) = 7{,}396 - 2{,}838 = 4{,}558$ ✓

(Note: $86^2 = 85^2 + (85 + 86) = 7{,}225 + 171 = 7{,}396$.

             $33 \times 86 = (30 \times 86) + (3 \times 86) = 2{,}580 + 258 = 2{,}838$.

             $7{,}396 - 2{,}838 = 7{,}396 - 2{,}800 - 30 - 8 \rightarrow 4{,}596 \rightarrow 4{,}566 \rightarrow 4{,}558$ ✓)

LEVEL 8 (HALVES, COMMON DENOMINATORS,
HALVES AND DOUBLES).......................................*4 STEPS*

Step 1   **53 x 86**

                                              26½ x 43 (x 4)

• $26\frac{1}{2} \times 43$: $20 \times 43 \rightarrow 860 \xrightarrow{+6 \times 43 = 258} 1{,}118 \xrightarrow{+\frac{1}{2} \times 43 = 21\frac{1}{2}} 1{,}139\frac{1}{2} \xrightarrow{\times 4} 4{,}558$ ✓

(Note: $1{,}139\frac{1}{2} \times 4 = (1{,}140 \times 4) - (\frac{1}{2} \times 4) = 4{,}560 - 2 = 4{,}558$ ✓)

Step 2   **53 x 86**

Closest common denominator is 43. (It's somewhat of a stretch.) We'll have to add $10 \times 86 =$ $\boxed{860}$ at the end.

                                              53 x 86

                                              43 x 86

It's $(43^2 \times 2) + (10 \times 86) = (1{,}849 \times 2) + \boxed{860} = 3{,}698 + \boxed{860} = 4{,}558$ ✓

Step 3   **53 x 86**

                                              106 x 43

• $106 \times 43 = 100 \times 43 \rightarrow 4{,}300 \xrightarrow{+6 \times 43 = 258} 4{,}558$ ✓

Step 4

$$53 \times 86$$
$$26\tfrac{1}{2} \times 172$$

Easiest:

- $26\tfrac{1}{2} \times 172 = (25 \times 172) + 1\tfrac{1}{2} \times 172 = 4{,}300 + 172 + 86 = 4{,}558$ ✓

(Note: 25×172: $^{172}/_2 = 86$. $^{86}/_2 = 43 \xrightarrow{\ \times 100\ } 4{,}300$)

LEVEL 9 (PLUS AND MINUS 10).. *4 STEPS*

Step 1

$$53 \times 86$$
$$43 \times 96$$

$\Delta = 86 \mid 53 = 33$. Result should be $(10 \times 33) + 100 = \boxed{430}$ less.

- Should be $4{,}558 - \boxed{430} = 4{,}128$ ✓

- $43 \times 96 = (43 \times 100) - (43 \times 4) = 4{,}300 - 172 = 4{,}128$ ✓

Step 2

$$53 \times 86$$
$$63 \times 76$$

$\Delta = 86 \mid 53 = 33$. Result should be $(10 \times 33) - 100 = \boxed{230}$ more.

- Result should be $4{,}558 + \boxed{230} = 4{,}788$ ✓

- $63 \times 76 = (63 \times 75) + 63$

- $63 \times 75 = 100 \,(^3/_4 \times 63)$. $^1/_4 \times 63 = 15\tfrac{3}{4}$. $^3/_4 \times 63 = 45^9/_4 = 47\tfrac{1}{4} \xrightarrow{\ \times 100\ } \boxed{4{,}725}$

- $63 \times 76 = \boxed{4{,}725} + 63 = 4{,}788$ ✓

Step 3

$$53 \times 86$$
$$43 \times 76$$

$\Sigma = (53 \times 86) = 139$. Result should be $(139 \times 10) - 100 = \boxed{1{,}290}$ less.

- Should be $4{,}558 - \boxed{1{,}290} = 3{,}268$ ✓

- $43 \times 76 \rightarrow 40 \times 75 \rightarrow 3{,}000 \xrightarrow{\ +40\,x\,1=40\ } 3{,}040 \xrightarrow{\ +3\,x\,76=228\ } 3{,}268$ ✓

Step 4   **53 x 86**

                                             63 x 96

- $\sum = 139$. Result should be $(10 \times 139) + 100 = \boxed{1,490}$ more.

- Result should be $4,558 + \boxed{1,490} = 6,048\checkmark$

- $63 \times 96 = (100 \times 63) - (4 \times 63) = 6,300 - 252 = 6,048\checkmark$

LEVEL 10 (FLIPS AND DIAGONALS: PART I)....................................... *7 STEPS*

Step 1   **53**
                                                 x86

- $8 \times 5 \to 40 \xrightarrow{\;\times 10\;} 400 \xrightarrow{\;+(3+8)+(6\times5)=54\;} 454 \xrightarrow{\;\times 10\;} 4,540 \xrightarrow{\;+3\times6=18\;} 4,558\checkmark$

Step 2: Vertical Flip   **53**
                                                 x86

                                                 56
                                                 x83

Δ of oners is 3; Δ of tenners is 30.

Result should be $3 \times 30 = 90$ more than $4,558 \to 4,648\checkmark$

- $5 \times 8 \to 40 \xrightarrow{\;\times 10\;} 400 \xrightarrow{\;+(6\times8)+(3\times5)=63\;} 463 \xrightarrow{\;\times 10\;} 4,630 \xrightarrow{\;+6\times3=18\;} 4,648\checkmark$

Step 3: Horizontal Derivative   **56**
                                                 x83

                                                 65
                                                 x38

- Product of oners is $6 \times 3 = 18$

- Product of tenners is $5 \times 8 = 40$

- $\Delta = 40 \mid 18 = 22$

- Therefore, the horizontal derivative should be 2,200 less and 22 more than 4,648.

- Result should be $4,648 - 2,200 + 22 = 2,470\checkmark$

- $65 \times 38 = (60 \times 38) + (5 \times 38) = 2,280 + 190 = 2,470\checkmark$

Step 4: First Diagonal Flip (1)

$$\begin{array}{r} 56 \\ \times\ \underline{83} \end{array}$$

$$\begin{array}{r} 58 \\ \times\ \underline{63} \end{array}$$

- $58 \times 63 = 60\tfrac{1}{2}^2 - 2\tfrac{1}{2}^2 = 3{,}660 - 6 = 3{,}654$ ✓

$\Delta_1 = 8\ |\ 6\ = 2$

Difference should be $-(200 \times 5) + (2 \times 3) = \boxed{-\ 1{,}000 + 6}$

- $4{,}648\ \boxed{-1{,}000 + 6}\ = 3{,}654$ ✓

Step 5: First Diagonal Flip (2)

$$\begin{array}{r} 56 \\ \times\ \underline{83} \end{array}$$

$$\begin{array}{r} 58 \\ \times\ \underline{63} \end{array}$$

- $58 \times 63 = 3{,}654$ (as per Step 4, above)

$\Delta_2 = 5\ |\ 3\ = 2$

Difference should be $-(200 \times 6) + (2 \times 8) = \boxed{-1{,}200 + 16}$

- $3{,}654\ \boxed{-1{,}200 + 16} = 2{,}470$ ✓

Step 6: Second Diagonal Flip (1)

$$\begin{array}{r} 56 \\ \times\ \underline{83} \end{array}$$

$$\begin{array}{r} 36 \\ \times\ \underline{85} \end{array}$$

- 36×85: two easy ways:

    1) $(40 \times 85) - (4 \times 85) = 3{,}400 - 340 = 3{,}060$ ✓, or

    2) $(100 \times 36) - (15 \times 36) = 3{,}600 - 540 = 3{,}060$ ✓

$\Delta_2 = 5\ |\ 3\ = 2$

Difference should be $+(800 \times 2) - (6 \times 2) = \boxed{+1{,}600 - 12}$

- $3{,}060\ \boxed{+1{,}600 - 12} = 4{,}648$ ✓

Step 7: Second Diagonal Flip (2)

$$56 \\ \underline{\times 83}$$

$$36 \\ \underline{\times 85}$$

- $36 \times 85 = 3{,}060$ (as per Step 6, above)

$\Delta_1 = 8 \mid 6 = 2$

Difference should be $-(200 \times 3) + (2 \times 5) = \boxed{-600 + 10}$

- $3{,}060 \; \boxed{-600 + 10} = 2{,}470\checkmark$

LEVEL 11 (SKEWED).. *2 STEPS*

Step 1   **53 x 86**

- $50 \times 80 \rightarrow 4{,}000 \xrightarrow{+(3+6)\times 53=477} 4{,}477 \xrightarrow{+3(80-50)=90} 4{,}567 \xrightarrow{-3^2=-9} 4{,}558\checkmark$

Step 2   **53 x 86**

- $50 \times 80 \rightarrow 4{,}000 \xrightarrow{+(3+6)\times 86=774} 4{,}777 \xrightarrow{-6(80-50)=-180} 4{,}594 \xrightarrow{-6^2=-36} 4{,}558\checkmark$

LEVEL 12 (FLIPS AND DIAGONALS: PART II) .... *5 STEPS*

Step 1: Horizontal Derivative

$$53 \\ \underline{\times 86}$$

$$35 \\ \underline{\times 68}$$

- Product of oners is $3 \times 6 = 18$

- Product of tenners is $5 \times 8 = 40$

- $\Delta = 40 \mid 8 = 22$

- Therefore, the horizontal derivative should be 2,200 less and 22 more than 4,558.

- Result should be $4{,}558 - 2{,}200 + 22 = 2{,}380$ ✓

- $35 \times 68 = (35 \times 70) - (2 \times 35) = 2 \times 35^2 - 70 = (2 \times 1{,}225) - 70 = 2{,}450 - 70 = 2{,}380$ ✓

Step 2: First Diagonal Flip (1)
$$\begin{array}{r} 53 \\ \times\, \underline{86} \end{array}$$
$$\begin{array}{r} 58 \\ \times\, \underline{36} \end{array}$$

- $58 \times 36 = (60 \times 36) - (2 \times 36) = 2{,}160 - 72 = 2{,}088$ ✓

$\Delta_1 = 8 \mid 3 = 5$

Difference should be $+(500 \times 5) - (5 \times 6) = \boxed{2{,}500 - 30}$

- $2{,}088 \boxed{+\, 2{,}500 - 30} = 4{,}558$ ✓

Step 3: First Diagonal Flip (2)
$$\begin{array}{r} 53 \\ \times\, \underline{86} \end{array}$$
$$\begin{array}{r} 58 \\ \times\, \underline{36} \end{array}$$

- $58 \times 36 = 2{,}088$ (as per step 2, above)

$\Delta_2 = 6 \mid 5 = 1$

Difference should be $(100 \times 3) - (1 \times 8) = \boxed{+\, 300 - 8}$

- $2{,}088 \boxed{+\, 300 - 8} = 2{,}380$ ✓

Step 4: Second Diagonal Flip (1)
$$\begin{array}{r} 53 \\ \times\, \underline{86} \end{array}$$
$$\begin{array}{r} 63 \\ \times\, \underline{85} \end{array}$$

- $63 \times 85 = (60 \times 85) + (3 \times 85) = 5{,}100 + 255 = 5{,}355$ ✓ or

- $63 \times 85 = (100 \times 63) - (15 \times 63) = 6{,}300 - 945 = 6{,}355 - 1{,}000 = 5{,}355$ ✓ or

- $63 \times 85 = (65 \times 85) - (2 \times 85) = 5{,}525 - 170 = 5{,}355$ ✓

$\Delta_2 = 6 \mid 3 = 1$

Difference should be $-(100 \times 8) + (1 \times 3) = \boxed{-800 + 3}$

- $5,355 \boxed{-800 + 3} = 4,558\checkmark$

Step 5: Second Diagonal Flip (2)

$$53$$
$$\underline{\times 86}$$

$$63$$
$$\underline{\times 85}$$

- $63 \times 85 = 5,355$ (as per Step 4, above)

$\Delta_1 = 8 \mid 3 = 5$

Difference should be $-(500 \times 6) + (5 \times 5) = \boxed{-3,000 + 25}$

- $5,355 \boxed{-3,000 + 25} = 2,380\checkmark$

LEVEL 13 (SQUARE OF HALF-SUM AND CENTERED ON 50) .... *3 STEPS*

Step 1   53 x 86

- $\Sigma(53 + 86) = 139; \ \Sigma/2 = 69\frac{1}{2}$

- $\Delta = 86 \mid 53 = 33$

- $53 \times 86 = 69\frac{1}{2}^2 - 16\frac{1}{2}^2 = 4,830 - 272 = 4,558\checkmark$

(Remember: $69\frac{1}{2}^2 = 70^2 - 70 = 4,900 - 70 = 4,830$)

Step 2   53 x 86

- $\Sigma(53 + 86) = 139$

- $139 - 100 = 39$

- $\Delta = 53 \mid 50 = 3$

- $53 \times 86 = 2,500 - 3^2 + (53 \times 39) = 2,500 - 9 + 2,067 = 4,558\checkmark$

(Note: $53 \times 39 = (53 \times 40) - 53 = 2,120 - 53 = 2,167 - 100 = 2,067$)

Step 3   **53 x 86**

- $\sum(53 + 86) = 139$

- $139 - 100 = 39$

- $\Delta = 86 \mid 50 = 36$

- $53 \times 86 = 2{,}500 - 36^2 + (86 \times 39) = 2{,}500 - 1{,}296 + 3{,}354 = 4{,}558\checkmark$

(Note: $86 \times 39 = (86 \times 40) - 86 = 3{,}440 - 86 = 3{,}454 - 100 = 3{,}354$)

LEVEL 14 (COMPLEMENT TO 10).. *2 STEPS*

Step 1   **53 x 86**

                              53 x 87 (make oners add to 10)

Subtract 1 x 53 = $\boxed{53}$ at the end.

- $80 + 10 = 90$

- $90 - 50 = 40$

- $53 \times 86 = (90 \times 50) + (3 \times 40) - 3^2 - \boxed{53} = 4{,}500 + 120 - 9 - \boxed{53} = 4{,}558\checkmark$

Step 2   **53 x 86**

                              54 x 86 (make oners add to 10)

Subtract 1 x 86 = $\boxed{86}$ at the end.

- $80 + 10 = 90$

- $90 - 50 = 40$

- $53 \times 86 = (90 \times 40) + (4 \times 40) - 4^2 - \boxed{86} = 4{,}500 + 160 - 16 - \boxed{86} = 4{,}558\checkmark$

LEVEL 15 (EQUAL ONERS AND TENNERS) .... *4 STEPS*

Step 1   **53 x 86**

                              53 x 83 (to equalize oners)

Add 3 x 53 = $\boxed{159}$ at the end.

- $50 \times 80 \rightarrow 4,000 \xrightarrow{\;+3(50+80)=390\;} 4,390 \xrightarrow{\;+3^2=9\;} 4,399 \xrightarrow{\;\boxed{+159}\;} 4,558\checkmark$

Step 2

53 x 86

56 x 86 (to equalize oners)

Subtract 3 x 86 = $\boxed{258}$ at the end.

- $50 \times 80 \rightarrow 4,000 \xrightarrow{\;+6(50+80)=780\;} 4,780 \xrightarrow{\;+6^2=36\;} 4,816 \xrightarrow{\;\boxed{-258}\;} 4,558\checkmark$

Step 3

53 x 86

53 x 56 (to equalize tenners)

Add 30 x 53 = $\boxed{1,590}$ at the end.

- $50^2 \rightarrow 2,500 \xrightarrow{\;+50(3+6)=450\;} 2,950 \xrightarrow{\;+3\times6=18\;} 2,968 \xrightarrow{\;\boxed{+1,590}\;} 4,558\checkmark$

Step 4

53 x 86

83 x 86 (to equalize tenners)

Subtract 30 x 86 = $\boxed{2,580}$ at the end.

- $80^2 \rightarrow 6,400 \xrightarrow{\;+80(3+6)=720\;} 7,120 \xrightarrow{\;+3\times6=18\;} 7,138 \xrightarrow{\;\boxed{-2,580}\;} 4,558\checkmark$

LEVEL 16 (STRIP THE TENNERS).. *2 STEPS*

Step 1

53 x 86

3 x 36 (eliminating the first tenner)

- $43 \times 86 = 50^2 + 50(3 + 36) + (3 \times 36) = 2,500 + 1,950 + 108 = 4,558\checkmark$

Step 2

53 x 86

-27 x 6 (eliminating the second tenner)

- $53 \times 86 = 80^2 + 80(-27 + 6) + (-27 \times 6) = 6,400 - 1,680 - 162 = 4,558\checkmark$

How about another one?

Problem #4

43 x 92

LEVEL 1 (THE EASIEST) .... *2 STEPS*

Step 1   43 x 92

- $(40 \times 92) + (3 \times 92)$

- $40 \times 92 = (40 \times 90) + (40 \times 2) = 3{,}600 + 80 \rightarrow 3{,}680$

- $3 \times 92 = (3 \times 90) + (3 \times 2) = 270 + 6 \rightarrow \underline{\quad 276\quad}$

$$\therefore \ 43 \times 92 = \underline{3{,}956} \ \checkmark$$

Step 2   43 x 92

- $(90 \times 43) + (2 \times 43)$

- $90 \times 43 = (90 \times 40) + (90 \times 3) = 3{,}600 + 270 \rightarrow 3{,}870$

- $2 \times 43 \hspace{5cm} \rightarrow \underline{\quad 86\quad}$

$$\therefore \ 43 \times 92 = \underline{3{,}956} \ \checkmark$$

LEVEL 2 (THE CLASSIC) .... *2 STEPS*

Step 1   43 x 92

- $(40 \times 90) + (3 \times 90) + (2 \times 40) + (3 \times 2)$

- $3{,}600 \xrightarrow{+3 \times 90 = 270} 3{,}870 \xrightarrow{(2 \times 4) = 80} 3{,}950 \xrightarrow{+3 \times 2 = 6} 3{,}956 \ \checkmark$

Step 2   43 x 92
$$(50 - 7) \times (100 - 8)$$

- $(50 \times 100) - (50 \times 8) - (100 \times 7) + (7 \times 8)$

- $5{,}000 \xrightarrow{-50 \times 8 = -400} 4{,}600 \xrightarrow{-100 \times 7 = -700} 3{,}900 \xrightarrow{+8 \times 7 = 56} \underline{3{,}956} \ \checkmark$

LEVEL 3 (CENTERED AROUND 5) .... *5 STEPS*

Step 1   **43 x 92**

- (45 x 95)   → 4,275

- For 43 x 95, subtract 2 x 95   → -190   → 4,085

- For 43 x 92, subtract 3 x 43   → <u>-129</u>   → 3,956

    Δ   → -319 ✓

Step 2   **43 x 92**

                                                  43 x 97

We will have to subtract 5 x 43 = $\boxed{215}$ at the end.

- (90 – 40)   =   50

- 3 – 5   =   -2

- -2 x 50   → -100

- – (-2²)   =   -4

- Subtract   → $\boxed{-215}$
                                                  ————
    Δ   →   -319 ✓

Step 3   **43 x 92**

                                                  48 x 92

We will have to subtract 5 x 92 = $\boxed{460}$ at the end.

- (90 – 40)   =   50

- 8 – 5 = 3

- 3 x 50   →   +150

- -3²   →   -9

- Subtract   → $\boxed{-460}$

       Δ   →   -319 ✓

Step 4   43 x 92

                              43 x 93

We will have to subtract 1 x 43 = $\boxed{43}$ at the end.

- 40 + 90 + 10   = 140
- 3 – 5   = -2
- -2 x 140   →   -280
- +(-2^2)   →   +4
- Subtract   → $\boxed{-43}$

       Δ   →   -319 ✓

Step 5   43 x 92
                              42 x 93

We will have to add 1 x 92 = $\boxed{92}$ at the end.

- 40 + 90 + 10   = 140
- 2 – 5   = -3
- -3 x 140   →   -420
- + (-3^2)   →   +9
- Add   → $\boxed{+92}$

       Δ   →   -319 ✓

LEVEL 4 (POWERS OF 2 OR 3, QUARTERS OR EIGHTHS) .... *3 STEPS*

Step 1   43 x 92

                              48 x 92

We will have to subtract 5 x 92 = $\boxed{460}$ at the end.

- 184 → 368 → 736 → 1,472 → 2,944
  (x2)   (x4)   (x8)   (x16)   (x32)

- 1,472 + 2,944 − 460 = 3,956✓

Step 2

$$43 \times 92$$
$$50 \times 92$$

We will have to subtract 7 x 92 = 644 at the end.

- 50 x 92 → 4,600 —−644→ → 3,956 ✓

Step 3

$$43 \times 92$$

$$43 \times 100$$

We will have to subtract 8 x 43 = 344 at the end.

- 43 x100 → 4,300 —−344→ 3,956 ✓

LEVEL 5 (FLIPS) .... *2 STEPS*

Step 1

$$43 \times 92$$
$$43 \times 34$$

After we have arrived at 43 x 34, we must bring it to 43 x 92. The easiest way to do this is to multiply the result of 43 x 34 by 3, which brings us to 43 x 102. Subtract 10 x 43 = 430 to get to 43 x 92.

But first we have to solve 43 x 34.

- 43×34 → 40×30 → $1,200 \xrightarrow{+10(4^2+3^2)=250} 1,450 \xrightarrow{+3 \times 4 = 12} 1,462 \xrightarrow{\times 3} 4,386 \xrightarrow{\boxed{-1,430}} 3,956$ ✓

Step 2

$$43 \times 92$$
$$29 \times 92$$

We will have to add $14 \times 92 = \boxed{1,288}$ at the end.

(Note: $14 \times 92 = (14 \times 100) - (14 \times 8) = 1,400 - 112 = 1,288$.)

- $29 \times 92 = 20 \times 90$ → $1,800 \xrightarrow{+10(9^2+2^2)=850} 2,650 \xrightarrow{+9 \times 2 = 18} 2,668 \xrightarrow{\boxed{+1,288}} 3,956$ ✓

LEVEL 6 (COMPLEMENTS TO 100) .... *2 STEPS*

Step 1

$$43 \times 92$$
$$4,300 - (8 \times 43)$$

- $8 \times 43 = 344$

- $43 \times 92 = 4,300 - 344 = 3,956$ ✓

Step 2

$$43 \times 92$$
$$9,200 - (57 \times 92)$$

- $57 \times 92 = (57 \times 100) - (57 \times 8) = 5,700 - 456 = 5,244$

- $43 \times 92 = 9,200 - 5,244 = 9,256 - 5,300 = 3,956$ ✓

LEVEL 7 (COMPLEMENT SQUARES) .... *2 STEPS*

Step 1

$$43 \times 92$$
$$\Delta = 49$$

- $43^2 + (49 \times 43) = 1,849 + 2,107 = 3,956$ ✓

(Note: $43^2 = 40^2 + (6 \times 40) + 3^2 = 1,600 + 240 + 9 = 1,849$

- $49 \times 43 = (50 \times 43) - (1 \times 43) = 2,150 - 43 = 2,107$)

Step 2 $\qquad$ **43 x 92**

$$\Delta = 49$$

- $92^2 = 90^2 + (4 \times 90) + 2^2 = 8,100 + 360 + 4 = 8,464$

- $49 \times 92 = (50 \times 92) - (1 \times 92) = 4,600 - 92 = 4,508$

- $43 \times 92 = 92^2 - (49 \times 92) = 8,464 - 4,508 = 3,956$ ✓

LEVEL 8 (HALVES, COMMON DENOMINATORS, HALVES AND DOUBLES) .... *4 STEPS*

Step 1 $\qquad$ **43 x 92**

21½ x 46 (x 4)

- 21½ x 46: $20 \times 46 \rightarrow 920 \xrightarrow{1\frac{1}{2} \times 46 = 46 + 23 = 69} 989 \xrightarrow{\times 4} 3,956$ ✓

Step 2 $\qquad$ **43 x 92**

Closest common denominator is 43.

43 x 92

43 x 86

We will have to add 6 x 43 = $\boxed{258}$ at the end.

- $43 \times 92 = (43^2 \times 2) + \boxed{258} = (1,849 \times 2) + \boxed{250} = 3,698 + 250 = 3,956$ ✓

Step 3 $\qquad$ **43 x 92**

86 x 46

Solved by same-last-digit method: $86 \times 46 \rightarrow 3,200 + \xrightarrow{+6(80+40)=720} 3,920 \xrightarrow{+6^2=36} = 3,956$ ✓

Step 4   **43 x 92**

21½ x 184

- 21½ x 184 = (20 x 184) + (1 x 186) + (½ x 186) = 3,680 + 184 + 92 = 3,956 ✓

LEVEL 9 (PLUS AND MINUS 10) .... *4 STEPS*

Step 1   **43 x 92**

33 x 102

$\Delta = 92 \mid 43 = 49$. Result should be (10 x 49) + 100 = $\boxed{590}$ less.

- Should be 3,956 − $\boxed{590}$ = 3,366 ✓

- 33 x 102 = (33 x 100) + (33 x 2) = 3,366 ✓

Step 2   **43 x 92**

53 x 82

$\Delta = 92 \mid 43 = 49$. Result should be (10 x 49) − 100 = $\boxed{390}$ more.

- Should be 3,956 + $\boxed{390}$ = 4,346 ✓

- 53 x 82 = (50 x 82) + (3 x 82) = 4,100 + 246 = 4,346 ✓

Step 3   **43 x 92**

33 x 82

$\Sigma = 135$. Result should be (10 x 135) − 100 = $\boxed{1,250}$ less.

- Should be 3,956 − $\boxed{1,250}$ = 2,706 ✓

- 33 x 82 = (30 x 82) + (3 x 82) = 2,460 + 246 = 2,706 ✓

Step 4   **43 x 92**

53 x 102

$\Sigma = 135$. Result should be $(10 \times 135) + 100 = \boxed{1,450}$ more.

- Result should be $3,956 + \boxed{1,450} = 5,406$ ✓

- $53 \times 102 = (53 \times 100) + (53 \times 2) = 5,300 + 106 = 5,406$ ✓

LEVEL 10 (FLIPS AND DIAGONALS: PART 1) .... *7 STEPS*

Step 1
$$\begin{array}{r} 43 \\ \times\ \underline{92} \end{array}$$

- $4 \times 9 \to 36 \xrightarrow{\times 10} 360 \xrightarrow{+(3 \times 9)+(2 \times 4)=35} 395 \xrightarrow{\times 10} 3,950 \xrightarrow{+3 \times 2=6} 3,956$ ✓

Step 2: Vertical Flip
$$\begin{array}{r} 43 \\ \times\ \underline{92} \end{array}$$

$$\begin{array}{r} 42 \\ \times\ \underline{93} \end{array}$$

Δ of oners is 1, Δ of tenners is 50

Result should be $1 \times 50 = 50$ less than $3,956 \to 3,906$✓

- $4 \times 9 \to 36 \xrightarrow{\times 10} 360 \xrightarrow{+(2 \times 9)+(3 \times 4)=30} 390 \xrightarrow{\times 10} 3,900 \xrightarrow{+(2 \times 3)=6} 3,906$ ✓

Step 3: Horizontal Derivative
$$\begin{array}{r} 42 \\ \times\ \underline{93} \end{array}$$

$$\begin{array}{r} 24 \\ \times\ \underline{39} \end{array}$$

- Product of oners is $2 \times 3 = 6$

- Product of tenners is $4 \times 9 = 36$

  $\Delta = 36 \,|\, 6 = 30$

- Therefore, the horizontal derivative should be 3,000 less and 30 more than 3,906.

- Result should be $3,906 - 3,000 + 30 = 936$ ✓

- $24 \times 39 = (24 \times 40) - (24 \times 1) = 960 - 24 = 936$ ✓

Step 4: First Diagonal Flip (1)

$$\begin{array}{r} 42 \\ \underline{\times 93} \end{array}$$

$$\begin{array}{r} 49 \\ \underline{\times 23} \end{array}$$

- $49 \times 23 = (50 \times 23) - (1 \times 23) = 1{,}150 - 23 = 1{,}127\checkmark$

  $\Delta = 9 \mid 2 = 7$

- Difference should be $+ (700 \times 4) - (7 \times 3) - \boxed{+\,2{,}800 - 21}$

- $1{,}127 \boxed{+2{,}800 - 21} = 3{,}906\checkmark$

Step 5: First Diagonal Flip (2)

$$\begin{array}{r} 42 \\ \underline{\times 93} \end{array}$$

$$\begin{array}{r} 49 \\ \underline{\times 23} \end{array}$$

- $49 \times 23 = (50 \times 23) - (1 \times 23) = 1{,}150 - 23 = 1{,}127\checkmark$

- Difference should be $- (100 + 2) + (1 \times 9)\ \boxed{-\,200 + 9}$

- $1{,}127 \boxed{-\,200 + 9} = 936\checkmark$

Step 6: Second Diagonal Flip (1)

$$\begin{array}{r} 42 \\ \underline{\times 93} \end{array}$$

$$\begin{array}{r} 32 \\ \underline{\times 94} \end{array}$$

- $32 \times 94 = (32 \times 100) - (32 \times 6) = 3{,}200 - 192 = 3{,}008\checkmark$

  $\Delta = 4 \mid 3 = 1$

- Difference should be $+ (100 \times 9) - (1 \times 2) - \boxed{+\,900 - 2}$

- $3{,}008 + \boxed{900 - 2} = 3{,}906\checkmark$

Step 7: Second Diagonal Flip (2)

$$\begin{array}{r} 42 \\ \underline{\times 93} \end{array}$$

$$\begin{array}{r} 32 \\ \underline{\times 94} \end{array}$$

- $32 \times 94 = (32 \times 100) - (32 \times 6) = 3,200 - 192 = 3,008$ ✓

  $\Delta = 9 \mid 2 = 7$

- Difference should be $- (700 + 3) + (7 \times 4)$ $\boxed{-2,100 + 28}$

- $3,008$ $\boxed{- 2,100 + 28}$ $= 936$ ✓

LEVEL 11 (SKEWED) .... *2 STEPS*

Step 1

43 x 92

- $(40 \times 90) = 3,600 \xrightarrow{+(3+2)\times 43=215} 3,815 \xrightarrow{+3(90-40)=150} 3,965 \xrightarrow{-3^2=-9} 3,956$ ✓

Step 2

43 x 92

- $40 \times 90 = 3,600 \xrightarrow{+(3+2)\times 92=460} 4,060 \xrightarrow{-2(90-40)=-100} 3,960 \xrightarrow{-2^2=-4} 3,956$ ✓

LEVEL 12 (FLIPS AND DIAGONALS: PART II) .... *5 STEPS*

Step 1: Horizontal Derivative

43
x <u>92</u>

34
x <u>29</u>

- Product of oners is $3 \times 2 = 6$

- Product of tenners is $4 \times 9 = 36$

  $\Delta = 36 \mid 6 = 30$

- Therefore, the horizontal derivative should be 3000 less and 30 more than 3,956.

- Result should be 3,956 – 3,000 + 30 = 986 ✓

- 34 x 29 = (34 x 30) – 34 = 1,020 – 34 = 986 ✓

(Note: 1,020 – 34 = 1,086 – 100 = 986 ✓ or 1,020 – 20 – 14 = 986 ✓)

Step 2: First Diagonal Flip (1)

$$43$$
$$\text{x } 92$$

$$49$$
$$\text{x } 32$$

- 49 x 32 = (50 x 32) – (1 x 32) = 1,600 – 32 = 1,568 ✓

$\Delta = 9 \mid 3 = 6$

- Difference should be + (600 x 4) – 6 x 2) = $\boxed{+\ 2,400 - 12}$

- 1,568 $\boxed{+\ 2,400 - 12}$ = 3,956 ✓

Step 3: First Diagonal Flip (2)

$$43$$
$$\text{x } 92$$

$$49$$
$$\text{x } 32$$

- 49 x 32 = 1,568 ✓

$\Delta = 4 \mid 2 = 2$

Difference should be – (200 x 3) + (2 x 9) = $\boxed{-\ 600 + 18}$

- 1,568 $\boxed{-\ 600 + 18}$ = 986 ✓

Step 4: Second Diagonal Flip (1)

$$43$$
$$\text{x } 92$$

$$23$$
$$\text{x } 94$$

- $23 \times 94 = (23 \times 100) - (23 \times 6) = 2{,}300 - 138 = 2{,}162$ ✓

$\Delta = 4 \mid 2 = 2$

Difference should be $+ (200 \times 9) - (2 \times 3) = \boxed{+ 1{,}800 - 6}$

- $2{,}162 \boxed{+ 1{,}800 - 6} = 3{,}956$ ✓

Step 5: Second Diagonal Flip (2)

$$\begin{array}{r} 43 \\ \times\ \underline{92} \end{array}$$

$$\begin{array}{r} 23 \\ \times\ \underline{94} \end{array}$$

- $23 \times 94 = 2{,}162$ ✓

$\Delta = 9 \mid 3 = 6$

Difference should be $- (600 \times 2) + (6 \times 4) = \boxed{- 1{,}200 + 24}$

- $2{,}162 \boxed{- 1{,}200 + 24} = 986$ ✓

LEVEL 13 (SQUARE OF HALF-SUM AND CENTERED ON 50) .... *3 STEPS*

Step 1   43 x 92

- $\Sigma (43 \times 92) = 135$

- $\Sigma \mid 2 = 67\frac{1}{2}$

$\Delta = 67\frac{1}{2} \mid 43 = 24\frac{1}{2}$

- $43 \times 92 \ = \ 67\frac{1}{2}^2 - 24\frac{1}{2}^2$

- $67\frac{1}{2}^2 = 70^2 - (5 \times 70) + 2\frac{1}{2}^2 = 4{,}900 - 350 + 6\,(.25) = 4{,}556\,(.25)$

- $24\frac{1}{2}^2 = 25^2 - 25 = 600\,(.25)$

- $67\frac{1}{2}^2 - 24\frac{1}{2}^2 = 4{,}556 - 600 = 3{,}956$ ✓

320

<u>**Step 2**</u>   **43 x 92**

- Σ (43 + 92) = 135

- 135 – 100 = 35

  $\Delta = 50 \mid 43 = 7$

- 43 x 92   = $2,500 - 7^2 + (43 \times 35) = 2,500 - 49 + 1,505 = 3,956$ ✓

(Note: 43 x 35 = (40 x 35) + (3 x 35) = 1,400 + 105 = 1,505)

<u>**Step 3**</u>   **43 x 92**

- Σ (43 x 92) = 135

- 135 – 100 = 35

  $\Delta = 92 \mid 50 = 42$

- 43 x 92   = $2,500 - 42^2 + (92 \times 35) = 2,500 - 1,764 + 3,220 = 3,956$ ✓

(Note: $42^2 = 40^2 + (4 \times 40) + 2^2 = 1,600 + 160 + 4 = 1,764$.

  92 x 35 = (100 x 35) – (8 x 35) = 3,500 – 280 = 3,220.)

LEVEL 14 (COMPLEMENT TO 10) .... *2 STEPS*

<u>**Step 1**</u>   **43 x 92**

                                                   43 x 97 (to make oners add to 10)

Subtract 5 x 43 = $\boxed{215}$ at the end.

- 90 + 10 = 100

- 100 – 40 = 60

- 43 x 92   = $(100 \times 40) + (3 \times 60) - 3^2 - \boxed{215} = 4,000 + 180 - 9 - 215 = 3,956$ ✓

<u>**Step 2**</u>   **43 x 92**

                                                   48 x 92 (to make oners add to 10)

Subtract 5 x 92 = $\boxed{460}$ at the end.

- $90 + 10 = 100$

- $100 - 40 = 60$

- $43 \times 92 = (100 \times 40) + (8 \times 60) - 8^2 - \boxed{460} = 4{,}000 + 480 - 64 - \boxed{460} = 3{,}956\checkmark$

LEVEL 15 (EQUAL ONERS AND TENNERS) .... *4 STEPS*

Step 1   **43 x 92**

43 x 93 (to equalize oners)

Subtract $1 \times 43 = \boxed{43}$ at the end.

- $40 \times 90 \rightarrow 3{,}600 \xrightarrow{+3(40+90)=390} 3{,}990 \xrightarrow{+3^2=9} 3{,}999 \xrightarrow{\boxed{-43}} 3{,}956\checkmark$

Step 2   **43 x 92**

42 x 92 (to equalize oners)

Add $1 \times 92 = \boxed{92}$ at the end.

- $40 \times 90 \rightarrow 3{,}600 \xrightarrow{+2(40+90)=260} 3{,}860 \xrightarrow{+2^2=4} 3{,}864 \xrightarrow{\boxed{+92}} 3{,}956\checkmark$

Step 3   **43 x 92**

43 x 42 (to equalize tenners)

Add $50 \times 43 = \boxed{2{,}150}$ at the end.

- $40^2 \rightarrow 1{,}600 \xrightarrow{+40+(3 \times 2)=200} 1{,}800 \xrightarrow{+3 \times 2=6} 1{,}806 \xrightarrow{\boxed{+2{,}150}} 3{,}956\checkmark$

Step 4   **43 x 92**

93 x 92 (to equalize tenners)

Subtract $50 \times 92 = \boxed{4{,}600}$ at the end.

- $90^2 \rightarrow 8{,}100 \xrightarrow{+90(3+2)=450} 8{,}550 \xrightarrow{+3 \times 2=6} 8{,}556 \xrightarrow{\boxed{-4{,}600}} 3{,}956\checkmark$

LEVEL 16 (STRIP THE TENNERS) .... *2 STEPS*

<u>Step 1</u>   **43 x 92**

                                                    3 x 52 (eliminating the first tenner)

- $43 \times 92 = 40^2 + 40(3 + 52) + (3 \times 52) = 1{,}600 + 2{,}220 + 156 = 3{,}956\checkmark$

<u>Step 2</u>   **43 x 92**

                                                    -47 x 2 (eliminating the second tenner)

- $43 \times 92 = 90^2 + 90(-47 + 2) + (-47 \times 2) = 8{,}100 - 4{,}050 - 94 = 3{,}956\checkmark$

Are you getting the hang of it? Let's do another one together…

Problem #5

52 x 79

LEVEL 1 (THE EASIEST) .... *2 STEPS*

<u>Step 1</u>   **52 x 79**

- $(50 \times 79) + (2 \times 79)$

- $50 \times 79 \;=\; (50 \times 70) + (50 \times 9) \;=\; 3{,}500 + 450 \;\rightarrow\; 3{,}950$

- $2 \times 79 \;\;=\; (2 \times 70) + (2 \times 9) \;\;=\; 140 + 18 \;\;\rightarrow\; \underline{+158}$

$$\therefore \textbf{52 x 79} \;\;=\; \underline{4{,}108}\checkmark$$

<u>Step 2</u>   **52 x 79**

- $(70 \times 52) + (9 \times 52)$

- $70 \times 52 \;=\; (70 \times 50) + (70 \times 2) \;=\; 3{,}500 + 140 \;\rightarrow\; 3{,}640$

- $9 \times 52 \;\;=\; (9 \times 50) + (9 \times 2) \;\;=\; 450 + 18 \;\;\rightarrow\; \underline{+468}$

$$\therefore \textbf{52 x 79} \;\;=\; \underline{4{,}108}\checkmark$$

LEVEL 2 (THE CLASSIC) .... *2 STEPS*

<u>Step 1</u>   **52 x 79**

- $(50 \times 70) + (50 \times 9) + (2 \times 70) + (2 \times 9)$

- $3{,}500 \xrightarrow{+50\times9=450} 3{,}950 \xrightarrow{+2\times70=140} 4{,}090 \xrightarrow{+2\times9=18} 4{,}108 \checkmark$

<u>Step 2</u>   **52 x 79**
                                      (60 − 8) x (80 − 1)

- $(60 \times 80) - (60 \times 1) - (80 \times 8) + (8 \times 1)$

- $4{,}800 \xrightarrow{-60\times1=-60} 4{,}740 \xrightarrow{-80\times8=-640} 4{,}100 \xrightarrow{+8\times1=8} 4{,}108 \checkmark$

LEVEL 3 (CENTERED AROUND 5) .... *5 STEPS*

<u>Step 1</u>   **52 x 79**

- 55 x 75   →   4,125

- For 52 x 75, subtract 3 x 75   →   -225   →   3,900

- For 52 x 79, add 4 x 52   →   <u>+208</u>   →   4,108✓

     Δ   →   -17✓

<u>Step 2</u>   **52 x 79**

                                                          52 x 78

We will have to add 1 x 52 = 52 at the end.

- 70 – 50   =   20

- 2 – 5   =   -3

- -3 x 20   →   -60

- $- (-3^2)$ →   -9

- Add: →   <u>+52</u>

     Δ   →   -17✓

<u>Step 3</u>   **52 x 79**

                                                          51 x79

We will have to add 1 x 79 = 79 at the end.

- 70 – 50   =   20

- 1 – 5   =   -4

- -4 x 20   →   -80

- $- (-4^2)$ →   -16

- Add: → $\boxed{+79}$
                _____

  Δ   →   -17✓

Step 4   **52 x 79**

           52 x 72

We will have to add 7 x 52 = $\boxed{364}$ at the end.

- 50 + 70 + 10   =   130

- 2 – 5   =   -3

- -3 x 130   →   -390

- $+ (-3^2)$ →   +9

- Add: → $\boxed{+364}$
                _____

  Δ   →   -17✓

Step 5   **52 x 79**

           59 x 79

We will have to subtract 7 x 59 = $\boxed{553}$ at the end.

- 50 + 70 + 10   =130

- 9 – 5   =   4

- 4 x 130   →   520

- $+ 4^2$ →   +16

- Subtract: → $\boxed{-553}$
                _____

  Δ   →   -17✓

LEVEL 4 (POWERS OF 2 OR 3, QUARTERS OR EIGHTHS)............... *3 STEPS*

Step 1

$$52 \times 79$$
$$52 \times 81$$

We will have to subtract 2 x 52 = $\boxed{104}$ at the end.

- $156 \rightarrow 468 \rightarrow 1,404 \rightarrow 4,212 \xrightarrow{\boxed{-104}} 4,108$ ✓
  (x3)   (x9)   (x27)   (x81)

Step 2

$$52 \times 79$$
$$50 \times 79$$

We will have to add 2 x 79 = $\boxed{158}$ at the end.

- $5 \times 79 \rightarrow 395 \xrightarrow{\times 10} 3,950 \xrightarrow{\boxed{+158}} 4,108$ ✓

Step 3

$$52 \times 79$$
$$52 \times 75$$

We will have to add 4 x 52 = $\boxed{208}$ at the end.

- $52 \times 25 = (\tfrac{1}{4} \times 52) \times 100 = 1,300$

- $52 \times 75 = 3 \times 1,300 = 3,900$

- $52 \times 79 = 3,900 + \boxed{208} = 4,108$ ✓

LEVEL 5 (FLIPS) .... *2 STEPS*

Step 1

$$52 \times 79$$
$$52 \times 25$$

After having arrived at 52 x 25, we have to bring it back to 52 x 79. We do that just as we did above in Step 3 of Level 4: We multiply the result by 3 (to get to 52 x 75) and then add 4 x 52 = 208 (to get to 42 x 79).

But first we have to solve 52 x 25 by Level 5 method.

- $52 \times 25 \rightarrow 50 \times 20 \rightarrow 1,000 \xrightarrow{+10(5^2 + 2^2) = 290} 1,290 \xrightarrow{+5 \times 2 = 10} 1,300$

- 52×70: $1,300 \xrightarrow{\text{x3}} 3,900 \xrightarrow{\boxed{+208}} 4,108$ ✓

Step 2

$$52 \times 79$$
$$97 \times 79$$

We'll have to get from 97×79 to 52×79. The easiest way to do this is to add $7 \times 79 =$ $\boxed{553}$ which brings us to 104×79. We divide that by 2 and get to 52×79.

- 97×79: $90 \times 70 \rightarrow 6,300 \xrightarrow{+10(7^2+9^2)=1,300} 7,600 \xrightarrow{+7 \times 9 = 63} 7,663$

- 52×79: $7,663 \xrightarrow{+7 \times 79 = \boxed{553}} 8,216 \xrightarrow{/2} 4,108$ ✓

LEVEL 6 (COMPLEMENTS TO 100) .... *2 STEPS*

Step 1

$$52 \times 79$$
$$5,200 - (21 \times 52)$$

- $21 \times 52 \rightarrow 20 \times 52 \rightarrow 1,040 \xrightarrow{+1 \times 52 = 52} 1,092$

- $5,200 - 1,092 = 4,108$ ✓

(Note: $5,200 - 1,092 = 5,208 - 1,100 = 4,108$ ✓)

Step 2

$$52 \times 79$$
$$7,900 - (48 \times 79)$$

- $48 \times 79 = (50 \times 79) - (2 \times 79) = 3,950 - 158 = 3,792$

- $7,900 - 3,792 = 7,908 - 3,800 = 4,108$ ✓

LEVEL 7 (COMPLEMENT SQUARES)..................................... *2 STEPS*

Step 1

$$52 \times 79$$
$$\Delta = 27$$

- $52^2 + (27 \times 52) = 2,704 + 1,404 = 4,108$ ✓

(Note: $52^2 = 50^2 + (4 \times 50) + 2^2 = 2,500 + 200 + 4 = 2,704$)

$\qquad 27 \times 52 = (30 \times 52) - (3 \times 52) = 1,560 - 156 = 1,404$, or

$\qquad 27 \times 52 = (50 \times 27) + (2 \times 27) = 1,350 + 54 = 1,404$)

Step 2 $\qquad\qquad\qquad\qquad\qquad$ **52 x 79**

$\qquad\qquad\qquad\qquad\qquad\qquad\qquad$ **Δ = 27**

• $79^2 - (27 \times 79) = 6,241 - 2,133 = 4,108$ ✓

(Note: $79^2 = 80^2 - (80 + 79) = 6,400 - 159 = 6,241$

$\qquad 27 \times 79 = (30 \times 79) - (3 \times 79) = 2,370 - 237 = 2,133$

$\qquad 30 \times 79 = (30 \times 80) - (30 \times 1) = 2,400 - 30 = 2,370$)

LEVEL 8 (HALVES, COMMON DENOMINATORS, HALVES AND DOUBLES)..*4 STEPS*

Step 1 $\qquad\qquad\qquad\qquad\qquad$ **52 x 79**

$\qquad\qquad\qquad\qquad\qquad\qquad\qquad$ **26 x 39½ (x 4)**

• $(26 \times 39\frac{1}{2}) = (26 \times 40) - (26 \times \frac{1}{2}) = 1,040 - 13 = 1,027$

• $1,027 \times 4 = 4,108$ ✓

Step 2 $\qquad\qquad\qquad\qquad\qquad$ **52 x 79**

Closest common denominator is 26, because $3 \times 26 = 78$.

$\qquad\qquad\qquad\qquad\qquad\qquad\qquad$ **52 x 79**

$\qquad\qquad\qquad\qquad\qquad\qquad\qquad$ **52 x 78**

We will have to add $1 \times 52 = \boxed{52}$ at the end.

• $52 \times 79 = 26^2 \times 6 + \boxed{52} = (676 \times 6) + 52 = 4,056 + \boxed{52} = 4,108$ ✓

Step 3 $\qquad\qquad\qquad\qquad\qquad$ **52 x 79**

$\qquad\qquad\qquad\qquad\qquad\qquad\qquad$ **104 x 39½**

• $104 \times 39\frac{1}{2} = (100 \times 39\frac{1}{2}) + (4 \times 39\frac{1}{2}) = 3,950 + 158 = 4,108$ ✓, or

• $104 \times 39\frac{1}{2} = (104 \times 40) - (104 \times \frac{1}{2}) = 4,160 - 52 = 4,108$ ✓

Step 4   **52 x 79**
                                                       26 x 158

- 26 x 158 = (26 x 100) + (26 x 50) + (26 x 8) = 2,600 + 1,300 + 208 = 4,108✓

LEVEL 9 (PLUS AND MINUS 10)..*4 STEPS*

Step 1   **52 x 79**
                                                       42 x 89

Δ = 79 | 52 = 27. Result should be (10 x 27) + 100 = $\boxed{370}$ less.

- Should be 4,108 – $\boxed{370}$ = 3,738✓

- 42 x 89 = (42 x 100) – (42 x 11) = 4,200 – 462 = 4,238 – 500 = 3,738✓

Step 2   **52 x 79**
                                                       62 x 69

- Δ = 79 | 52 = 27. Result should be (10 x 27) - 100 = $\boxed{170}$ more.

- Result should be 4,108 + $\boxed{170}$ = 4,278✓

Two easy way to solve 62 x 69:

  1. 62 x 69 = (62 x 70) – (62 – 1) = 4,340 – 62 = 4,278, or

  2. 62 x 69 (by square-of-half-sum method) $65\frac{1}{2}^2 - 3\frac{1}{2}^2 - 4,290 - 12 = 4,278$.

(Note: $65\frac{1}{2}^2 = 65^2 + 65 = 4,225 + 65 = 4,290$)

Step 3   **52 x 79**
                                                       42 x 69

Σ = 131. Result should be (10 x 131) – 100 = $\boxed{1,210}$ less.

- Should be 4,108 – $\boxed{1,210}$ = 2,898✓

- 42 x 69 = (40 x 70) – (40 x 1) + (2 x 69) = 2,800 – 40 + 138 = 2,898✓

Step 4   **52 x 79**
                                                       62 x 89

- Σ = 131. Result should be (10 x 131) + 100 = $\boxed{1,410}$ more.

- Result should be 4,108 + $\boxed{1,410}$ = 5,518 ✓

- 62 x 89 = (62 x 100) – (62 x 11) = 6,200 – 682 = 6,218 – 700 = 5,518 ✓

LEVEL 10 (FLIPS AND DIAGONALS: PART I)..................................... *7 STEPS*

<u>**Step 1**</u>

$$\begin{array}{r} 52 \\ \text{x } \underline{79} \end{array}$$

- 5 x 7 $\to$ 35 $\xrightarrow{\text{x10}}$ 350 $\xrightarrow{+(2\,x\,7)+(9\,x\,5)=59}$ 409 $\xrightarrow{\text{x10}}$ 4,090 $\xrightarrow{+2\,x\,9=18}$ 4,108 ✓

<u>**Step 2: Vertical Flip**</u>

$$\begin{array}{r} 52 \\ \text{x } \underline{79} \end{array}$$

$$\begin{array}{r} 59 \\ \text{x } \underline{72} \end{array}$$

Δ of oners is 7; Δ of tenners is 20.

Result should be 7 x 20 = 140 more than 4,108 $\to$ 4,248 ✓

- 5 x 7 $\to$ 35 $\xrightarrow{\text{x10}}$ 350 $\xrightarrow{+(9\,x\,7)+(\,x\,5)=73}$ 423 $\xrightarrow{\text{x10}}$ 4,230 $\xrightarrow{+9\,x\,2=18}$ 4,248 ✓

<u>**Step 3: Horizontal Derivative**</u>

$$\begin{array}{r} 59 \\ \text{x } \underline{72} \end{array}$$

$$\begin{array}{r} 95 \\ \text{x } \underline{27} \end{array}$$

- Product of oners is 9 x 2 = 18

- Product of tenners is 5 x 7 = 35

- Δ = 35 | 18 = 17

- Therefore, the horizontal derivative should be 1,700 less and 17 more than 4,248.

- Result should be 4,248 – 1,700 + 17 = 2,565 ✓

- 95 x 27 = (100 x 27) – (5 x 27) = 2,700 – 135 = 2,565 ✓

Step 4: First Diagonal Flip (1)

$$59$$
$$\times 72$$

$$57$$
$$\times 92$$

- $57 \times 92 = (57 \times 100) - (57 \times 8) = 5{,}700 - 456 = 5{,}244 \checkmark$

$\Delta_1 = 9 \mid 7\ = 2$

Difference should be $-\ (200 \times 5) + (2 \times 2) = \boxed{-1{,}000 + 4}$

- $5{,}244\ \boxed{-1{,}000 + 4} = 4{,}248 \checkmark$

Step 5: First Diagonal Flip (2)

$$59$$
$$\times 72$$

$$57$$
$$\times 92$$

- $57 \times 92 = 5{,}244$ (see Step 4, above) $\checkmark$

$\Delta_2 = 5 \mid 2 = 3$

Difference should be $-\ (300 \times 9) + (3 \times 7) = \boxed{-2{,}700 + 21}$

- $5{,}244\ \boxed{-2{,}700 + 21} = 2{,}565 \checkmark$

Step 6: Second Diagonal Flip (1)

$$59$$
$$\times 72$$

$$29$$
$$\times 75$$

- $29 \times 75 = (30 \times 75) - (1 \times 75) = 2{,}250 - 75 = 2{,}175 \checkmark$

- $\tfrac{1}{4}$ of $29 = 7\tfrac{1}{4} \xrightarrow{\ \times 3\ } 21\ ^3/_4 \rightarrow 21.75 \xrightarrow{\ \times 100\ } 2{,}175 \checkmark$

$\Delta_2 = 5 \mid 2\ = 3$

Difference should be $+\ (300 \times 7) - (3 \times 9) = \boxed{+\,2{,}100 - 27}$

- $2{,}175\ \boxed{+2{,}100 - 27} = 4{,}248 \checkmark$

Step 7: Second Diagonal Flip (2)

$$\begin{array}{r} 59 \\ \times 72 \\ \hline \end{array}$$

$$\begin{array}{r} \mathbf{29} \\ \underline{\times 75} \end{array}$$

- $29 \times 75 = 2{,}175$ (See Step 6, above)✓

$\Delta_1 = 9 \mid 7 = 2$

Difference should be $+(200 \times 2) - (2 \times 5) = \boxed{+\,400 - 10}$

- $2{,}175 \ \boxed{+\,400 - 10} = 2{,}565$✓

LEVEL 11 (SKEWED)... *2 STEPS*

Step 1   **52 x 79**

- $50 \times 70 \rightarrow 3{,}500 \xrightarrow{+(2+9)\times 52 = 572} 4{,}072 \xrightarrow{+2(70-50)=40} 4{,}112 \xrightarrow{-2^2 = -4} 4{,}108$✓

Step 2   **52 x 79**

- $50 \times 70 \rightarrow 3{,}500 \xrightarrow{+(2+9)\times 79 = 869} 4{,}369 \xrightarrow{-9(70-50)=-180} 4{,}189 \xrightarrow{-9^2 = -81} 4{,}108$✓

LEVEL 12 (FLIPS AND DIAGONALS: PART II) .... *5 STEPS*

Step 1: Horizontal Derivative

$$\begin{array}{r} 52 \\ \underline{\times 79} \end{array}$$

$$\begin{array}{r} 25 \\ \underline{\times 97} \end{array}$$

- Product of oners is $2 \times 9 = 18$

- Product of tenners is $5 \times 7 = 35$

- $\Delta = 35 \mid 18 = 17$

- Therefore, the horizontal derivative should be 1,700 less and 17 more than 4,108.

- Result should be $4{,}108 - 1{,}700 + 17 = 2{,}425$✓

- $25 \times 97 = (25 \times 100) - (25 \times 3) = 2,500 - 75 = 2,425$ ✓

Step 2: First Diagonal Flip (1)

$$\begin{array}{r} 52 \\ \underline{\times 79} \end{array}$$

$$\begin{array}{r} 57 \\ \underline{\times 29} \end{array}$$

- $57 \times 29 = (57 \times 30) - (57 \times 1) = 1,710 - 57 = 1,753 - 100 = 1,653$ ✓

$\Delta_1 = 7 \mid 2 = 5$

Difference should be $+ (500 \times 5) - (5 \times 9) = \boxed{+2,500 - 45}$

- $1,653 \boxed{+2,500 - 45} = 4,108$ ✓

Step 3: First Diagonal Flip (2)

$$\begin{array}{r} 52 \\ \underline{\times 79} \end{array}$$

$$\begin{array}{r} 57 \\ \underline{\times 29} \end{array}$$

- $57 \times 29 = 1,653$ (See Step 2, above) ✓

$\Delta_2 = 9 \mid 5 = 4$

Difference should be $+ (400 \times 2) - (4 \times 7) = \boxed{+ 800 - 28}$

- $1,653 \boxed{+ 800 - 28} = 2,425$ ✓

Step 4: Second Diagonal Flip (1)

$$\begin{array}{r} 52 \\ \underline{\times 79} \end{array}$$

$$\begin{array}{r} 92 \\ \underline{\times 75} \end{array}$$

- $92 \times 75 = (100 \times 75) - (8 \times 75) = 7,500 - 600 = 6,900$ ✓, or

$92 / 4 = 23 \xrightarrow{\times 3} 69 \xrightarrow{\times 100} 6,900$ ✓

$\Delta_2 = 9 \mid 5 = 4$

Difference should be $- (400 \times 7) + (4 \times 2) = \boxed{-2,800 + 8}$

334

- $6,900 \boxed{-2,800 + 8} = 4,108 \checkmark$

Step 5: Second Diagonal Flip (2)

$$\begin{array}{r} 52 \\ \underline{\times 79} \end{array}$$

$$\begin{array}{r} 92 \\ \underline{\times 75} \end{array}$$

- $92 \times 75 = 6,900$ (see Step 4, above)$\checkmark$

$\Delta_1 = 7 \mid 2 = 5$

Difference should be $-(500 \times 9) + (5 \times 5) = \boxed{-4,500 + 25}$

- $6,900 \boxed{-4,500 + 25} = 2,425 \checkmark$

LEVEL 13 (SQUARE OF HALF-SUM AND CENTERED ON 50) .... *3 STEPS*

Step 1   **52 x 79**

- $\sum(52 + 79) = 131. \quad \sum/2 = 65\frac{1}{2}$

- $\Delta = 65\frac{1}{2} \mid 52 = 13\frac{1}{2}$

- $52 \times 79 = (65\frac{1}{2})^2 - (13\frac{1}{2})^2 = 4,290 - 182 = 4,108 \checkmark$

(Remember:

1. In subtracting a square of a number ending in $\frac{1}{2}$ from the square of another number also ending in $\frac{1}{2}$, we always eliminate the .25 with which all squares of .$\frac{1}{2}$ end.

2. $65\frac{1}{2}^2 = 65^2 + 65. \quad 65^2 = 100 (6 \times 7) + 25 = 4,225; 65\frac{1}{2}^2 - 4,225 + 65 = 4,290.$

   $13\frac{1}{2}^2 = 13^2 + 13 = 169 + 13 = 182)$

Step 2   **52 x 79**

- $\sum(52 + 79) = 131$

- $131 - 100 = 31$

  $\Delta = 52 \mid 50 = 2$

- $52 \times 79 = 2{,}500 - 2^2 + (52 \times 31) = 2{,}500 - 4 + 1{,}612 = 4{,}108$ ✓

Step 3   **52 x 79**

- $\sum(52 + 79) = 131$

- $131 - 100 = 31$

- $\Delta = 79 \mid 50 = 29$

- $52 \times 79 = 2{,}500 - 29^2 + (79 \times 31) = 2{,}500 - 841 + 2{,}449 = 4{,}108$ ✓

(Note: $29^2 = 30^2 - (30 + 29) = 900 - 59 - 841$

79 x 31: Solve by square of half-sum method.

$79 + 31 = 110$

$\frac{1}{2} \times 110 = 55$

$55^2 = \boxed{3{,}025}$

$55 - 31 = 24$

$24^2 = 576$

$79 \times 31 = \boxed{3{,}025} - \boxed{576} = 3{,}049 - 600 = 2{,}449)$

LEVEL 14 (COMPLEMENT TO 10)... *2 STEPS*

Step 1   **52 x 79**

                                     52 x 78 (make oners add to 10)

Add $1 \times 52 = \boxed{52}$ at the end.

- $70 + 10 = 80$

- $80 - 50 = 30$

- $52 \times 79 = (80 \times 50) + (2 \times 30) - 2^2 + \boxed{52} = 4{,}000 + 60 - 4 + \boxed{52} = 4{,}108$ ✓

Step 2   **52 x 79**

51 x 79 (make oners add to 10)

Add 1 x 79 = $\boxed{79}$ at the end.

- $70 + 10 = 80$

- $80 - 50 = 30$

- $52 \times 79 = (80 \times 50) + (1 + 30) - 1^2 + \boxed{79} = 4{,}000 + 30 - 1 + \boxed{79} = 4{,}108 \checkmark$

LEVEL 15 (EQUAL ONERS AND TENNERS) .... *4 STEPS*

Step 1   **52 x 79**

52 x 72 (to equalize oners)

Add 7 x 52 = $\boxed{364}$ at the end.

- $50 \times 70 \rightarrow 3{,}500 \xrightarrow{+2(50+70)=240} 3{,}740 \xrightarrow{+2^2=4} 3{,}744 \xrightarrow{\boxed{+364}} 4{,}108 \checkmark$

Step 2   **52 x 79**

59 x 79 (to equalize oners)

Subtract 7 x 79 = $\boxed{553}$ at the end.

- $50 \times 70 \rightarrow 3{,}500 \xrightarrow{+9(50+70)=1{,}080} 4{,}580 \xrightarrow{+9^2=81} 4{,}661 \xrightarrow{\boxed{-553}} 4{,}108 \checkmark$

Step 3   **52 x 79**

52 x 59 (to equalize tenners)

Add 20 x 52 = $\boxed{1{,}040}$ at the end.

- $50^2 \rightarrow 2{,}500 \xrightarrow{50(2+9)=550} 3{,}050 \xrightarrow{+2\times9=18} 3{,}068 \xrightarrow{\boxed{+1{,}040}} 4{,}108 \checkmark$

Step 4   **52 x 79**

72 x 79 (to equalize tenners)

Subtract 20 x 79 = $\boxed{1{,}580}$ at the end.

- $70^2 \rightarrow 4{,}900 \xrightarrow{+70(2+9)=770} 5{,}670 \xrightarrow{+2\times9=18} 5{,}688 \xrightarrow{\boxed{-1{,}580}} 4{,}108 \checkmark$

LEVEL 16 (STRIP THE TENNERS).. *2 STEPS*

<u>**Step 1**</u>   **52 x 79**

                                             2 x 29 (eliminating the first tenner)

- $52 \times 79 = 50^2 + 50 (2 + 29) + (2 \times 29) = 2{,}500 + 1{,}550 + 58 = 4{,}108$ ✓

<u>**Step 2**</u>   **52 x 79**

                                             -18 x 9 (eliminating the second tenner)

- $52 \times 79 = 70^2 + 70 (-18 + 9) + (-18 \times 9) = 4{,}900 - 630 - 162 = 4{,}108$ ✓

Now let's do one last problem together.

Problem #6

62 x 89

LEVEL 1 (THE EASIEST) .... *2 STEPS*

Step 1   **62 x 89**

- $(60 \times 89) + (2 \times 89)$

- $60 \times 89 \ = \ (60 \times 80) + (6 \times 9) \ = \ 4{,}800 + 540 \ \rightarrow 5{,}340$

- $2 \times 89 \ \ = \ (2 \times 80) + (2 \times 9) \ \ = \ 160 + 18 \ \ \ \rightarrow \ \ \underline{178}$

$$\therefore \ \textbf{62 x 89} \ \ \ = \ \underline{5{,}518}\checkmark$$

Step 2   **62 x 89**

- $(80 \times 62) + (9 \times 62)$

- $80 \times 62 \ \ = \ (80 \times 60) + (80 \times 2) = \ 4{,}800 + 160 \ \rightarrow \ \ 4{,}960$

- $9 \times 62 \ \ \ = \ (9 \times 60) + (9 \times 2) \ \ \ = \ 540 + 18 \ \ \ \ \rightarrow \underline{\ \ +558}$

$$\therefore \ \textbf{62 x 89} \ \ \ = \ \ \underline{5{,}518}\checkmark$$

LEVEL 2 (THE CLASSIC) .... *2 STEPS*

Step 1   **62 x 89**

- $(60 \times 80) + (2 \times 80) + (60 \times 9) + (2 \times 9)$

- $4{,}800 \xrightarrow{\ +2\times80=160\ } 4{,}960 \xrightarrow{\ +60\times9=540\ } 5{,}500 \xrightarrow{\ +2\times9=18\ } 5{,}518 \checkmark$

Step 2   **62 x 89**
$$(70 - 8) \text{ x } (90 - 1)$$

- $(70 \times 90) - (8 \times 90) - (70 \times 1) + (8 \times 1)$

- $6{,}300 \xrightarrow{\ -8\times90=-720\ } 5{,}580 \xrightarrow{\ -70\times1=-70\ } 5{,}510 \xrightarrow{\ +8\times1=8\ } 5{,}518 \checkmark$

LEVEL 3 (CENTERED AROUND 5) .... *5 STEPS*

Step 1

62 x 89

- 65 x 85[*]   →   5,525
- For 62 x 65, subtract 3 x 85   →   -255   →   5,270
- For 62 x 89, add 4 x 62   →   +248   →   5,518✓
-    Δ   →   -7✓

Step 2

62 x 89

62 x 88

We will have to add 1 x 62 = $\boxed{62}$ at the end.

- 80 – 60   =   20
- 2 – 5   =   -3
- -3 x 20   →   -60
- $-(-3^2)$ →   -9
- Add: → $\boxed{+62}$
                                                     ─────────
-    Δ   →   -7✓

Step 3

62 x 89

61 x 89

We will have to add 1 x 89 = $\boxed{89}$ at the end.

- 80 – 60   =   20

───────────────────────

*Remember how to multiply two numbers ending in 5? Here is a refresher:

65 x 85

6 x 8	=	48
(6 + 8)/2	=	7
		55
attach		25
65 x 85	=	5,525✓

- $1 - 5 \qquad = \qquad -4$

- $-4 \times 20 \qquad = \qquad\qquad\qquad \rightarrow \qquad -80$

- $-(-4^2) \qquad\qquad\qquad\qquad \rightarrow \qquad -16$

- Add: $\qquad\qquad\qquad\qquad \rightarrow \qquad \boxed{+89}$

- $\Delta \qquad\qquad\qquad\qquad\qquad \rightarrow \qquad -7 \checkmark$

Step 4

$$62 \times 89$$
$$62 \times 82$$

We will have to add 7 x 62 = $\boxed{434}$ at the end.

- $60 + 80 + 10 \qquad = 150$

- $2 - 5 \qquad\qquad = \ -3$

- $3 \times 150 \qquad\qquad\qquad \rightarrow \qquad -450$

- $+(-3^2) \qquad\qquad\qquad \rightarrow \qquad +9$

- Add: $\qquad\qquad\qquad\qquad \rightarrow \qquad \boxed{+434}$

- $\Delta \qquad\qquad\qquad\qquad\qquad \rightarrow \qquad -7 \checkmark$

Step 5

$$62 \times 89$$
$$69 \times 89$$

We will have to subtract 7 x 89 = $\boxed{623}$ at the end.

- $60 + 80 + 10 \qquad = 150$

- $9 - 5 \qquad\qquad = \ 4$

- $4 \times 150 \qquad\qquad\qquad \rightarrow \qquad +600$

- $+4^2 \qquad\qquad\qquad\qquad \rightarrow \qquad +16$

- Subtract: $\qquad\qquad\qquad\qquad \rightarrow \qquad \boxed{-623}$

- $\Delta \qquad\qquad\qquad\qquad\qquad \rightarrow \qquad -7 \checkmark$

LEVEL 4 (POWERS OF 2 OR 3, QUARTERS OR EIGHTHS) .... *3 STEPS*

Step 1

$$62 \times 89$$
$$64 \times 89$$

We will have to subtract 2 x 89 = $\boxed{178}$ at the end.

- 178 $\rightarrow$ 356 $\rightarrow$ 712 $\rightarrow$ 1,424 $\rightarrow$ 2,848 $\rightarrow$ 5,696 $\xrightarrow{\boxed{-178}}$ 5,518 ✓
  (x2)   (x4)   (x8)   (x16)   (x32)   (x64)

Step 2

$$62 \times 89$$
$$62\tfrac{1}{2} \times 89 \; (\tfrac{5}{8} \times 89 \times 100)$$

We will have to subtract ½ x 89 = $\boxed{44\tfrac{1}{2}}$ at the end.

(Remember: If we subtract ½ from ½ we can forget about the ½ in both numbers.)

- 89/8 = $11\tfrac{1}{8}$ $\xrightarrow{x5}$ $55\tfrac{5}{8}$ $\rightarrow$ 55.625 $\xrightarrow{x100}$ 5,562(½) $\xrightarrow{\boxed{-44(1/2)}}$ 5,518 ✓

Step 3

$$62 \times 89$$
$$62 \times 100$$

We will have to subtract 11 x 62 = $\boxed{682}$ at the end.

- 100 x 62 $\rightarrow$ 6,200 $\xrightarrow{\boxed{-682}}$ 5,518 ✓

LEVEL 5 (FLIPS) .... *2 STEPS*

Step 1

$$62 \times 89$$
$$62 \times 26$$

After we have arrived at 62 x 26, we have to bring it back to 62 x 89. The best way of doing this is to multiply the result of 62 x 26 by 3, which brings you to 62 x 78. Add 62 x 11 = $\boxed{682}$, which brings you to 62 x 89.

- 62 x 89 = (62 x 26) x 3 + $\boxed{682}$

• $62 \times 89 \rightarrow 20 \times 0 \rightarrow 1{,}200 \xrightarrow{+10(6^2+2^2)=400} 1{,}600 \xrightarrow{+(2\times6)=12} 1{,}612 \xrightarrow{\times 3} 4{,}836 \xrightarrow{\boxed{+682}} 5{,}518 \checkmark$

Step 2

$$62 \times 89$$
$$98 \times 89$$

After you solve for 98 x 89, the easiest way to get to 62 x 98 is to subtract 8 x 89 = $\boxed{712}$ from the result, which brings you to 90 x 89. Divide by 3 and multiply by 2, which brings you to 60 x 89. Add 2 x 89 = $\boxed{178}$ to get you to where you want to be: 62 x 89.

First let's solve 98 x 89. In "real life," the easy way, of course, would be to figure 100 x 89 = 8,900 and then subtract 2 x 89 = 178 and get the result 8,728.

But we are committed to do it the somewhat harder way, by Level 5 method, so here goes.

• $62 \times 89 = [(98 \times 89) - (8 \times 89)] \times \tfrac{2}{3} + (2 \times 89)$

• $62 \times 89 \rightarrow (90 \times 80) \rightarrow 7{,}200 \xrightarrow{10\times(9^2+8^2)=1{,}450} 8{,}650 \xrightarrow{+9\times8=72} 8{,}722 \xrightarrow{\boxed{-712}} 8{,}010$

$\xrightarrow{/3} 2{,}670^{(1)} \xrightarrow{\times 2} 5{,}340 \xrightarrow{\boxed{+178}} 5{,}518 \checkmark$

LEVEL 6 (COMPLEMENTS TO 100) .... *2 STEPS*

Step 1

$$62 \times 89$$
$$6{,}200 - (62 \times 11)$$

• $62 \times 11 \;=\; \boxed{682}$

• $62 \times 89 \;=\; 6{,}200 - \boxed{682} = 5{,}518 \checkmark$

---

(1) How do you (mentally) divide 8,010 by 3? First of all, of course, you determine that the number is indeed divisible by 3. The sum of digits of 8,010 is 9, so, yes, it is divisible by 3. 80 is not divisible by 3. The next lower number that is divisible by 3 is 78 → 7,800. 7,800 divided by 3 is 2,600. The remainder is 210; that divided by 3 is of course 70. So, 8,010 divided by 3 is 2,600 and 70 = 2,670.

I go into so much detail because I want you to acquire the facility in doing these mental calculations -- yes, even divisions!

LEVEL 6 (COMPLEMENTS TO 100) .... *2 STEPS*

<u>Step 1</u> 62×89

$$6{,}200 - 62, (100 - 89), \text{ or}$$
$$6{,}200 - (62 \times 11)$$

- $62 \times 11 \ = \ \boxed{682}$

- $62 \times 89 \ = \ 6{,}200 - \boxed{682} = 5{,}518 \checkmark$

<u>Step 2</u> 62×89
$$8{,}900 - (89 \times 38)$$

- $89 \times 38 \ (\text{easiest}) = (100 \times 38) - (11 \times 38) = 3{,}800 - 418 = \boxed{3{,}382}$

- $62 \times 89 = 8{,}900 - \boxed{3{,}382} = 8{,}918 - 3{,}400 = 5{,}518 \checkmark$

LEVEL 7 (COMPLEMENT SQUARES) .... *2 STEPS*

<u>Step 1</u> 62×89
$$\Delta = 89 \,|\, 62 = 27$$

- $62 \times 89 \ = 62^2 + (27 \times 62)$

- $27 \times 62 \ = (30 \times 62) - (3 \times 62) = 1{,}860 - 186 = \boxed{1{,}674}$

- $62^2 = 60^2 + (4 \times 60) + 2^2 = 3{,}600 + 240 + 4 = \boxed{3{,}844}$

- $62 \times 89 \ = \boxed{1{,}674} + \boxed{3{,}814} = 5{,}518 \checkmark$

<u>Step 2</u> 62×89
$$\Delta = 27$$

- $62 \times 89 \ = \ 89^2 - (27 \times 89)$

- $27 \times 89 \ = \ (30 \times 89) - (3 \times 89) = 2{,}670 - 267 = \boxed{2{,}403}$

- $89^2 \ = \ 90^2 - (90 + 89) = 8{,}100 - 179 = \boxed{7{,}921}$

- $62 \times 89 = \ \boxed{7{,}921} - \boxed{2{,}403} = 5{,}518 \checkmark$

LEVEL 8 (HALVES, COMMON DENOMINATORS, HALVES AND DOUBLES).. *4 STEPS*

Step 1

$$62 \times 89$$
$$31 \times 44\tfrac{1}{2} \ (\times 4)$$

- $31 \times 44\tfrac{1}{2}$: $30 \times 40 \to 1,200 \xrightarrow{+30 \times 4 = 120} 1,320 \xrightarrow{+1 \times 44 = 44} 1,364 \xrightarrow{+31 \times 1/2 = 15 1/2}$

$$1,379\tfrac{1}{2} \xrightarrow{\times 4} 5,518 \checkmark$$

(Note: $1,379\tfrac{1}{2} \times 4 = (1,380 \times 4) - (\tfrac{1}{2} \times 4) = 5,200 + 320 - 2 = 5,518 \checkmark$)

Step 2

$$62 \times 89$$

Closest common denominator is 31.

$$62 \times 89$$
$$62 \times 93$$

We will have to subtract $4 \times 62 = \boxed{248}$ at the end.

- $62 = 2 \times 31$

- $93 = 3 \times 31$

- $31^2 = 30^2 + (30 + 31) = \boxed{961}^{(1)}$

- $62 \times 89 = 6 \times 31^2 - \boxed{248} = 6 \times 961 - \boxed{248} = 5,766 - 248^{(2)} = 5,518 \checkmark$

(Note: (1) 961×6 (easiest) $= (6 \times 900) + (6 \times 60) + (6 \times 1) = 5,400 + 360 + 6 = 5,766$, or

$961 \times 6 = (6 \times 1,000) - (6 \times 39) = 6,000 - 234 = 5,766$.

(2) $5,766 - 248 = 5,766 - 200 - 40 - 8 \to 5,566 \to 5,526 \to 5,518 \checkmark$)

Step 3

$$62 \times 89$$
$$124 \times 44\tfrac{1}{2}$$

- Solve by 124×44 by same-last-digit method and add $124 \times \tfrac{1}{2} = \boxed{+62}$

- $124 \times 44\tfrac{1}{2} \to 12\text{-} \times 4\text{-} \to \xrightarrow{+(120+40) \times 4 = 640} 5,440 \xrightarrow{+4^2 = 16} 5,456 \xrightarrow{\boxed{+62}} 5,518 \checkmark$

Step 4   **62 x 89**
                                             31 x 178

- $31 \times 178 = (30 \times 178) + (1 \times 178)$

- $31 \times 178 = 30 \times 170 \rightarrow 5{,}100 \xrightarrow{+30 \times 8 = 240} 5{,}340 \xrightarrow{+1 \times 178 = 178} 5{,}518$ ✓

LEVEL 9 (PLUS AND MINUS 10).. *4 STEPS*

Step 1   **62 x 89**
                                             52 x 99

$\Delta = 89 \mid 62 = 27$. Result should be $(10 \times 27) + 100 = \boxed{370}$ less.

- Should be $5{,}518 - \boxed{370} = 5{,}148$ ✓

- $52 \times 99 = (52 \times 100) - 52 = 5{,}200 - 52 = 5{,}148$ ✓

Step 2   **62 x 89**
                                             72 x 79

- $\Delta = 89 \mid 62 = 27$. Result should be $(10 \times 27) - 100 = \boxed{170}$ more.

- Result should be $5{,}518 + \boxed{170} = 5{,}688$ ✓

- $72 \times 79 = (72 \times 80) - 72 = 5{,}760 - 72 = 5{,}688$ ✓

Step 3   **62 x 89**
                                             52 x 79

- $\Sigma = 62 + 89 = 151$. Result should be $(10 \times 151) - 100 = \boxed{1{,}410}$ less.

- Should be $5{,}518 - \boxed{1{,}410} = 4{,}108$ ✓

- 52×79: 1. 52×25 (¼ of 5,200) $\rightarrow 1{,}300$

        $52 \times 79 = 1{,}300 \xrightarrow{\times 3} 3{,}900 \xrightarrow{+4 \times 52 = 208} 4{,}108$ ✓, or

      2. $52 \times 79 = (50 \times 79) + (2 \times 79) = 3{,}950 + 158 = 4{,}108$ ✓, or

3. $52 \times 79 = (52 \times 80) - 52 = 4,160 - 52 = 4,108$ ✓

So many ways to skin a cat. Get used to it!

Step 4   **62 x 89**
                                                     72 x 99

- $\Sigma = 151$. Result should be $(10 \times 151) + 100 = \boxed{1,610}$ more.

- Result should be $5,518 + \boxed{1,610} = 7,128$ ✓

- $72 \times 99 = (72 \times 100) - (72 \times 1) = 7,200 - 72 = 7,128$ ✓

LEVEL 10 (FLIPS AND DIAGONALS: PART I)....................................... *7 STEPS*

Step 1   **62**
                                                     x89

- $6 \times 8 \rightarrow 48 \xrightarrow{\text{x10}} 480 \xrightarrow{+(2\times8)+(9\times6)=70} 550 \xrightarrow{\text{x10}} 5,500 \xrightarrow{+2\times9=18} 5,518$ ✓

Step 2: Vertical Flip   **62**
                                                     x89

                                                     69
                                                     x82

Δ of oners is 7; Δ of tenners is 20

Result should be $7 \times 20 = 140$ more than $5,518 \rightarrow 5,658$ ✓

- $6 \times 8 \rightarrow 48 \xrightarrow{\text{x10}} 480 \xrightarrow{+(9\times8)+(2\times6)=84} 564 \xrightarrow{\text{x10}} 5,640 \xrightarrow{+9\times2=18} 5,658$ ✓

Step 3: Horizontal Derivative   **69**
                                                     x82

                                                     96
                                                     x28

- Product of oners is $9 \times 2 = 18$

- Product of tenners is $6 \times 8 = 48$

- $\Delta = 48 \mid 18 = 30$

- Therefore, the horizontal derivative should be 3,000 less and 30 more than 5,658.

- Result should be $5,658 - 3,000 + 30 = 2,688$ ✓

- $96 \times 28 = (96 \times 25) + (96 \times 3)$; ¼ of 96 = 24 ✓

- $96 \times 25 = 2,400.$ $96 \times 3 = 288$

- Therefore, $96 \times 28 = 2,400 + 288 = 2,688$ ✓, or

- $96 \times 28 = (100 \times 28) - (4 \times 28) = 2,800 - 112 = 2,688$ ✓

Step 4: First Diagonal Flip (1)

$$\begin{array}{r} 69 \\ \times\ \underline{82} \end{array}$$

$$\begin{array}{r} 68 \\ \times\ \underline{92} \end{array}$$

- Solve 68×92 by square of half-sum $= 80^2 - 12^2 = 6,400 - 144 = 6,256$ ✓

$\Delta_1 = 9|8\ = 1$

Difference should be $-(100 \times 6) + (1 \times 2) = \boxed{-\ 600 + 2}$

- $6,256 - \boxed{600 + 2}\ = 5,658$ ✓

Step 5: First Diagonal Flip (2)

$$\begin{array}{r} 69 \\ \times\ \underline{82} \end{array}$$

$$\begin{array}{r} 68 \\ \times\ \underline{92} \end{array}$$

- $68 \times 92 = 6,256$ (see Step 4 above)

$\Delta_2 = 6 \mid 2 = 4$

Difference should be $-\ (400 \times 9) + (4 \times 8) = \boxed{-3,600 + 32}$

- $6,256 \boxed{-\ 3,600 + 32} = 2,688$ ✓

Step 6: Second Diagonal Flip (1)
$$\begin{array}{r} 69 \\ \underline{\times 82} \end{array}$$

$$\begin{array}{r} 29 \\ \underline{\times 86} \end{array}$$

- $29 \times 86 = (30 \times 86) - (1 \times 86) = 2,580 - 86 = 2,494\checkmark$

$\Delta_2 = 6 \mid 2 = 4$

Difference should be $(400 \times 8) - (4 \times 9) = \boxed{+3,200 - 36}$

- $2,494 \boxed{+3,200 - 36} = 5,658\checkmark$

Step 7: Second Diagonal Flip (2)
$$\begin{array}{r} 69 \\ \underline{\times 82} \end{array}$$

$$\begin{array}{r} 29 \\ \underline{\times 86} \end{array}$$

- $29 \times 86 = 2,494\checkmark$ (see Step 6 above)

$\Delta_1 = 9 \mid 8 = 1$

Difference should be $+ (100 \times 2) - (1 \times 6) = \boxed{+200 - 6}$

- $2,494 \boxed{+ 200 - 6} = 2,688\checkmark$

LEVEL 11 (SKEWED)... *2 STEPS*

Step 1   **62 x 89**

- $60 \times 80 \rightarrow 4,800 \xrightarrow{+(9+2)\times62=682} 5,482 \xrightarrow{+2(80-60)=40} 5,522 \xrightarrow{-2^2=-4} 5,518\checkmark$

Step 2   **62 x 89**

- $60 \times 80 \rightarrow 4,800 \xrightarrow{+(2+9)\times89=979} 5,779 \xrightarrow{-9(80-60)=-180} 5,599 \xrightarrow{-9^2=-81} 5,518\checkmark$

LEVEL 12 (FLIPS AND DIAGONALS: PART II) .... *5 STEPS*

Step 1: Horizontal Derivative

$$62$$
$$\times 89$$

$$26$$
$$\times 98$$

- Product of oners is 2 x 9 = 18.

- Product of tenners is 6 x 8 = 48.

- Δ = 48 | 18 = 30.

- Therefore, the horizontal derivative should be 3,000 less and 30 more than 5,518.

- Result should be 5,518 – 3,000 + 30 = 2,548✓

- 26 x 98 = (26 x 100) – (26 x 2) = 2,600 – 52 = 2,548✓

Step 2: First Diagonal Flip (1)

$$62$$
$$\times 89$$

$$68$$
$$\times 29$$

- 68 x 29 = (68 x 30) – (68 x 1) = 2,040 – 68 = 1,972✓

Δ_1 = 8 | 2 = 6

Difference should be +(600 x 6) – (6 x 9) = $\boxed{+3,600 - 54}$

- 1,972 $\boxed{+ 3,600 - 54}$ = 5,518✓

Step 3: First Diagonal Flip (2)

$$62$$
$$\times 89$$

$$68$$
$$\times 29$$

- 68 x 29 = 1,972 (See Step 2 above)✓

Δ_2 = 9 | 6 = 3

Difference should be + (300 x 2) − (3 x 8) = $\boxed{+\,600 - 24}$

- 1,972 $\boxed{+\,600 - 24}$ = 2,548✓

Step 4: Second Diagonal Flip (1)

$$62$$
$$\underline{\text{x}89}$$

$$92$$
$$\underline{\text{x}86}$$

Solve 92 x 86 (easiest) by square of half sum: $92 \times 86 = 89^2 - 3^2$

- $89^2 = 90^2 - (90 + 89) = 8{,}100 - 179 = 7{,}921$

- $92 \times 86 = 7{,}921 - 3^2 = 7{,}921 - 9 = 7{,}912$✓

$\Delta_2 = 9 \mid 6 = 3$

- Difference should be − (300 x 8) + (3 x 2) $\boxed{-\,2{,}400 + 6}$

- 7,912 − $\boxed{2{,}400 + 6}$ = 5,518✓

Step 5: Second Diagonal Flip (2)

$$62$$
$$\underline{\text{x}89}$$

$$92$$
$$\underline{\text{x}86}$$

- 92 x 86 = 7,912 (see Step 6 above)

$\Delta_1 = 8 \mid 2 = 6$

Difference should be - (600 x 9) + (6 x 6) = $\boxed{-5{,}400 + 36}$

- 7,912 $\boxed{-5{,}400 + 36}$ = 2,548✓

LEVEL 13 (SQUARE OF HALF-SUM AND CENTERED ON 50) .... *3 STEPS*

Step 1

$$62 \times 89$$

- $\sum(62 + 89) = 151.$ $\sum/2 = 75\tfrac{1}{2}$

- $\Delta = 75\tfrac{1}{2} - 62 = 13\tfrac{1}{2}$

- $62 \times 89 = 75\frac{1}{2}^2 - 13\frac{1}{2}^2 = 5,700 - 182 = 5,518\checkmark$

(Remember: $75\frac{1}{2}^2 = 75^2 + 75 = 5,625 + 75 = 5,700$

$\qquad\qquad 13\frac{1}{2}^2 = 13^2 + 13 = 169 + 13 = 182$)

Since we subtract two equals, we can disregard the .25 that dangles from every square of -.$\frac{1}{2}$)

Step 2 $\qquad\qquad$ 62 x 89

- $\sum(62 + 89) = 151$

- $151 - 100 = 51$

$\Delta = 62 \mid 50 = 12$

- $62 \times 89 = 2,500 - 12^2 + (51 \times 62) = 2,500 - 144 + 3,162 = 5,518\checkmark$

(Note: $(51 \times 62) - (50 \times 62) + (1 \times 62) = 3,100 + 62 = 3,162$)

Step 3 $\qquad\qquad$ 62 x 89

- $\sum(62 + 89) = 151$

- $151 - 100 = 51$

$\Delta = 89 \mid 50 = 39$

- $62 \times 89 = 2,500 - 39^2 + (89 \times 51) = 2,500 - 1,521 + 4,539 = 5,518\checkmark$

(Note: $39^2 = 40^2 - (40 + 39) = 1,600 - 79 = 1,521$

$\qquad 89 \times 51$: Easiest $\rightarrow (100 \times 51) - (11 \times 51) = 5,100 - 561 = 5,139 - 600 = 4,539$, or

$\qquad 89 \times 51 = 70^2 - 19^2 = 4,900 - 361 = 4,539$)

LEVEL 14 (COMPLEMENT TO 10)...*2 STEPS*

Step 1 $\qquad\qquad$ 62 x 89

$\qquad\qquad\qquad\qquad$ **62 x 88 (make oners add to 10)**

Add $1 \times 62 = \boxed{62}$ at the end.

- $80 + 10 = 90$

- $90 - 60 = 30$

- $62 \times 89 = (90 \times 60) + (2 \times 30) - 2^2 + \boxed{62} = 5{,}400 + 60 - 4 + \boxed{62} = 5{,}518\checkmark$

<u>**Step 2**</u>   **62 x 89**

                              61 x 89 (make oners add to 10)

Add $1 \times 89 = \boxed{89}$ at the end.

- $80 + 10 = 90$

- $90 - 60 = 30$

- $62 \times 89 = (90 \times 60) + (1 \times 30) - 1^2 + \boxed{89} = 5{,}400 + 30 - 1 + \boxed{89} = 5{,}518\checkmark$

LEVEL 15 (EQUAL ONERS AND TENNERS) .... *4 STEPS*

<u>**Step 1**</u>   **62 x 89**

                              62 x 82 (to equalize oners)

Add $7 \times 62 = \boxed{434}$ at the end.

- $60 \times 80 \rightarrow 4{,}800 \xrightarrow{+2(60+80)=280} 5{,}080 \xrightarrow{+2^2=4} 5{,}084 \xrightarrow{\boxed{+434}} 5{,}518\checkmark$

<u>**Step 2**</u>   **62 x 89**

                              69 x 89 (to equalize oners)

Subtract $7 \times 89 = \boxed{623}$ at the end.

(Note: $7 \times 89 = (7 \times 90) - (7 \times 1) = 630 - 7 = 623$)

- $60 \times 80 \rightarrow 4{,}800 \xrightarrow{+9(60+80)=1{,}260} 6{,}060 \xrightarrow{+9^2=81} 6{,}141 \xrightarrow{\boxed{-623}} 5{,}518\checkmark$

<u>**Step 3**</u>   **62 x 89**

                              62 x 69 (to equalize tenners)

Add $20 \times 62 = \boxed{1{,}240}$ at the end.

- $60^2 \rightarrow 3{,}600 \xrightarrow{+60(2+9)=660} 4{,}260 \xrightarrow{+2 \times 9=18} 4{,}278 \xrightarrow{\boxed{+1{,}240}} 5{,}518\checkmark$

<u>**Step 4**</u>   **62 x 89**

82 x 89 (to equalize tenners)

Subtract 20 x 89 = $\boxed{1{,}780}$ at the end.

- $80^2 \rightarrow 6{,}400 \xrightarrow{\ +80(2+9)=880\ } 7{,}280 \xrightarrow{\ +2 \times 9 = 18\ } 7{,}298 \xrightarrow{\ \boxed{-1{,}780}\ } 5{,}518\checkmark$

LEVEL 16 (STRIP THE TENNERS).. *2 STEPS*

<u>**Step 1**</u>   **62 x 89**

2 x 29 (eliminating the first tenner)

- $62 \times 89 = 60^2 + 60(2+29) - (2 \times 29) = 3{,}600 + 1{,}860 + 58 = 5{,}518\checkmark$

<u>**Step 2**</u>   **62 x 89**

-18 x 9 (eliminating the second tenner)

- $62 \times 89 = 80^2 + 80(-18 + 9) + (-18 \times 9) = 6{,}400 - 720 - 162 = 5{,}518\checkmark$

I hope that you have enjoyed this journey that we took together through the 16-Level Paradigm. I know that it is a little difficult at first, especially if you have not much previous experience in working with numbers. But do practice and you will be rewarded. You possibly already feel how your mind has been sharpened and how your memory has improved. I promise you that it will get better and better as you go along. As you get the hang of it and as you make progress, you will find your mind becoming more and more alive and the problems becoming easier and easier to solve.

The next section (Section IV) deals with the algebra of the 16-Level Paradigm. As I told you in the beginning, this section is optional – some people just can't stand algebra. But I urge you to give it a try. You will find it most rewarding.

There are also some small bonuses in that section that don't really pertain to the 16-Level Paradigm. You will enjoy them. I even show you how you can make a little extra money with some startling "propositions."

In the last section of this book (Section V), I give you 25 practice examples. I shall help you with the first five; on the last twenty you are pretty much on your own.

Section IV

THE ALGEBRA OF THE 16-LEVEL PARADIGM

I have promised you that I would not burden you with algebra in the main part of this book, and that I would reserve it for this special section. I've kept the promise. And algebra isn't really what this book is about.

This book is about how to sharpen your mind and hone your memory by the discipline of the 16-Level Paradigm that we just went through together.

If you stayed with me and if you did all of the exercises, you should surely feel a substantial improvement in your mental capacity by now.

And this mental acuity, this great memory, will further improve as you practice the 16-Level Paradigm on your own, as we discussed in the previous section.

As to the algebra: We will refer to the algebra that may be involved in each of the levels. At the end, we will have some comments on probability (even show you how to make a little money by winning some "sure-thing" bar bets), and on second-degree (quadratic) equation.

LEVEL 1 (THE EASIEST) .... *2 STEPS*

All of our examples are of the order:

$$(10a + b)(10c + d)$$

Multiplying each term of the first factor by each term of the second factor, we get:

356

$(10a + b)(10c + d) = 100ac + 10ad + 10bc + bd$

or $\quad = 100ac + 10(ad + bc) + bd$

Step 1

The procedure in Step 1 is:

$10a(10c + d) + b(10c + d)$, which works out to:

$100ac + 10ad + 10bc + bd$

This is of course what it should be.

Step 2

Step 2 is the mirror image of Step 1, so there is no need to go through the algebra of that.

We find that sometimes, when the oners of one (or both) of the factors is/are close to 10 (such as 7, 8, or 9), it might be simpler to express $10a + b$ as $10(a + 1) - (10 - b)$.

For instance, if $(10a + b)$ is, say 58 (i.e., a = 5 and b = 8), we could instead think of $(10 \times 6) - (2) = 58$.

The algebra would then work as follows:

$[10(a + 1) - (10 - b)] \times (10c + d) =$

$[10a + \cancel{10} - \cancel{10} + b] \times (10c + d) =$

$(10a + b)(10c + d)$ (which, not surprisingly, is the same as if we had worked with $(10a + b)$.

If the oners of both factors are close to 10 – suppose the case of 58 x 79 (with terms c = 7 and d = 9 for the second factor), we could work it advantageously as:

$[10(a + 1) - (10 - b)] \times [10(c + 1) - (10 - d)] =$

$[10a + \cancel{10} - \cancel{10} + b] \times [10c + \cancel{10} - \cancel{10} + d] =$

$(10a + b)(10c + d)$ (which, again, is of course the same as if we had worked with $(10a + b)$ and $(10c + d)$, instead of with the complements).

<u>Note</u>: In both examples, we have struck through + 10 and − 10, two terms that eliminate each other. We shall do that in many of our equations in the future. So please remember that.

LEVEL 2 (THE CLASSIC)..*2 STEPS*

We call this level "classic" because, in both Steps 1 and 2, we work exactly in accordance with the binomial expression, namely

$$(10a + b)(10c + d) = 100ac + 10ad + 10\ bc + bd$$

For instance, if we multiply 37 x 82 (in which a = 3, b = 7, c = 8, and d = 2), we follow this sequence

1. 30 x 80 = 100ac

2. +7 x 80 = +10bc

3. + 2 x 30 = +10ad

4. +7 x 2 = + bd

You will note that I changed the sequence slightly, which does not make any difference, of course. It's just more convenient for me. It will also be more convenient for you.

In Step 2 of Level 2, we express (10a + b) (10c + d) as

$$[10\ (a + 1) − (10 − b)] \times [10\ (c + 1) − (10 − d)]$$
$$\quad (1) \qquad\quad (2) \qquad\qquad (3) \qquad\quad (4)$$

Multiplying the terms of each factor with each of the terms of the other factor, we get

$$10\ (a + 1) \times 10\ (c + 1) − 10\ (a + 1)(10 − d) − (10 − b) \times 10(c + 1) + (10 − b)(10 − d)^{*}$$
$$\ (1)\ \ \text{x}\ \ (2) \qquad − \qquad (1)\ \ \text{x}\ \ (3) \quad − \quad (2)\ \ \text{x}\ \ (3) \quad + \quad (2)\ \ \text{x}\ \ (4)$$

---

[*] As we go along, we shall in many cases omit the "x" to signify multiplication. It is a convention and it is understood that the operation performed is multiplication if no sign between two terms is shown.

So, with our present problem (37 x 82) in which a = 3, b = 7, c = 8, and d = 2, the separate terms become

$$10(4) + 10(9) - 10(4 \times 8) - 10(3 \times 9) + (3 \times 8)$$
$$3,600 \quad - \quad 320 \quad - \quad 270 \quad + \quad 24 \quad = 3,304 \checkmark$$

LEVEL 3 (CENTERED AROUND 5).. *5 STEPS*

Let's show algebraically how the rule of how to multiply two numbers that end in 5 comes about. With the same binomial as before, in which b and d respectively are 5, we have

$$(10a + 5)(10c + 5) =$$

$$100ac + 50a + 50c + 25 \text{ or}$$

$$100ac + 50(a + c) + 25 \text{ or}$$

$$100ac + 100 + \left(\frac{a+c}{2}\right) + 25 \text{ or}$$
$$100\left(ac + \frac{a+c}{2}\right) + 25$$

It is clear that if (a + c) is an odd number, $100 \frac{a+c}{2}$ will be a multiply of 100 with a remainder of 50. In that case, we could call the term $100 \frac{a+c}{2} = 100 \frac{a+c-1}{2} + 50$, in which case we would have to add 50 to the "dangling" 25, making this 75.

For instance, in the case of

45 x 85

in which a = 4 and c = 8 and therefore (a + c) is even.

$$45 \times 85 = 100(4 \times 8) + 100\left(\frac{4+8}{2}\right) + 25$$

$$= 100\left[(4 \times 8) + \left(\frac{4+8}{2}\right)\right] + 25$$

$$= 100(32 + 6) + 25 \qquad = \underline{3,825} \checkmark$$

Let's take a case in which (a + c) is odd, for instance

45 x 75

In this case

$$100 \left(ac + \frac{a+c}{2}\right) + 25 \text{ becomes}$$

$$100 \left(4 \times 7 + \frac{4+7}{2}\right) + 25 =$$

$$100 (28 + 5.5) + 25 =$$

$$100 (28 + 5) + 50 + 25 =$$

$$(100 \times 33) + 75 \qquad\qquad = \underline{3,375} \checkmark$$

Suppose the problem is

43 x 79

In this case we have to find the gap Δ_5[*] between 45 x 75 and 43 x 79

We know empirically that Δ_5 will be 2 x 75 (150) less and 4 x 43 (172) more than 45 x 75

(3,375) or 172 – 150 (22) more = 3,375 + 22 = 3,397. Δ_5 = 22.

How does it work algebraically?

With a = 4, b = 3, c = 7, and d = 9, and expressing

43 x 79 as

(10a + b) (10c + d), what we just did corresponds to

$$\Delta_5 = (b - 5) (10c + 5) + (d - 5) (10a + b) \text{ or}$$
$$(\text{-}2 \times 75) \qquad + \qquad (4 \times 43) = 22$$

$$\Delta_5 = -\, 50 (a + c) + 10 (ad + bc) + bd - 25$$
$$-\ 550 \qquad + \qquad 570 \quad + 27 - 25 = 22,$$

---

[*] For this level, we designate Δ_5 as the gap between the problem as posed (in this case, 43 x 79) and the oners of the problem changed to 5's (in this case, 45 x 75).

which looks (and is) a little more complex than the "empirical" way. But that is algebra for you.

Steps 2 & 3

These two steps, in which we adjust the oners to add up to 10 are identical to each other algebraically. The only difference is that in Step 2, we adjust the second oner and in Step 3, we adjust the first oner.

You will remember that, if we adjust one of the oners (d, the oner of the second factor in Step 2, and a, the oner of the first factor in Step 3) the gap (we'll call it Δ_{10}) between that product and the product if both oners are made to be 5 is in Step 2

$$\Delta_{10} = 10\,(c - a)\,(b - 5) - (b - 5)^2$$

In our example of

43 x 79, which becomes
43 x 77

this works out to

$$\Delta_{10} = 10\,(7 - 4)\,(3 - 5) - (3 - 5)^2 =$$
$$(30 \quad x \quad -2) \quad - \quad 4 \quad = -64$$

But we need to adjust this to 43 x 79, which means that we have to add 2 x 43 = 86 to that, which brings us, as expected, to 22.

This adjustment is expressed algebraically as follows:

Adjustment = $(10a + b)\,[d - (10 - b)]$ =

$(10a + b)\,(b + d - 10)$ and substituting as control
$\qquad\qquad$ 43 $\quad$ x $\quad$ 2 $\qquad$ = 86
Algebraically:

$$\Delta_5 = \Delta_{10} + \text{Adjustment, or}$$

$$\Delta_5 = -50(a + c) + 10\,(ad + bc) + bd - 25 = 10(c - a)\,(b - 5) - (b - 5)^2 + (10a + b)\,(b + d - 10), \text{ or}$$

$$\Delta_5 = -50a - 50c + 10ad + 10bc + bd - 25 = 10bc - 50c - 10ab + 50a - b^2 + 10b - 25$$
$$+\, 10ab + 10ad - 100a + b^2 + bd - 10b$$

Simplifying and rearranging:

$$\Delta_5 = \text{-}50a - 50c + 10ad + 10bc + bd - 25 = \text{-}50a - 50c + 10ad + 10bc + bd - 25$$

The two sides are the same, they are equal. If you have the time to put in our usual controls ($a = 4$, $b = 3$, $c = 7$, and $d = 9$), you will see that, as expected, they add up to Δ_5 22.

Step 3, in which we keep d as is and adjust b to add up to 10 with d, is algebraically analogous and we don't have to go through it.

In Steps 4 and 5, we adjust the respective oners to be equal.

In Step 4, we adjust the oner of the second factor to be the same as b, the oner of the first factor: In Step 5 we adjust the oner b of the first factor to be the same as d, the oner of the second factor. Both steps are algebraically analogous and we need to examine only one of them --- Step 4.

Having made this "equalization" and calling this gap Δ_0, you will remember that

$$\Delta_0 = 10 (a + c + 1) (b - 5) + (b - 5)^2$$

Checking with our control

43 x 79, which becomes
43 x 73

$\Delta_0 = 120 (\text{-}2) + (\text{-}2)^2$
$ = -240 \quad + 4 = \text{-}236$

But we need to adjust this to 43 x 79, which means that we have to add 6 x 43 = 258 to that, which, as expected, brings us again to $\Delta_5 = 22$.

This adjustment is expressed algebraically as follows:

$(10a + b) (d - b)$, and inserting our control
$43 \quad \text{x} \quad 6 \; = \; 258$

Algebraically:

$$\Delta_5 = \Delta_0 + \text{Adjustment}$$

$\Delta_5 = \Delta_0 + \text{Adjustment}$

$$\Delta_5 = -50\,(a + c) + 10\,(ad + bc) + bd - 25 = 10\,(a + c + 1)\,(b - 5) + (b - 5)^2 +$$

$$(10a + b)\,(d - b)$$

$$\Delta_5 = -50a - 50c + 10ad + 10bc + bd - 25 = 10ab - 50a + 10bc - 50c + 10b - 50 +$$

$$b^2 - 10b + 25 + 10ad - 10ab + bd - b^2$$

Simplifying and rearranging:

$$\Delta_5 = -50a - 50c + 10ad + 10bc + bd - 25 = -50a - 50c + 10ad + 10b + bd - 25, \text{q.e.d.}^*$$

As in Step 2, the two sides are the same, they are equal. You probably have already inserted our control (a = 4, b = 3, c = 7, and d = 9), and, as expected, you will have found that the two sides add up to 22.

As we have already agreed, Step 5 of this level is algebraically analogous to Step 4, so we don't have to analyze it.

LEVEL 4 (POWERS OF 2 OR 3, QUARTERS OR EIGHTHS)................*3 STEPS*

There is no algebra applicable to this level. All we do is work with powers of 2 or 3 in Step 1 and with eighths and quarters in Steps 2 and 3. It's all arithmetic, no algebra.

LEVEL 5 (FLIPS)..*2 STEPS*

---

* Q.e.d What is that? It is an abbreviation of the Latin term "quod erat demonstrandum," which means "that which had to be proven or demonstrated." Mathematicians like to use it, so may you when it is appropriate. You will impress your friends and relatives with your erudition

In this level we multiply each of the factors with its horizontal flip and then add (in Step 1) or subtract (in Step 2) the product of the factor and the difference between it and the other factor.

To refresh your memory: If the factors are, say, 36 and 84, we would multiply 36 x 63 (by the rule) and then add 21 x 36 in order to get to 36 x 84.

The algebra that follows will refer to that. But please, understand that after you have followed the rule in multiplying the factor by its horizontal flip, you can use any method you please to get to the final result.

For instance, let's say that your problem is 36 x 84, which is 3,024. After you have "fulfilled your commitment" by multiplying 36 x 63 by following the rule, yielding 2,268, you can come to your result (36 x 84) by adding 21x 36 (756), which will bring you to 3,024. More elegantly, realizing that 63 = 3 x 21 and 84 = 4 x 21, you can divide your intermediate result (2,268) by 3, which is 756 and then multiply it by 4, which brings you quickly to the final result of 3,024.

I know that this section is about algebra, but let's stop for a moment and think how we can quickly (and mentally, of course) divide 2,268 by 3 and multiply the result 756 by 4.

In looking at 2,268, think which is the closest lower hundred that is divisible by 3. It obviously is 2,100, and it divided by 3 is 700. That leaves 168. The closest lower tenner divisible by 3 is 150, and it divided by 3 is 50. We add that to the 700 and we have 750. The remainder is 18 and, of course, it divided by 3 is 6. So, 2,268 divided by 3 is 756. It takes approximately five times as long to explain it as you will be able to do it -- really in only seconds.

Multiplying 756 by 4 is even easier and quicker. You should realize instantly that 4 x 75 = 300 and therefore 4 x 750 = 3,000. Add 4 x 6 = 24 and you have your result of 3,024. As you go through this book but, more importantly, as you go through life and as you become more familiar and more comfortable with numbers, you will find many occasions to simplify arithmetical operations.

As, in this example, to bring 36 x 63 to 36 x 84, that is not an algebraic, but an arithmetic problem and we have discussed how to do that.

Before we proceed, let's just look at the rule itself.

To refresh your memory, it was:

$$(10a + b) (10b + a) = 100ab + 10(a^2 + b^2) + ab,$$ and with our control 36 x 63

$$(30 + 6) (60 + 3) = 1,800 + 450 + 18 \qquad = 2,268 \checkmark$$

which is clearly correct. You will note that we could "simplify" this by reducing the expression to

$$101ab + 10(a^2 + b^2)$$

but, while obviously the same, would make the mental process somewhat more difficult.

You will recall, when we dealt with Level 5 in Section II, that in most, though not in all cases, the gap (Δ) between the flip of one of the factors and the other factor would be the flip of the corresponding operation performed with the other factor, but with the opposite sign.

For instance

$$38 ---- 87: 83 - 87 = \textbf{-04}; 78 - 38 \; = \textbf{40} \quad \text{flip}$$

$$25 ---- 82: 52 - 82 = \textbf{-30}; 28 - 25 \; = \textbf{03} \quad \text{flip}$$

$$43 ---- 76: 34 - 76 = \textbf{-42}; 67 - 43 \; = \textbf{24} \quad \text{flip}$$

$$58 ---- 93: 85 - 93 = \textbf{-08}; 39 - 58 \; = \textbf{-19} \quad \text{no flip}$$

Note: There are certain pairs of numbers which, if the first (lower) number is flipped it will be one-half of the second (higher) number. And if the second number is flipped, it will be twice the lower number. In other words, if the two numbers are $(10a + b)$ and $(10c + d)$, respectively, $(10b + a)$ will be $\frac{1}{2}(10c + d)$, and $(10d + c)$ will be $2(10a + b)$. In all of those pairs, c = 2b and d = 2a. Of course, this works only if the flip does not result in a 3-digit number. For instance, 34 → 43 and 86 → 68. 43 = ½ x 86 and 68 = 2 x 34. Apart from the trivial cases of numbers ending in 0 (10, 20, etc.), and numbers divisible by 11 (11, 22, etc.), the following numbers fulfill this requirement: 12 – 42; 13 – 62; 14 – 82; 21 – 24; 23 – 64; 24 – 84; 31 – 26; 32 – 46; 34 – 86; 41 – 28; 42 – 48; 43 – 68.

Take the case of 43 ---- 65 in which, 1 = 4, b = 3, c = 6 and d = 5.

Of course, since this is algebra, these numbers are for control only and for checking and proving that our work is correct.

The gap (Δ_1) between the flip of the lower number (43), which is 34, and the higher number (65) is 34 – 65 = -31.

The gap (Δ_2) between the flip of the higher number (65), which is 56 and the lower number (43) is 56 – 43 = 13.

And of course, -31 is the flip of 13, but with the opposite sign.

Let's do the algebra.

What is $\Delta_2 - \Delta_1$? It is

$$[(10d + c) - (10a + b)] - [(10b + a) - (10c + d)]$$
$$(56 - 43) \qquad - \qquad (34 - 65) = 44$$

which, (just checking for accuracy) works out to 44 which is, of course, correct.

Multiplying and simplifying, this becomes

$$10d + c - 10a - b - 10b - 1 + 10c + d = 11 (c - a + d - b)$$

Regardless of whether the expression (c – a + d – b) is a positive or a negative number, the Δ_1 and Δ_2 have to be flips of each other, because any 2-digit number divisible by 11 (11, 22, 33…99) has to be composed either by two equal numbers (only, of course, in the cases of even numbers such as 22, 44…88), or of two numbers that are flips of each other such as 23 + 32 = 55 or 16 + 61 = 77, etc.

In order for this to work, however, Δ_1 and Δ_2 must be negative and positive (or positive and negative) respectively. Thus, if one is subtracted from the other we have either + and + or – and -, the two Δ's adding up to a positive or negative number that is divisible by 11.

The two numbers can relate in nine different ways to each other.

Each number, when flipped, can assume three positions.

1.   It can fall "outside." That means that the lower number becomes smaller when flipped and the higher number becomes larger.

For instance, if you have 43 x 67, flipping 43, it becomes 34, which is smaller and therefore "outside" the 43 ---- 67 range.

If you flip 67, it becomes 76, which is larger and therefore "outside" the 43 -- 67 range.

Thus, both numbers (43 and 67) are "outside" in this example.

2.   It can be "inside." That means that the lower number when flipped is higher than the number itself but smaller than the higher number – it falls inside (between) the lower and the higher numbers.

The same applies to the higher number.

For instance, if you have 45 x 68, if you flip 45 it becomes 54 which is inside the 45 ---- 68 range.

If you flip 68, it becomes 86 which is "outside" because it is outside the 45 ---- 68 range being greater than 68.

So in this example, one number (45) is "inside" when flipped and the other (68) is "outside."

3. It can be "beyond." That means that if the lower number is flipped it will be greater than the higher number. If the higher number is flipped, it will be smaller than the lower number.

    For instance: 28 x 71. Flip 28 and it becomes 82 which is greater than 71 and is therefore "beyond." Flip 71 and it becomes 17 which is smaller than 28 and therefore also "beyond."

    Or take 39 x 64. Flip 39 and it becomes 93 which is beyond 64. Flip 64 and it becomes 46 which is inside (the 39 ---- 64) range.

With these definitions we can set up a matrix as follows:

Upper Number

		IN	OUT	BEYOND
	IN	1 ✓	2 ✓	3 ☒
Lower Number	**OUT**	4 ✓	5 ✓	6 ☒
	BEYOND	7 ☒	8 ☒	9 ✓

In accordance with the algebra that we have developed, in these five fields in which we have a check mark (5 out of 9; 56%), either number of the pair that is flipped will be the flip of the other flipped number. In those fields in which we have a cross, rather than a check, that will not be the case (4 out of 9; 44%).

368

The first case (56%) applies to all pairs in which both numbers fall either outside or inside and in which both numbers fall beyond.

The second case (44%) applies to all pairs in which one of the numbers falls either outside or inside and the other number falls beyond.

This has been a rather lengthy excursion, but it gave us the change of doing some interesting out-of-the-way algebra and I trust that you benefited from it and that you enjoyed it.

LEVEL 6 (COMPLEMENTS TO 100)..*2 STEPS*

In the two steps of this level we work with the complements of first of one and second of the other of the two numbers to be multiplied.

The rule is that we multiply either number by 100 and subtract from that the product of the complement (to 100) of the other number times the first number.

For instance:

$$37 \times 82 = 3,700 - 37 \times (100 - 82)$$
$$= 3,700 - (37 \times 18) \qquad = 3,304 \checkmark$$

How does that look algebraically?

$$(10a + b)(10c + d) = 100(10a + b) - (10a + b)[100 - (10c + d)]$$

Let's multiply both sides out and see whether this is indeed an equation, in other words that both sides are the same.

$$100ac + 10ad + 10bc + bd = \cancel{1,000a} + \cancel{100b} - \cancel{1,000a} + 100ac + 10ad - \cancel{100b} + 10bc + bd$$

Take a minute and look at the terms on both sides of this equation. You can eliminate all terms on either side of the equation if their signs are opposite.

For instance: $1,000a - 1,000a$ obviously is 0; therefore, the two terms eliminate each other so we strike them out.

You can also eliminate all terms that are the same, with the same sign on opposite sides of the equation.

For instance, you can eliminate 100ac on the left side as against 100ac on the right side of this equation.

By the time you get through with doing this, you will find that you have eliminated all terms of this equation which is of course indicative of the two sides being equal.

We went through a lot of variations with this, mostly because I wanted to further strengthen you in algebra. But we could have made this a whole lot easier, namely by calling (10a + b) = A and (10c + d) = B. Then it becomes:

$$A \times B = 100A - A(100 - B)$$

Multiply it out and you can see that it is an equation. The two terms on the right side (100A and – 100A) cancel each other so the equation becomes A x B = A x B, q.e.d.

LEVEL 7 (COMPLEMENT SQUARES) .... *2 STEPS*

This level is another no-brainer as far as algebra is concerned.

The two steps are the mirror images of each other, so if we understand one, we understand the other.

You will recall that in this level, we square one of the numbers and (in Step 1), having squared the lower number, add the product of the "gap" (Δ = the difference between the lower and the higher number) and the lower number to that square.

We do the opposite in Step 2, square the higher number and subtract the product of Δ and the higher number.

Once you have squared either number, you can continue any way you want to. You do not have to add or subtract. Suppose, for instance, that your problem is 38 x 74. You can do it two ways.

Square 38 (you have to do that because that is your "commitment" on this level). And then add 36 (Δ) x 38 to that square.

Let's do it:

1. • $38^2 = 40^2 - (4 \times 40) + 2^2 = 1,600 - 160 + 4 = 1,444$

    • Solve the product of Δ x 38 by square of half sum.

    $36 \times 38 = 37^2 - 1^2 = 1,369 - 1 = 1,368.$

    ∴ $38^2 + (36 \times 38) = 1,444 + 1,368 = 2,812$ ✓

    • 37^2 is, of course, $40^2 - (6 \times 40) + 3^2 = 1,600 - 240 + 9 = 1,369$

2. Double 38^2, which gives you 38 x 76 and then subtract 2 x 38 (76) to bring you to 38 x 74.

    • $38^2 \rightarrow 1,444 \xrightarrow{\text{x2}} 2,888 \xrightarrow{-76} 2,812$ ✓

Take your pick, whichever is easier for you.

But for purposes of generalized algebra of this level we think in terms of adding/subtracting.

Let's again make it easy on ourselves. Let's call $(10a + b) = A$ and $(10c + d) = B$.

We then have the following:

Step 1

$$A \times B = A^2 + A (B - A)$$

$$A \times B = A^2 + AB - A^2, \text{ q.e.d}$$

Step 2

$$A \times B = B^2 - B(B-A)$$

$$A \times B = B^2 - B^2 + BA, \text{ q.e.d.}$$

LEVEL 8 (HALVES, COMMON DENOMINATORS, HALVES AND DOUBLES)..*2 STEPS*

This level has four steps. Step 1 and Step 2 are different from each other.

Step 3 and Step 4 are the mirror image of each other. If we explain the algebra of one, we have explained the algebra of the other.

Step 1 is quite easy if both numbers are even or if one number is even and the other odd. (Things get a little more difficult algebraically when both numbers are odd.)

The principle, and again, let's call the two numbers A and B, respectively, instead of $(10a + b)$ and $(10c + d)$, is quite easy, as you will see.

As to Step 1, we can agree that if we multiply one-half of both factors with each other, we have to multiply that result by 4 to come to the right answer.

$$(A/2 \times B/2) = AB/4$$

$$4(AB)/4 = AB, \text{ q.e.d.}$$

We have learned that if both numbers are odd and therefore if halving them will result in expressions that end in ½, things are a little more difficult. We have to multiply the halved numbers (without considering the ½) with one another; then, add to that result one-half of the sum of these numbers (again, disregarding any halves). We then multiply that result by 4. If the last halving does not leave a remainder of ½, we add 1 to the result; if it leaves a remainder of ½, we must add 3 to the result.

How come?

Let's consider these two cases.

1.   The two numbers do not have a remainder of ½ in the second halving.

Calling the first number A and the second number B, we state that

A x B = 4 (A/2 x B/2)

If both A and B are odd, we have

$$A \times B = 4\left[(\frac{A-1}{2} \times \frac{B-1}{2}) + \frac{1}{2}(\frac{A-1}{2}) + \frac{1}{2}(\frac{B-1}{2}) + \frac{1}{4}\right]$$

$$= 4\left[(\frac{A-1}{2} \times \frac{B-1}{2}) + \frac{1}{2}(\frac{A-1}{2})\right] + 1$$

Let's do a numerical example, say

A x B = 15 x 31 = 465 ✓

$$15 \times 31 = 4\left[(\frac{15-1}{2} \times \frac{31-1}{2}) + \frac{1}{2}(\frac{15-1}{2}) + \frac{1}{2}(\frac{31-1}{2}) + \frac{1}{4}\right]$$

$$= 4\left[(\frac{15-1}{2} \times \frac{31-1}{2}) + \frac{1}{2}(\frac{15+31-2}{2})\right] + 1$$

$$= 4\left[(7 \times 15) + \frac{1}{2}(\frac{44}{2})\right] + 1$$

$$= 4(105 + 11) + 1$$

$$= (4 \times 116) + 1 = 465 ✓, \text{q.e.d.}$$

2.   The two numbers do leave a remainder of ½ in the second halving.

We have initially the same, namely:

$$A \times B = 4\left[(\frac{A-1}{2} \times \frac{B-1}{2}) + \frac{1}{2}(\frac{A+B-2}{2})\right] + 1$$

or, which is the same

$$A \times B = 4 \left[\left(\frac{A-1}{2} \times \frac{B-1}{2} \right) + \frac{1}{2} \left(\frac{A+B-4}{2} \right) \right] + 3$$

Let's do a numerical example, say

$A + B = 15 \times 33 = 495$ ✓

$$15 \times 33 = 4 \left[\left(\frac{15-1}{2} \times \frac{33-1}{2} \right) + \frac{1}{2} \left(\frac{15+33-4}{2} \right) \right] + 3$$

$$= 4 \left[(7 \times 16) + \frac{1}{2} \left(\frac{44}{2} \right) \right] + 3$$

$$= 4 (112 + 11) + 3$$

$$= (4 \times 123) + 3 = 495 \text{ ✓, q.e.d.}$$

Step 2 of this level is somewhat of a soft proposition, because you cannot generalize whether there is going to be a common denominator or anything close to it. But for the purpose of algebra, let's assume that the lower number is A and the higher number B is gA + h.

With this assumption

$A \times B = gA^2 + hA$

This is clear since B = gA + h.

$A \times B = gA^2 + hA$ or $A (gA + h)$

Let's try it with a numerical example in which A = 17 and B = 56.

$17 \times 56 \qquad = 952$ ✓

B is $(3 \times 17) + 5$, which means that g = 3 and h = 5.

$A \times B = gA^2 + hA = (3 \times 289) + (5 \times 17) = 867 + 85 \quad = 952$ ✓

Step 3 and Step 4 are mirror images of each other. In Step 3 we double A and halve B, and in Step 4 we halve A and double B.

The algebra involved is minimal. It is obvious that

2A x B/2 = A x B and that A/2 x 2B also A x B

For instance, if A = 38 and B = 75₁, Step 3 will be

76 x 37½

and Step 4 will be

19 x 150

In solving such problems you have no "commitment" at all. You can use the fastest and easiest "real life" method that you can come up with.

For instance, I would solve Step 3 (76 x 37½) by instantly recognizing that 37½ = $\frac{3}{8}$ of 100. 1/8 of 76 is 9.5 (divide 76/2 → 38 → 19 → 9.5). Multiply that by 3 (you get $\frac{3}{8}$) which brings you to 28.5. Multiply that by 100 and you have the result of 2,850 ✓.

It really shouldn't take more than 15 seconds and won't take you any longer once you have finished this book and followed the regimen of regular mental exercise.

Step 4 is even easier.

To solve 19 x 150 you go first to 20 x 150 which is, of course, 3,000. Subtract 1 x 150 (150) and you get 2,850 which is the result.

Another easy way of solving such a problem is by realizing that 19 x 150 is (19 x 100) + (19 x 50), which would be 1,900 + 950, again 2,850 ✓.

Or, finally, you can think of it as (20 x 150) – 150 = 3,000 – 150 = 2,850 ✓. Take your pick!

LEVEL 9 (PLUS AND MINUS 10).. *4 STEPS*

In this level we have four steps in various combinations of adding and subtracting 10 from the factors.

- In Step 1 we subtract 10 from the lower factor and add 10 to the higher factor.

- In Step 2 we add 10 to the lower factor and subtract 10 from the higher factor.

- In Step 3 we subtract 10 from both the lower and the higher factors.

- In Step 4 we add 10 to both the lower and the higher factors.

- In algebraic terms, the Rules were as follows (again, we shall, for simplicity's sake, call $(10a + b) = A$ and $(10c + d) = B$.

Step 1

$(A - 10)(B + 10) = AB - 10(B - A) - 100$

Let's check it out by extending both sides.

$AB + 10A - 10B - 100 = AB - 10B + 10A - 100$

The two sides are identical, q.e.d.

Step 2

$(A + 10)(B - 10) = AB + 10(B - A) - 100$

Checking it by extension:

$AB - 10A + 10B - 100 = AB + 10B - 10A - 100$

Again, the two sides are the same, q.e.d.

Step 3

$(A - 10)(B - 10) = AB - 10(A + B) + 100$

Checking it by extension:

$AB - 10A - 10B + 100 = AB - 10A - 10B + 100$

It checks, q.e.d.

Step 4

$(A + 10)(B + 10) = AB + 10(A + B) + 100$

Checking it by extension:

$AB + 10A + 10B + 100 = AB + 10A + 10B + 100$

Add the checks, the two sides are equal, the Rule is correct, q.e.d.

LEVEL 10 (FLIPS AND DIAGONALS, PART I) .... *7 STEPS*

You remember it; it was a tough one, with seven steps and flips and criss-crosses. But the algebra is interesting and you won't find it all that difficult.

In order to help ourselves along and to check our work we'll run a parallel numerical example with the algebra (let's make it 47 x 86 = 4,042).

In this, a = 4, b = 7, c = 8 , and d = 6.

You will remember that in this level (and also in Level 12) you will stack the factors, like this.

$$10a + b \qquad (10 \times 4) + 7$$
$$\underline{10c + d} \qquad \underline{(10 \times 8) + 6}$$

Here is how the rule works for Step 1.

Step 1

$$[10\,(ab) + ad + bc] \times 10 + bd$$

$$[10\,(4 \times 8) + (4 \times 6) + (7 \times 8)] \times 10 + (7 \times 6)$$

$$(320 + 80) \times 10 + 42 = 4{,}042 \checkmark$$

Step 2

We exchange the oners by making a vertical flip and it becomes

$$10a + d \qquad (10 \times 4) + 6$$
$$\underline{10c + b} \qquad \underline{(10 \times 8) + 7}$$

The rule was that the difference between the original problem and the vertically flipped problem would be the difference between the oners times the difference between the full tenners. The flipped result would be larger if the first oner (b) is smaller than the second oner (d), and vice versa.

For instance, in our numerical example:

47
x 86

46
x 87

The difference between the oners is 1 and the difference between the full tenners is 40; b (7) is larger than d (6); therefore 46 x 87 should be 1 x 40 = 40 smaller than 47 x 86, and indeed it is: it's 4,002.

But we have to prove this algebraically.

$(10a + b)(10c + d) - (10a + d)(10c + b) = (10c - 10a)(b - d)$

$\cancel{100ac} + 10ad + 10bc + \cancel{bd} - \cancel{100ac} - 10ab - 10cd - \cancel{bd} = 10bc - 10cd - 10ab + 10ad$

The two sides are the same, q.e.d.

Just for fun, you may wish to substitute our numerical example. For example, the left side of the equation will be $(47 \times 86) - (46 \times 87) = 4,042 - 4,002 = 40$. The right side of the equation is $560 - 480 - 280 + 240 = 40$, q.e.d.

Step 3

After having performed the vertical flip in Step 2, we flip both factors horizontally and arrive at what we've called the "horizontal derivative."

```
10a + d → 10d + a        46 → 64
10c + b → 10b + c        87 → 78
```

The rule was that the difference between the result of the "original" problem (which in this case is the already vertically flipped one) and the horizontal derivative was 99 times the difference between the product of the oners and the product of the tenners. The horizontal

378

derivative would be larger if the product of the oners was greater than the product of the tenners and vice versa. We also agreed that 99 was $(100 - 1)$, which was much easier to work with.

How does the algebra work?

The "original" (vertically flipped) problem works out as follows (as we determined in Step 2).

$(10a + d) (10c + b) = 100ac + 10ab + 10cd + bd$. The horizontal derivative is:
$\underline{(10d + a) (10b + c) =\quad ac\quad + 10ab + 10cd + 100bd}$, and subtracting:

$$\Delta \quad = \quad 99ac \quad\quad - 99bd$$
$$= \quad 99\,(ac - bd), \text{ q.e.d.}$$

And plugging in our numerical example of 47 x 86, which after Step 2 becomes 46 x 87, we find that:

$$\Delta \quad = 99\,[(4 \times 8) - (6 \times 7)] = 99\,(-10)$$

And indeed, as expected,

46 x 87 = 4,002

-64 x 78 = -4,992

$\Delta = \quad -990 = 99\,(-10)$ ✓

As a practical matter and for purposes of quick computation, you determine the difference between the product of the oners (in this case 6 x 7 = 42) and of the tenners (in this case 4 x 8 = 32). The difference is $(42 - 32) = 10$. Since the product of the oners is larger than that of the tenners, the resultant derivative will be larger by $100\Delta - 1\Delta$. In this case:

4,002 + (100 x 10) – (1 x 10) = 4,992.

Steps 4 to 7

Here's where we start with diagonal flips -- through Step 7.

Since we have done the vertical flip in Step 2, our starting problem is:

$$\begin{array}{cc} (10a + d) & 46 \\ x\,(10c + b) & x\,87 \end{array}$$

You will remember that we worked with the two diagonals. Diagonal 1 being the NE|SW one (Δ_1 = NE|SW), and Diagonal 2 the NW|SE one (Δ_2 = NW|SE).

Here is the diagram again to refresh your memory.

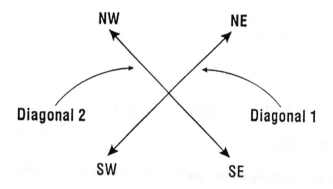

$$\Delta_1 = NE\,|\,SW$$

$$\Delta_2 = NW\,|\,SE$$

Δ_1 is the gap between (in this case) c and d, and Δ_2 is the gap between (in this case) a and b.

Referring to our present configuration:

$$\begin{array}{l} (10a + d) \\ x\,(10c + b) \end{array}$$

If diagonal 1 is flipped, the result will be larger or smaller by

$\pm\,(100 \times \Delta_1 \times a)\mp\,(1x\,\Delta_1 \times b)$ than the (vertically flipped) original

It will be

$\pm\,100\,\Delta_2 \times d \mp 1\,\Delta_2 \times c$

larger or smaller than the horizontal derivative.

Before we go into the algebra of it, let's see how it works with our numerical example, 47 x 86, which, from Step 2 forward, has been 46 x 87.

We know that this "original" (46 x 87) is 4,002 and that the horizontal derivative (64 x 78) is 4,992.

$$\begin{array}{ll} (10a + d) & 46 \\ \underline{x\,(10c + b)} & \underline{x\,87} \end{array}$$

$$\Delta_1 = 8|6 = 2 \quad \Delta_2\ 7|4 = 3$$

Step 4 - Diagonal 1 Flipped Compared to Original

This flip brings us to

$$\begin{array}{ll} (10a + c) & 48 \\ \underline{x\,(10d + b)} & \underline{x\,67} \end{array}$$

$$48 \times 67 : 50 \times 67 \rightarrow 3{,}350 \xrightarrow{\ -2x67 = 134\ } 3{,}216$$

This is $4{,}002 - 3{,}216 = 786$ smaller than the original 4,002.

Let's check it.

$\Delta = -\,(100\,\Delta_1 \times a) + (1\Delta_1 \times b)$

$-\,(100 \times 2 \times 4) + (2 \times 7) = -800 + 14 = -786$, q.e.d.

This flip (3,216) is 1,776 smaller than the horizontal derivative (4,992)

Let's check it.

$$\Delta = -\,(100\,\Delta_2 \times d) + (1\,\Delta_2 \times c)$$

$$= -\,(100 \times 3 \times 6) + (1 \times 3 \times 8) = -1{,}800 + 24 = -1{,}776, \text{ q.e.d.}$$

Now let's look at the algebra of it:

Again, compared to the original.

FLIPPED	**ORIGINAL**

$(10a + c) (10d + b) - (10a + d) (10c + b)$

$100ad + \cancel{10ab} + \cancel{10cd} + bc - 100ac - \cancel{10cd} =$

$100ad - 100ac + bc - bd =$

$100a (d-c) + \quad b (c-d)$

$400 (-2) + 7 (2) = -800 + 14 \qquad = -786$ ✓

$(100a - b) (d - c)$

$\quad 393 \quad x \quad (-2) \qquad\qquad = 786$ ✓

Step 5 - Diagonal 1 Flipped Compared to Horizontal Derivative

FLIPPED	**HORIZONTAL DERIVATIVE**

$(10a + c) (10d + b) - (10d + a) (10b + c)$

$100ad + \cancel{10ab} + \cancel{10cd} + bc - 100bd - \cancel{10cd} - \cancel{10ab} - ac$

$100ad - 100bd + bc - ac =$

$100d (a - b) - c (a - b)$

$600 (-3) - 8 (-3) = -1,800 + 24 \qquad\qquad = -1,776$ ✓

$(100d - c) (a - b)$

$\quad 592 \quad (-3) \qquad\qquad\qquad = -1,776$ ✓

We have now proved the Rules for Steps 4 and 5, comparing the diagonally flipped problem with the original and with the horizontal derivative.

The same (analysis) holds true for Steps 6 and 7 in which, instead of flipping Diagonal (NW|SW) we flip Diagonal 2 (NW|SE).

Since it's really the same I won't bore you with the repetition of the algebra, but I'll summarize for you algebraically the four steps and then we'll run the numerical example through those four steps.

With our "original" (vertically flipped) problem being

$$
\begin{array}{ll}
10a + d & 46 \\
\underline{\times\ 10c + b} & \underline{\times\ 87} \qquad = 4{,}002
\end{array}
$$

The first diagonal flipped (Steps 4 and 5) becomes

$$
\begin{array}{ll}
10a + c & 48 \\
\underline{\times\ 10d + b} & \underline{\times\ 67} \qquad = 3{,}216
\end{array}
$$

And the horizontal derivative flip being

$$
\begin{array}{ll}
10d + a & 64 \\
\underline{\times\ 10b + c} & \underline{\times\ 78} \qquad = 4{,}992
\end{array}
$$

$\Delta_1\ c|d = 2$

$\Delta_2\ b|a = 3$

The second diagonal flip (Steps 6 and 7) becomes

$$
\begin{array}{ll}
10b + d & 76 \\
\underline{\times\ 10c + a} & \underline{\times\ 84} \qquad = 6{,}384
\end{array}
$$

The Δ's for the four steps are:

Step 4 – Diagonal Flipped 1 Compared to Original

FLIPPED   **ORIGINAL**

$$\Delta = (10a + c)\,(10d + b) - (10a + d)\,(10c + b)$$

$$48\ \times\ 67\ -\ 46 \times\ 87\ =\ -786\ \checkmark$$

$$\Delta = -100\Delta_1 a + \Delta_1 b$$

$$= -800 + 14 \qquad\qquad\qquad\qquad = -786\ \checkmark$$

Step 5 – Diagonal Flipped 1 Compared to Horizontal Derivative

FLIPPED   **ORIGINAL**

$$\Delta = (10a + c)\,(10d + b) - (10d + a)\,(10b + c) =$$

$$48 \quad x \quad 67 \quad - \quad 64 \; x \; 78 \qquad\qquad = \; -1{,}776 \; \checkmark$$

$$\Delta = \; -100\Delta_2 d + \Delta_2 c$$

$$-1{,}800 + 24 \qquad\qquad = \; -1{,}776 \; \checkmark$$

Step 6 – Diagonal Flipped 2 Compared to Original

FLIPPED	DIAGONAL

$$(10b + d)\,(10c + a) - (10a + d)\,(10c + b)$$

$$76 \quad x \quad 84 \quad - \quad 46 \; x \; 87 \qquad = \; 2{,}382 \; \checkmark$$

$$\Delta = 100 \; \Delta_1 c - \Delta_2 d$$

$$= 2{,}400 \quad - 18 \qquad\qquad = \; 2{,}382 \; \checkmark$$

Step 7 – Diagonal Flipped 2 Compared to Horizontal Derivative

$$(10b + d)\,(10c + a) - (10b + a)\,(10b + c)$$

$$76 \quad x \quad 84 \quad - \quad 64 \; x \; 78 \quad = \; 1{,}392 \; \checkmark$$

$$\Delta = 100\Delta_1 b - \Delta_1 a$$

$$1{,}400 \quad - 8 \qquad\qquad = \; 1{,}392 \; \checkmark$$

Wow. The algebra of this level was somewhat of what the French call a *tour de force* – a feat of strength or skill. But if you are interested in algebra and are used to it by now, it will profit you to review this level and the summaries.

Keep in mind, that in this level, Δ (without a suffix) always refers to the differences established by the step and that Δ_1 and Δ_2 refer to the "gap" of the first and second diagonal, respectively.

Just for kicks, and to get you started in this review, let's work out together the last summary, that of Step 7 just above.

$$(10b + d) (10c + a) - (10d + a) (10b + c)$$

$$100bc + \cancel{10ab} + \cancel{10cd} + ad - 100bd - \cancel{10cd} - \cancel{10ab} - ac$$

$100bc - 100bd$	$- a (c - d)$
$100b (c - d)$	$- a (c - d)$
$100b\Delta_1$	$- a \Delta_1$
$100 \times 7 \times 2$	$- 4 \times 2 = 1{,}392$ q.e.d.

LEVEL 11 (SKEWED) ....*2 STEPS*

This level is very easy, certainly compared to Level 10.

The two steps are reverses of each other.

We call this level "skewed" because it isn't really "symmetrical."

According to the Rule, in Step 1, we first multiply the full tenners with each other, then we add the product of the sum of the oners with the lower factor, we then add the product of the oner of the lower factor and the difference of the full tenners between the two factors, and finally subtract the square of the oner of the lower factor.

In Step 2, we first multiply the full tenners with each other, then we add the product of the sum of the oners with the higher factor, we then subtract the product of the oner of the higher factor and the difference of the full tenners between the two factors, and finally subtract the square of the oner of the higher factor.

To clarify once again: The "full tenner" is the digit representing the tenner times ten. For instance, in, say, 43, the full tenner is 40 and not 4.

Expressing it algebraically (and substituting, again, for demonstration let's use as our example 46 x 87 = 4,002 in which a = 4, b = 6, c = 8, d = 7):

Step 1

$$(10a + b)(10c + d) \quad = \quad 10a \times 10c \quad + \quad (b + d)(10a + b) \quad + \quad b(10c - 10a) - b^2$$

$$(56 \times 87) \quad = \quad 3{,}200 \quad + \quad (13 \times 49) \quad + \quad (6 \times 40) \quad - 36$$

$$4{,}002 \quad = \quad 3{,}200 \quad + \quad 598 \quad + \quad 240 \quad - 36 \text{, or}$$

$$100ac + 10ad + 10bc + bd = 100ac + \cancel{10ab} + \cancel{b^2} - 10ad + bd + 10bc - \cancel{10ab} - \cancel{b^2}$$

As you can see, after canceling those items on the right side of this equation that are equal

but opposed in sign, the left side and the right sides are the same, which is therefore correct – q.e.d.

Step 2

$$(10a + b)(10c + d) \quad = \quad 10a \times 10c \quad + \quad (b + d)(10c + d) - d(10c - 10a) \quad - d^2$$

$$(40 \times 87) \quad = \quad 3{,}200 \quad + \quad (13 \times 87) \quad - \quad (7 \times 40) \quad - 49$$

$$4{,}002 \quad = \quad 3{,}200 \quad + \quad 431 \quad - \quad 280 \quad - 49 \text{, or}$$

$$100ac + 10ad + 10bc + bd = 100bc + 10bc + bd + \cancel{10cd} + \cancel{d^2} - \cancel{10cd} + \cancel{10ad} - \cancel{d^2}$$

Again, we have the same items on both sides of the equation, which is therefore correct – q.e.d.

LEVEL 12 (FLIPS AND DIAGONALS, PART II)..*5 STEPS*

Good news! There is no algebra for this level. Why? Because it is exactly the same as

the algebra for Level 10 except

      Step 3 in Level 10   is   Step 1 in Level 12

      Step 4 in Level 10   is   Step 2 in Level 12

      Step 5 in Level 10   is   Step 3 in Level 12

      Step 6 in Level 10   is   Step 4 in Level 12

      Step 7 in Level 10   is   Step 5 in Level 12

And since we started out with the vertical flip in Level 10

$$10a + d$$
$$\underline{x\ 10c + b}$$

and since we start with the "original original" in Level 12

$$10a + b$$
$$\underline{x\ 10c + d}$$

the notations of each step are correspondingly different. But everything else, and specifically the algebra, are the same as for Level 10.

(We don't want to go through that again, do we?)

LEVEL 13 (SQUARE OF HALF-SUM AND CENTERED ON 50) ....*3 STEPS*

This level has three steps: The first is "unique," the second and third are reflections of each other.

Step 1

This step is the square of the half sum. You remember how to do that.

- You square one-half of the sum of the factors.

- You subtract from that the square of the difference between that half sum and either of the factors.

$$(\frac{A+B}{2})^2 - (\frac{B-A}{2})^2$$

$$\frac{A^2+2AB+B^2-B^2+2AB-A^2}{4}$$

$$\frac{4AB}{4} = AB, \text{ q.e.d}$$

Let's do a simple numerical example, again A x B = 46 x 87 = 4,002.

$$AB \quad = \quad (\frac{A+B}{2})^2 - (\frac{B-A}{2})^2$$

$$46 \times 87 = 66\frac{1}{2}^2 - 20\frac{1}{2}^2$$

$$46 \times 87 = 4{,}422\ (.25) - 420\ (.25) \qquad = 4{,}002\ \checkmark$$

(A little refresher, though you probably don't need it):

$$66\frac{1}{2}^2 = 70^2 - (2 \times 3.5 \times 70) + 3\frac{1}{2}^2 = \text{(eliminating the .25's)}$$

$$4{,}900 - 490 + 12 \qquad = 4{,}422$$

$$20\frac{1}{2}^2 = 20^2 + (1 \times 20) + \frac{1}{2}^2 \qquad = \text{(eliminating the .25's)} \qquad 420$$

Steps 2 and 3

In these steps, you start with the base of $50^2 = 2{,}500$.

You subtract the square of the difference between 50 and the factor and you add the product of that factor and the sum of both factors less 100.

If the sum of the factors is less than 100, the difference would be a negative number, of course.

In Step 2, the above would apply to the first factor. In Step 3 it would apply to the second factor.

Algebraically, again for simplicity sake, we'll make $(10a + b) = A$ and $(10c + d) = B$. And once again, we'll use $46 \times 87 = 4{,}002$ as our numerical example $(46 + 87 = 133)$.

Step 2

$$A + B = 2{,}500 - (50 - A)^2 + (A + B - 100) \times A \text{ or}$$

$$= 2{,}500 - 4^2 + (33 \times 46) = 2{,}500 - 16 + 1{,}518 = 4{,}002\ \checkmark$$

And here is the algebra:

$$A \times B = 2{,}500 - (50 - A)^2 + (A + B - 100)\,A$$

$$A \times B = \cancel{2{,}500} - \cancel{2{,}500} + \cancel{100A} - A^2 + A^2 + AB - \cancel{100A}$$

The two sides are equal – q.e.d.

Step 3

$$A \times B = 2{,}500 - (50 - B)^2 + (A + B - 100) \times B$$

$$= 2{,}500 - (-37)^2 + (33 \times 87)$$

$$= 2{,}500 - 1{,}369 + 2{,}871 \qquad = 4{,}002 \checkmark$$

(A refresher: Remember that the square of a negative number is a positive number, therefore $-37^2 = 1{,}369$ but $-(-37)^2$ is $-1{,}369$.

How do you multiply 33 x 87? Two easy ways:

1. $\quad 33 \times 87 = (30 \times 87) + (3 \times 87) = 2{,}610 + 261 = 2{,}871$ or

2. $\quad 33 \times 87 = \left[\dfrac{33 + 87}{2}\right]^2 - 27^2 = 3{,}600 - 729 = 2{,}871$

Let's just do one example in which the sum of the factors is less than 100. For instance,

$$\mathbf{23 \times 64 = 1{,}472}$$

$$\Sigma \quad = \quad 23 + 64 \quad = \quad 87$$
$$\Delta_1 \quad = \quad 50 \,|\, 23 \quad = \quad 27$$
$$\Delta_2 \quad = \quad 64 \,|\, 50 \quad = \quad 14$$

$$A \times B = 2{,}500 - (50 - A)^2 + (A + B - 100) \times A$$
$$= 2{,}500 - 27^2 + (-13 \times 23)$$
$$= 2{,}500 - 729 - 299 \qquad = 1{,}472 \checkmark$$

LEVEL 14 (COMPLEMENT TO 10)..*2 STEPS*

In this level, just as we did in Steps 2 and 3 of Level 3, we must make the oners of the two factors equal 10. In Step 1 we adjust the oner of the second factor so as to complement the oner of the first factor to 10. In Step 2 we adjust the oner of the first factor so as to complement the oner of the second factor to 10. Naturally, in a problem like 34 x 86, the oners already add to 10 so only one step would be required.

Step 1

The rule is that we multiply the lower full tenner (10a) with the upper full tenner plus 10 (10c + 10). We add to that the product of the lower oner (b) with the difference between the lower full tenner and the upper full tenner plus 10, and we finally subtract the square of the lower full oner.

Naturally, if the oners did not originally add up to 10, we must, at the end, add or subtract the product of the difference of the oner that had been adjusted and the factor whose oner had not been adjusted. But that's not an algebraic procedure.

Let's see how it works in algebra. Let's use 32 x 84 = 2,688 as our numerical control.

32 x 84 becomes
32 x 88 = 2,816

We must subtract 4 x 32 = 128 at the end.

Let's go back to the equation, multiply it out and work the algebra.

$$(10a + b)(10c + 10 - b) = 10a(10c + 10) + b(10c + 10 - 10a) - b^2$$

$$100ac + 100a - 10ab + 10bc + 10b - b^2 = 100ac + 100a + 10bc + 10b - 10ab - b^2$$

As you can see, items on the left side of the equation are exactly the same as those on the right side of the equation, although in somewhat different sequence. Therefore the rule is correct, q.e.d.

Using the numerical control:

$$(10a + b)(10c + 10 - b) = 10a(10c + 10) + b(10c + 10 - 10a) - b^2$$

32	x	88	= 30 x 90	+ 2 (60)		− 4
	2,816		= 2,700	+ 120		− 4 = 2,816 q.e.d.

We now have 32 x 88.

Naturally, in order to get to 32 x 84 we have to subtract 4 x 32 = 128 and get the final result of 2,688 ✓

Step 2

Step 2 is, of course, almost exactly the same, except that instead of adjusting to b, we adjust to d.

For this purpose, 32 x 84 becomes 36 x 84, and at the end we'll have to subtract 4 x 84 = 336, which, again, is not a matter of algebra.

So let's do it.

$$(10a + 10 - d)(10c + d) = 10a(10c + 10) + (10 - d)(10c + 10 - 10a) - (10 - d)^2$$

$$(36 \quad x \quad 84) = (30 \times 90) + (6 \times 60) \quad - 36 = 3{,}024 \checkmark$$

Let's multiply it out and see whether the equation balances.

$$100ac + 10\,ad + 100c + 10d - 10cd - d^2 =$$

$$100ac + \cancel{100a} + 100c - \cancel{100a} + \cancel{100} - 10cd + 10ad - 10d - \cancel{100} + 20d - d^2$$

Yes, complicated tough it looks, the two sides are equal. Check it out for yourself. The terms +100a and –100a cancel out on the right side of the equation and so do the two 100's; –10d and +20d is equal to 10d, corresponding to the left side of the equation. And so, as you can see, the two sides are the same, q.e.d.

LEVEL 15 (EQUAL ONERS AND TENNERS) ....*4 STEPS*

This level has four steps. The first two are a reflection of each other, and so are the second two.

In the first two steps, the oners are made equal and, at the end, the difference to the actual problem is added or subtracted.

Thus, for instance, if the problem is, say, for instance, 38 x 64, in Step 1, we would adjust the second oner and would consider 38 x 68 and subtract 4 x 38 at the end. In Step 2, we would adjust the first oner and would consider 34 x 64 and add 4 x 64 at the end.

Naturally, if the two oners are the same, as in, say 37 x 97, no adjustment is necessary and Steps 1 and 2 meld into one.

In Steps 3 and 4, the tenners are equalized and, at the end, the difference to the actual problem is added or subtracted.

Thus, for instance, if the problem is, again, 38 x 64, you would, in Step 3, consider 38 x 34 and add 30 x 38 at the end. In Step 4, you would consider 68 x 64 and would subtract 30 x 64 at the end.

And, of course, if the two tenners are the same, say 63 x 62, no adjustment would be required and Steps 3 and 4 meld into one.

The at-the-end adjustment in any of these steps is not a matter of algebra and we shall therefore not consider it.

So let's go through the algebra of the four steps and let's take 38 x 64 = 2,432 as our numerical control.

We have studied these four steps in Section 1 (Arithmetic) of this book. Steps 1 and 2 correspond to the same-last-digit procedure; Steps 3 and 4 correspond to the same-first-digit procedure.

Step 1

Equalize oners, making second oner (d) equal to first oner (b).

$$(10a + b)(10c + b) = 100ac + 10ab + 10bc + b^2$$
$$= 100ac + 10b(a + c) + b^2$$

$$38 \quad x \quad 68 = 1,800 + \quad 720 \quad + 64 \quad = \quad 2,584$$

Subtract: 4 x 38 = 152.

$$2,584 - 152 \quad = \quad \underline{2,438} \checkmark$$

Step 2

Equalize oners, making first oner (b) equal to second oner (d).

$$(10a + d)(10c + d) = 100ac + 10ad + 10cd + d^2$$
$$= 100ac + 10d(a + c) + d^2$$

| 34 | x | 64 | = 1,800 | + | 360 | +16 | = | 2,176 |

Add: 4 x 64 = 256.

$$2,176 + 256 = \underline{2,432} \checkmark$$

Step 3

Equalize tenners, making second tenner (c) equal to first tenner (a).

$$(10a + b)(10a + d) = 100a^2 + 10ad + 10ab + bd$$
$$= 100a^2 + 10a(b + d) + bd$$

| 38 | x | 34 | = 900 | + | 360 | + 32 | = | 1,292 |

Add: 30 x 38 = 1,140.

$$1,292 + 1,140 = \underline{2,432} \checkmark$$

Step 4

Equalize tenners, making first tenner (a) equal to second tenner (c).

$$(10c + b)(10c + d) = 100c^2 + 10cd + 10bc + bd$$
$$= 100c^2 + 10c(b + d) + bd$$

| 68 | x | 64 | = 3,600 | + | 720 | + 32 | = | 4,352 |

Subtract: 30 x 64 = 1,920

$$4,352 - 1,920 = \underline{2,432} \checkmark$$

LEVEL 16 (STRIP THE TENNERS)..*1 STEP*

We now come to the end, to the last level of the algebra of the Paradigm.

Level 16 has two steps, but the algebra for both is the same.

In Step 1, we "strip" the tenner of the first factor; in Step 2, we "strip" the tenner of the second factor.

The "complication" is that in Step 2 you will have to work with a negative first factor, which may be problematic when you first do it. In algebra, of course, it makes no difference at all.

The rule is that the result is the square of the full stripped tenner ($10a$ or $10c$, respectively), plus the product of that full tenner and the sum of the stripped factors, plus the product of the stripped factors.

Let's look at the algebra of this.

According to the rule, the truncated factors will look as follows, with $38 \times 94 = 3,572$, again as our numerical control.

Step 1

We "strip" the tenners and

$$38 \times 94 = 3,572 \text{ becomes}$$
$$8 \times 64$$

Stripping the lower tenners ($10a = 30$) from both factors, becomes

$$(10a + b)(10c + d) = (10a)^2 + 10a(b + 10c - 10a + d) + b(10c - 10a + d)$$

$$38 \quad \times \quad 94 \quad = \quad 700 + 2,100 \quad\quad\quad\quad + 512 = 3,572$$

$$100ac + 10ad + 10bc + bd = \cancel{100a^2} + \cancel{10ab} + 100ac - \cancel{100a^2} + 10ad + 10bc - \cancel{10ab} + bd$$

Considering the terms that are equal, but with opposite signs on the right hand of this equation and which therefore cancel each other, we find that the remaining terms on both sides of the equation are the same, which means that the two sides are the same, the rule is correct --- q.e.d.

Now let's do the same thing stripping the second tenner.

The algebra, of course, remains the same if we "strip" the second tenner, rather than the first tenner. The first factor will now be negative. But since you may not have much experience working with negative numbers, let's work it through with the same example, 38×94.

38 x 94 becomes
-52 x 4, because 38 – 90 = -52

$$(10a + b)(10c + d) = (10c)^2 + 10c(10a + b - 10c + d) + d(a + b - 10c)$$

38 x 94   = 8,100 + 90 (-52 + 4)   +   4(- 52)

38 x 94   = 8,100 –   4,320   –   208 = 3,572✓, q.e.d.

This is the end of the algebra for the 16-Level Paradigm. All of it is really quite elementary and if you haven't looked at an algebra book since you left high school this should have been quite interesting and enjoyable to you.

Before we go to the last section of this book, I'll give you a couple of unrelated or partly related algebra bonuses that you may enjoy.

—————————————— · ——————————————

UNRELATED AND PARTLY RELATED ALGEBRAIC TOPICS

Now that we have finished this section on algebra relating to the 16-Level Paradigm and hoping that your appetite is sufficiently whetted, let's discuss some unrelated or partly related topics of mathematics that may be of interest to you.

Combination and Permutations

In Levels 10 and 12, we flipped the digits of the two factors every which way. We may ask ourselves whether we exhausted all possible permutations of the four digits involved (assuming that we indeed had four different digits).

This opens an interesting window into permutations, a part of statistics.

Here is the rule: The number of possible permutations of n (n being any number) is n! which is spoken as "n factorial."

What does ! (the factorial sign) mean? It means to multiply all the numbers from 1 to n with each other.

For instance, 2! means 1 x 2 = 2.

3! means 1 x 2 x 3 = 6

4! means 1 x 2 x 3 x 4 = 24, etc.

Thus, the four digits involved in multiplying two 2-digit numbers with each other can be arranged in 4! or 24 different permutations. But these are really only twelve different permutations, because each set is counted twice. For instance (forgetting about the 10's for this purpose), we would count both abxcd and cdxab as only one because they are obviously the same.

We had seven steps in Level 10 and five steps in Level 12, twelve steps altogether. We may tend to think that we have exhausted all sorts of permutations in these two levels. But as you can see from the tabulation that follows, we have covered only eight of the twelve permutations. The reason for that is that Steps 4 and 5 and Steps 6 and 7 of Level 10 deal with only two permutations, looking at them from different angles. The same is true of Steps 2 and 3 and Steps 4 and 5 of Level 12.

1.	ab x cd	Level 10, Step 1
2.	ab x dc	No Match
3.	ac x bd	Level 12, Steps 2 and 3
4.	ac x db	Level 10, Steps 4 and 5
5.	ad x bc	No Match
6.	ad x cb	Level 10, Step 2
7.	ba x cd	No Match
8.	ba x dc	Level 12, Step 1

5.	bc x ad	No Match
9.	bc x da	Level 10, Step 3
3.	bd x ac	Level 12, Steps 2 and 3
10.	bd x ca	Level 10, Steps 6 and 7
10.	ca x bd	Level 10, Steps 6 and 7
11.	ca x db	Level 12, Steps 4 and 5
6.	cb x ad	Level 10, Step 2
12.	cb x da	No Match
1.	cd x ab	Level 10, Step 1
7.	cd x ba	No Match
9.	da x bc	Level 10, Step 3
12.	da x cb	No Match
4.	db x ac	Level 10, Steps 4 and 5
11.	db x ca	Level 12, Steps 4 and 5
2.	dc x ab	No Match
8.	dc x ba	Level 12, Step 1

Having numbered the permutations in this tabulations and having noted next to each of them to which level and step they correspond, you will note that ##2, 5, 7 and 12 are not covered by Levels 10 and 12. We could have done them, of course, also, but I feel you've had your fill of these permutations and we've ready to go onto something else.

But how about, as homework, for you to work out the algebra of (2), (5), (7), and (12), or, rather, I'll work with you on (2) and then you do the other three by yourself. How about that?

To "back up" our algebra, we'll use a numerical example, let's say 23 x 45, i.e., a = 2, b = 3, c = 4, and d = 5.

#2 is $(10a + b)(10d + c)$

$$(10a + b)(10c + d) = 100ac + 10ad + 10bc + bd = 1{,}035$$
$$23 \quad x \quad 45$$

$$(10a + b)(10d + c) = 10ac + 100ad + bc + 10bd = 1{,}242$$
$$23 \quad x \quad 54$$

$$90ac - 90ad + 9bc - 9bd = -207$$
$$= 9(10a + b)(c - d)$$
$$= 9(20 + 3)(4 - 5)$$
$$= 207 \quad x \quad (-1) \quad = -207, \text{ q.e.d.}$$

O.K. You are on your own for (5), (7), and (12).

Factorials, with which we've just become acquainted, can run into pretty large numbers. For instance, think of a group of ten friends who meet for dinner are sitting at a round table. They resolve to meet every evening but will change the seating arrangement at every meeting. How long will it take until all permutations are exhausted.

We know that the answer is 10! but how much is that? We've already figured up to 4! Then

$$5! = 4! \times 5 = 24 \times 5 = 120$$

$$6! = 5! \times 6 = 120 \times 6 = 720$$

$$7! = 6! \times 7 = 720 \times 7 = 5,040$$

$$8! = 7! \times 8 = 5,040 \times 8 = 40,320$$

$$9! = 8! \times 9 = 40,320 \times 9 = 362,880$$

$$10! = 9! \times 10 = 362,880 \times 10 = 3,628,800$$

3,628,800/365 days (forget about leap years) is 9,941 + almost 10,000 years. So it isn't likely that these fellows will ever come close to exhausting all seating arrangements, all permutations in their lifetimes.

Probability

This is an important area of mathematics. Let's just deal with two minor aspects, which are related to what this book is about.

The numbers that we're dealing with in our Paradigm go from 21 to 99. We have agreed that we would not be dealing with numbers smaller than 20 and that we would not be dealing with numbers ending in zero.

With these provisos, we have a total of 72 numbers available --- nine in the 20's, nine in the 30's --- up to nine in the 90's. That is 8 x 9 = 72 numbers.

Suppose the first of our numbers is 23. What are the chances that the second number that we would be picking at random would contain either a 2 or a 3?

All the remaining eight numbers in the 20's obviously contain a 2. All the nine numbers in the 30's contain a 3 (and one of them (32) also contains a 2). Two numbers each in the 40's to 90's contain both a 2 and 3. So that is 9 + 8 + (6 x 2) = 29. 29 numbers out of 71 = 29/71 = .408. 40.8% of the random numbers chosen as the second factor will contain either 2 or 3, and 59.2% won't. In other words, chances are that you will pick a random number containing one of the digits of the first number you have chosen is roughly 2 out of 5.

Suppose that your original number is a "doublet," say, 33. What is the probability that the second number chosen at random will contain a 3? It will be the eight remaining numbers in the 30's and 23, 43…93, seven such numbers ending in 3. Thus, there will be 8 + 7 = 15 such numbers altogether or 15/71 = 21+% or roughly 1 chance in 5 that there will be a match and 4 chances in 5 that there won't.

You can easily figure out for yourself what the answers are to pick another number with the same ending digit or the chances of picking another number with the same beginning digit.

Another probability problem to which you will find the answer to be somewhat surprising: Remember the tests that we applied to check whether our results were correct? I told you at the time that if your results passed the test, you could be pretty sure, but not 100% sure, that your result was correct. Let's look into this.

Assume our problem is 43 x 67 and that we arrive at the result of 2,881.

- The sum of digits of 43 is 7 and of 67 is 4. Therefore the sum of digits of result must be 7 x 4 = 28 → 1. The sum of digits of 2,881 is 19 → 1. So, our answer passes the first test.

- Since the product of the last digits (3 and 7) ends in 1 (21), the result must also end in 1. 2,881 does indeed end in 1. So our result passes the second test.

- The result of 43 x 67 must lie between 40 x 60 = 2,400 and 50 x 70 = 3,500. 2,881 does indeed lie within these limits. The result passes the third test.

Having passed these three tests, what is the mathematical likelihood that the result of 2,881 is correct? Can we be absolutely sure? Can it be 100%?

It is not, because upon analysis it is clear that the three conditions would be fulfilled every 90 numbers. Going backwards from 2,881 toward the lower limit of 2,400 we find that the following additional numbers fulfill the three requirements: 2,791, 2,701, 2,611, 2,521, and 2,431.

Going forward toward the upper limit of 3,500, the following additional numbers fulfill the three requirements: 2,971, 3,061, 3,151, 3,241, 3,331, and 3,431.

So we have, in addition to the correct result of 2,881, eleven numbers that will fill the requirements, twelve numbers altogether. Therefore, strictly applying the mathematical method, we find that the probability that our result is correct is 1 out of 12 = 8.3%. I admit that that is quite counter-intuitive. One would have thought it would be 100% or close to it.

But the following example will make it a little more understandable. Suppose you have a bowl containing 1,100 balls (the number between 2,400 and 3,500), and that 1,088 balls are black which is the number that does not fulfill the three requirement; and, twelve balls are red (the number that does fulfill the three requirements). Of these twelve balls, only one (the one corresponding to the right answer) contains a diamond. What are the chances that, blindfolded, you would pull out a red ball? The chances are 12/1,100 or just over 1% -- very small.

What are your chances that you would pull out the red ball containing the diamond? Even smaller, obviously – just 1/1,100 or just .09%.

But suppose that somebody had already pulled all 12 balls out for you and you have to pick the one containing the diamond. Not having any other clue, your chances of picking the right ball is 1/12 = 8.3%, just as in our example.

Let's try one more of those.

Suppose our problem is 45 x 75 and you arrive at the (correct) result of 3,375.

We apply three somewhat different tests.

- The sum of digits of the result must be 9 since the sum of digits of one of the factors (45) is 9. 3,375 passes this test.

- Two numbers ending in 5 multiplied with each other must end in either 25 or 75. If the digits proceeding the 5 are both even or both odd, the result must end in 25. If, as in our example one is even and the other is odd, the result must end in 75. 3,375 passes this test.

- The result must be between 40 x 70 = 2,800 and 50 x 80 = 4,000. 3,375 passes this test.

How assured can we be that 3,375 is the correct answer? Is it again 8% or something close to it as in the last example? No, in this case we can be 100% sure that 3,375 is the correct answer. Why so? Analysis shows that numbers ending in 75 and with a sum of digits of 9 occur only once in every 900 numbers. The number proceeding 3,375 that fulfills the conditions is 2,475 and the number following 3,375 that fulfills the conditions is 4,275. But both of them lie outside of the possible limits of 2,800 to 4,200. Therefore, there is no other number satisfies all three conditions and we can therefore be 100% sure that 3,375 is the correct result.

Here's one more thing that I'd like to pass by you and have you think about. We have decided that we have a universe of 72 numbers with which to operate. How many different operations are possible. You may have already figured it out yourself, but consider this:

The first eligible number is 21. We can multiply it by 22, 23, 24…all the way to 21 x 99. That's 71 combinations with 21. (Remember, we don't work with numbers ending in zero.) How about 22? We have already multiplied it with 21, but we can multiply it with 23, 24, 25…all the way to 22 x 99. That is 70 combinations. It's easy to see that we can do that all the way to the last possibility, which is 98 x 99. You can see that there are 71 possible combinations with 21, 70 with 22, 69 with 23, etc., until there is finally only one combination with 98, namely 98 x 99.

So the total number of combinations is the sum of all of these: 71 + 70 + 69…+ 3 + 2 + 1. How much is that?

You may have already figured it out. If you haven't, I'll tell you in a minute. In the meantime, however, let me tell you a true story.

Karl Friedrich Gauss (1777 to 1855) was a great German mathematician. As a little boy he attended a one-room rural school house. One day, when Gauss was 8 years old, the school superintendent came, on horseback, to make one of his periodic inspections of the school.

needed time to talk to the teacher and he instructed the teacher to give the students an assignment that would keep them occupied for a good while. The teacher gave them the assignment to add all the numbers from 1 to 100. Almost immediately, little Gauss raised his hand and announced that he had solved the problem. The teacher thought it was impossible. The superintendent was equally skeptical.

"What is the result?" he asked.

"5,050," Gauss replied.

"How did you arrive at that?"

"Well," Gauss said, "I realized that 1 + 100 = 101, that 2 + 99 = 101, 3 + 98 = 101, etc., all the way to 50 + 51 = 101. So I could do that 50 times, and 50 x 101 = 5,050."

Now that was smart, wasn't it?

Of course, Gauss went on to great fame and many much deeper insights.

You may have realized by now that we can apply young Gauss's reasoning to our little problem. What is the sum of the numbers from 1 to 71? It's 1 + 71, 2 + 70, 3 + 69…all the way to 35 + 37. We can do that 35 times --- 35 x 71 with 36 being left "unused" in the middle. So the total number of combinations is (35 x 71) + 36 = 2,556. That is the total number of different operations that you can perform with the restrictions that we have established.

Are you interested in the general formula for that? It is

$\Sigma = (1 + n) \times n/2$, in which n is the final number of the series --- 100 in the case of young Gauss, 71 in our case.

Let's check is out for our case.

$$\Sigma = (1 + 71) + \frac{71}{2} = 72 \times 35.5 = 2,556, \text{ q.e.d.}$$

Propositions

I told you in the foreword that I would show you how you could make a little money with this book. In fact, I told you that you could secure a "small but steady income" from what I'm going to teach you. I was exaggerating a little, of course, but you should be able to win quite a few bar room bets.

A "proposition," as used in this context usually refers to a bet in which the person to whom it is proposed (the "mark") believes to have a good advantage over the dumb sap that suggested it to him. Naturally, the exact opposite is the case. Here are two famous examples.

THE BIRTHDAY PROPOSITION: You bet the mark that of the first 35 people that you meet and ask, at least two will have the same birthday (month and day), or to scan any listing that contains the birthdays of the individuals in it. The mark figures that there are 365 days in a year, so the chance that two out of 35 people should have the same birthday would seem to be remote. He believes that he shall take the bet and that he is bound to win.

But, alas, the reality is quite different. Here is how it works (forgetting about leap year and 366th day for this purpose – it makes little difference).

Chances that the second person you ask will <u>not</u> have the same birthday as the first are 364/365. The chances that the third person will <u>not</u> have the same birthday as the first two is 364/365 x 363/365. The chances for the 35th person <u>not</u> to have the same birthday as the

404

preceding 34 is 364/365 x 363/365 x 362/365…x 330/365.   Multiplying this out brings you to the

result of .1856. [*]

That means that there is an 18% chance for there being no hit and an 82% chance of there

being a hit. The odds in your favor are $82/18$ = 4.5+ to 1, which is splendid for you, of course,

especially if you are betting even money.

If you are really greedy, you can propose to extend the list of those to be asked for their

birthday to 40. The chances of there not being a hit go down to .1071 and, therefore the chances

of there being a hit (which is what you are betting for), increase to .8929. Your odds are

.8929/.1071 = 8.3+. It's like taking candy from a baby, isn't it?

THE LICENSE PLATE (OR PHONE BOOK) PROPOSITION: Propose to the mark that in

the next 20 cars that you meet, at least will have the same 2 last digits in their license plate.

A quicker way to accomplish the same end is to ask the mark to pick any column on any

page in the phone book and to check the last 2 digits of the first 20 telephone numbers.

Again, the mark figures that since there are 100 possibilities of the two last digits, and that

therefore the chance that there would be a match in just 20 cars would be very small. Of course,

he is wrong – it is a disastrous bet for him. As in the birthday proposition, there chances of there

not being a hit are 99/100 x 98/100…x 80/100, or

.99 x .98 x…x .80.

---

[*] This sort of thing is very laborious to do by hand, the old fashioned way, and it would be difficult to avoid errors. It could be done by logarithms within a reasonable time and with good accuracy but now it can be done very quickly by computer or even by hand-held calculators.

The odds in the next problem (the License Plate Proposition) can be solved on a standard calculator in less than a minute by multiplying .9 x .89 x .88 … x .8, without, as in the Birthday Proposition, having to divide (by 365) at every step.

The result is .1040, a 10%+ chance of there not being a hit and a .8960 chance of there being a hit. Your odds are .8960/.1040 = 8.6+ to 1.

You are bound to make some money with that, aren't you?

Equations with Unknowns

Much of algebra deals with equations. Therefore, even though equations play no role in our 16-Level paradigm, I thought that we should take a stab at them. They are something that you may use very frequently, especially first-degree equations.

First-Degree Equations with One Unknown

A first-degree equation is one in which the unknown or unknowns are not elevated to a power, i.e., they are x or y but not x^2 or y^3.

You use these kinds of equations probably every day in your life and in your work, although you may have never before thought of them in those terms.

One point before we proceed: The unknown in any equation is conventionally called x. If there is a second unknown it is conventionally called y.

You see an ad for five pounds of cheese for $17.50. What is the cost of one pound of cheese? You probably do this quickly in your head, dividing $17.50 by 5 and determine, correctly, that one pound of cheeses costs $3.50. You have just solved a first-degree equation with one unknown.

In mathematical terms, with x being the cost of one pound of cheese

5x = $17.50

$$x = \frac{\$17.50}{5} = \$3.50$$

406

Equation, of course, means equality. The two sides of the equation are in equilibrium. The left side (5x) is the same as $17.50. In order to maintain this equilibrium you must, if you make any changes to one side of this equation, make the same adjustment to the other side of the equation.

In our case, we have divided both sides of the equation by 5.

As a practical matter, you can "bring any factor to the other side" by reversing it's function:

+ becomes −

− becomes +

x becomes / (divided by)

/ becomes x

Let's do another example and apply this rule.

You have a coupon that entitles you to a 20% discount on a purchase. The merchant tells you that your bill (after the discount) comes to $45.00. How much was the cost before the merchant applied the discount of 20%?

Call that cost x.

Then we have:

.8x = $45

Now we "bring the .8 to the other side" and by reversing it's function and the equation becomes:

$$x = \frac{\$45}{.8} = \$56.25$$

You can check your result, of course, by reversing the procedure. Is .8 x $56.25 = $45? Yes it is. Therefore your solution was correct.

Suppose the coupon would have entitled you to a discount of $20 rather than of 20%. You're bill is still $45. The equation would then look like this:

x - $20 = $45

You bring the -$20 to the other side of the equation by changing the sign and it becomes:

x = $45 + $20 = $65

That is, of course, correct.

First-degree equations are quite trivial. But I thought that we should cover this before we get to the next chapter, namely First-Degree Equations with Two Unknowns.

First-Degree Equations with Two Unknowns

In order to solve for two unknowns you need two equations, since one equation could not determine what the two unknowns are.

Suppose you would have x + y = 100. It is clear that there would be an infinity of possible solutions. Even if we confined ourselves only to full integers, and to positive ones at that, we would have 100 different solutions for x = 0 to x = 100 with corresponding y = 100 to 0.

But if we have

x + 3y = 230 and

2x – y = 5

we could determine, by trial and error, that x = 35 and y = 65. Try it and you'll see that it's right. I'll show you how to do it with algebra and without trial and error.

There are essentially two ways of solving this equation, namely by 1. substitution or 2. subtraction.

Let's do substitution.

From the first equation, and bringing y to the other side it's clear that $x = 230 - 3y$.

Substituting that expression into the second equation, we have

$2x - y = 5$ becomes

$2(230 - 3y) - y = 5$ or

$460 - 7y = 5$

Bring the 460 to the other side and you have

$-7y = 5 - 460$ or

$-7y = -455$

Divide both sides by (-7) which means divide by 7 and reverse the signs (changing – to +) and you have

$7y = 455$

$y = 65$

Let's introduce the value for y into either of the two equations to determine the value for x. Let's take the second equation.

$2x - y = 5$ or

$2x - 65 = 5$ or

$2x = 70$ or

$x = 35$

You can always prove to yourself that your result is correct by introducing the values ($x = 35$ and $y = 65$ in our case) in the original equation. Try it: It is correct.

Let's now do it by subtraction.

Again:

$x + 3y = 230$

$2x - y = 5$

In order to work with subtraction, we have to make one of the unknowns in the first equation equal to that unknown in the second equation.

Let's "equalize" the x's by multiplying the first equation by 2. Since we perform the same operation on both sides of the equation, the equation is still valid.

$$
\begin{aligned}
2x + 6y &= 460 \\
\underline{2x - y} &= \underline{5} \\
7y &= 455 \\
y &= 65
\end{aligned}
$$

And, as before, we find that $x = 35$.

What is the purpose of this you may ask. Let's try a practical example.

The sum of the ages of a father and son is 60 years. Ten years ago, the father was 3 times as old as his son. How old are both of them now?

With the father's age being F and the son's age being S, we can set this up as two equations as follows:

$F + S = 60$

$(F - 10) = 3 (S - 10)$

$F - 10 = 3S - 30$

Substitute, from the first equation, $F = 60 - S$ into the second equation and we get

$60 - S - 10 = 3S - 30$

And bringing the S's to the left side and the number to the right, we get

$-4S = -80$

$S = 20$

And putting that value into the first equation

F + 20 = 60

    F = 60 – 20

    F = 40

The father is 40 and the son is 20 years old.

How about another one?

You go shopping. You buy eight pounds of potatoes and five pounds of coffee. The total bill comes to $29.80. But you don't verify the cost of the individual items.

Next week you go shopping again. You have been assured that prices haven't been changed. This time you buy twelve pounds of potatoes and three pounds of coffee. Your bill comes to $24.00. What is the cost per pound of potatoes and of coffee?

Let's set it up as an equation, with the cost of potatoes as P and the cost of coffee as C.

8P + 5C = $29.80

12P + 3C = $24.00

By substitution:

8P = $29.80 – 5C

$$P = \frac{\$29.80}{8} - \frac{5}{8}C$$

$$= 3.725 - .625C$$

And substituting:

12 (3.725 – .625C) + 3C = $24.00

    44.70 – 7.5C + 3C = $24.00

              –4.5C = -$20.70

                C = $4.60

And substituting this value into the first equation, we get:

$8P + 5C \quad = \$29.80$

$8P + 23.00 = \$29.80$

$\quad 8P \quad\quad = \$6.80$

$\quad P \quad\quad\quad = \$.85$

It's a little more difficult to solve this by substitution but let's try it just for practice.

$8P + 5C \quad = \$29.80$

$12P + 3C = \$24.00$

If we want to eliminate C, for example, we'll have to multiply both equations in order to make the C's equal. We'll have to multiply the first equation by 3 and the second equation by 5.

Let's do it.

$\quad 24P + 15C = \$89.40$

$\quad 60P + 15C = \$120.00$

Let's subtract the first equation from the second, and we get:

$36\,P \quad = \$30.60$

$P \quad = \$.85$

And we easily determine C by introducing the value for P (.85) into either of the equations.

$8P + 5C \quad = \$29.80$

$\$6.80 + 5C = \$29.80$

$\quad 5C = \$23.00$

$\quad C \quad = \$4.60$

Let me give you a homework problem:

412

John and Mary each have a number of marbles.

John says to Mary, "Give me a dozen of your marbles and I'll have twice as many marbles as you have then."

Marcy replies, "You are too greedy, John. Give me twelve of your marbles and then I'll have as many marbles as you will have left."

How many marbles did John and Mary each have?

The solution is that John had 84 marbles and Mary had 60.

You should now be able to solve this and come to the solution by the methods that we have learned. If you have a problem with it, let me know and I will send you the solution.

Gerardo Joffe
c/o Jomira/Advance, Advance Books Division
470 Third Street, #211
San Francisco, CA 94107   Fax: (415) 356-7804

Please include a stamped, self-addressed envelope.

Second-Degree ("Quadratic") Equations with One Unknown

Although it involves a higher level of difficulty, let's take a stab at second-degree ("quadratic") equations, in which the unknown (x) is squared.

For instance

$6x^2 + 4x = 170$ or

$6x^2 + 4x - 170 = 0$

is a typical second-degree ("quadratic") equation. The solution to this equation is 5. Try it.

$(6 \times 25) + (4 \times 5) = 170$

Let me show you how to solve a quadratic equation. Please don't ask me why this works; the explanation would be too lengthy for our purpose. Just accept it.

In order to solve a quadratic equation it has to be brought to the form

$$x^2 + ax + b = 0$$

After having brought it to that form, the solution is

$$x = -a/2 \pm \sqrt{(a/2)^2 - b}$$

The "v" looking symbol above is called a square root. The square root of a number is another number[*] which, when multiplied by itself produces the first number.

For instance:

$\sqrt{9} = 3$, because 3 x 3 = 9

$\sqrt{144} = 12$, because 12 x 12 = 144

$\sqrt{12.25} = 3.5$, because 3.5 x 3.5 = 12.25

You are not expected to find the square root of a number on your own. Most calculators have a key that produces the square root of any number instantly.

Let's go back to our example.

$$6x^2 + 4x - 170 = 0$$

In order to bring it to the proper from for a solution, we have to divide the equation by 6, and we get:

$$x^2 + \frac{4}{6}x - \frac{170}{6} = 0$$

$$x^2 + .67x - 28.33 = 0$$

$$x = -.33 \pm \sqrt{.1089 + 28.33}$$

$$= -.33 \pm \sqrt{28.44}$$

---

[*] The square root of 1 is 1. It is the only number the square of which is the number itself.

414

$$= -.33 \pm \sqrt{28.44}$$

$$= -.33 \pm 5.33$$

$$x_1 = -.33 + 5.33 = 5$$

$$x_2 = -.33 - 5.33 = -5.66 = -5\tfrac{2}{3}$$

Here is something new: Every quadratic equation has two solutions, because of the $\pm$ in front of the square root. Let's try and see whether our equation

$6x^2 + 6x - 170 = 0$ works for both solutions

1.   (with x = 5): $(6 \times 5^2) + (4 \times 5) - 170 = 0$ ✓

2.   (with x = -5⅔): $6x\left[-\dfrac{17}{3}\right]^2 - 4 \times 5\tfrac{2}{3} - 170 = 0$

$$192.66 - 22.66 - 170 = 0$$

The two solutions are of importance primarily only in purely mathematical applications. In "real life" only one solution is usually applicable.

Let's take an example from real life.

You buy a piece of land, which is a perfect square, and are told by the seller that it is exactly one acre, 43,560 ft. sq. But you don't really trust the seller and decide to have your own surveyor re-measure it. He tells you that you have indeed been cheated and that you have to add a 20-foot strip to one side of the square to bring it up to a full acre. What was the length of the side (x) of the original square? Here is what it looks like:

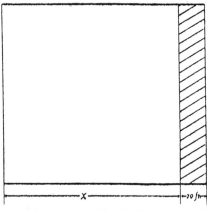

It is clear from the sketch that

$(x + 20) x = 43,560$ or

$x^2 + 20x - 43,560 = 0$

This equation is in proper form, so it's easy to solve.

$x = -10 \pm \sqrt{10^2 + 43,560}$

$= -10 \pm \sqrt{43,660}$

$= -10 \pm 208.95$

$x_1 = -218.95$ which is obviously not the correct solution

$x_2 = 198.95$ ✓

Let's check it out. If the side of the original square was indeed 198.95 ft. then new side (base) of the rectangle will be $198.95 + 20 = 218.95$ ft. and the size of the rectangle is

$218.95 \times 198.95 = 43,560$, q.e.d.

So as our final example, if you feel up to it, let's do one a little more complicated, since in order to solve it you'll have to know something else, namely the concept of "acceleration."

You know, of course, that if you drop something, say a stone, it will fall faster and faster as time goes by or, which is the same, cover more and more distance per second as time goes by (remember Galileo and that tower in Pisa?).

The formula for acceleration is:

$d = 16t^2$ ft. where d is distance in feet and t is time in seconds.

Suppose you're dropping a stone from a tower. It will fall

$d = 16 \times 3^2$ ft. $= 144$ ft. in 3 seconds, or

$d = 16 \times 5^2$ ft. $= 400$ ft. in 5 seconds

So here's our problem:

A parachutist descends at a steady rate of 20 ft./sec. As he is 100 ft. above the ground he loses one shoe. How long will the shoe have been on the ground before the parachutist gets there?

It is clear that the parachutist descending at a steady rate of 20 ft./sec. will take 5 seconds to reach the ground. How long will the shoe take?

If the shoe had no initial velocity, the formula:

$d = 16t^2$ or

$t^2 = d/16$ or

$t = \sqrt{d/16}$ would apply.

But the shoe does have an initial velocity of 20 ft./sec., which has to be added to the distance covered by the acceleration. So the total time required for the shoe to drop from 100 ft. with an initial velocity of 20 ft./sec. is

$$d \qquad\qquad = 16t^2 + 20t, \text{ and since } d = 100$$

$$100 \qquad\qquad = 16t^2 + 20t, \text{ or}$$

$$16t^2 + 20t - 100 = 0, \text{ and dividing by } 16$$

$$t^2 + 1.25t - 6.25 = 0, \text{ and according to our formula}$$

$$t \qquad\qquad = -.625 \pm \sqrt{.625^2 + 6.25}$$

$$= -.625 \pm \sqrt{.3906 + 6.25}$$

$$= -.625 \pm \sqrt{6.6406}$$

$$= -.625 \pm 2.57$$

$$x_1 \qquad\qquad = -3.19 \text{ secs. (No!)}$$

$$x_2 \qquad\qquad = 1.95 \text{ secs. (Yes!)}$$

Since the parachutist will take 5 seconds to reach the ground, the shoe will be on the ground $5 - 1.95 = 3.05$ seconds before the parachutist.

Now that you know about accelerations and how to solve quadratic equations, let me give you a homework problem as a goodbye present.

A pile-driving steam hammer is to be adjusted to strike 30 blows per minute. It is raised at the rate of five feet per second. After it hits, it rests for .1 second. How high does the hammer have to be raised to strike those required 30 blows per minute?

It's a neat problem and you should now be able to solve it. To check your work: The answer is 6.35 ft.

If you have difficulty with these, let me know and I'll send you the solutions.

Gerardo Joffe
c/o Jomira/Advance, Advance Books Division
470 Third Street, #211
San Francisco, CA 94107   Fax: (415) 356-7804

Please include a stamped self-addressed envelope and, of course, I welcome any comment that you might have about this book.

Dear Friend and Reader:

This is the end of what this book is about. The last part, the algebra section was really "optional," but I hope that you went through it, that you learned something from it (or refreshed what you learned or should have learned in school), and that you enjoyed it.

But the most important part of this book, of course, is the 16-Level Paradigm. Please make a real and honest effort to master it. Always keep one problem going in your head. Work on it on your way to work, during your lunch hour, on your way back home and before you fall asleep.

Your mind should already be in a whole lot better shape than it was before you started on this book and your memory also should by now have greatly improved. But full success doesn't come in a day or two. Just as with any other exercise program (yes, think of your brain as a "muscle" for this purpose) it takes patience and perseverance to be successful.

Section V, the final pages that follow, contains a few odds and ends, among them some homework exercises, how you can get your Achievement Certificate, and how you can get this book for free (get your money back) as I promised you in the foreword.

Finally, as I also promised you in the foreword, I'll show you a little "parlor trick," namely how to instantly determine the day of the week corresponding to any date in the twentieth and twentieth-first centuries. How about that?

Section V

FINAL WRAP-UP AND ODDS & ENDS

We are now coming to the end of the road. This section (as the title shows) will bring you a few odds and ends. In the first part of this section, I give you 25 problems, which I want you to run through the 16-Level Paradigm, just as we have done in the six problems of Section III. I shall give you some help on the first five examples. You will be on your own on the last twenty. Also, in the first five examples, I shall show you what the preferred "real life" solution to the problem is (i.e. without the constraints of the paradigms).

As you know, this book is not about making you a "lightning calculator", but you will inevitably become one and that will be a special bonus. The "trick" is to recognize in each case what the quickest and easiest method is to get to your result. In most cases, it will be the Level 1 method, but in many cases other methods will bring you quicker results.

In this book and in the 16-Level Paradigm, we deal only with the multiplication of two 2-digit numbers. It isn't really too different in dealing with 3-digit numbers -- or at least if one of the two numbers is a 3-digit number.

Take the case of, for instance, 146 x 73. You would first calculate 46 x 73, by thinking of it as $(50 \times 73) - (4 \times 73)$ or as $3{,}650 - 292$, which is equal to $3{,}658 - 300$, which is 3,358. To that we add 100 x 73, which is 7,300. We easily get to the total result of 10,658. Or how about thinking of 73 x 146 as $73^2 \times 2 = (4{,}900 + 6 \times 70 + 3^2) = 5{,}329 \times 2 = 10{,}658.$ ✓

Once you get into the swing of it and into the habit, I shall expect you to work one problem every day – through all sixteen levels of the Paradigm. But for those first 25, I shall allow you two days for each problem – say Levels 1 through 9 (the easy ones) the first day, and Levels 10 through 16 (with the tough Levels 10 and 12) the second day.

After you have done 25 problems in two months (or less), you may wish to fill out the form on page 441 of this book and apply for your **Certificate of Achievement**. Naturally, that is strictly on the honor system.

Final Homework Problems

I am now going to give you some examples, twenty-five altogether, that I want you to run through the 16-Level Paradigm. With the first five, I am going to give you some applicable hints and comments, and I'll show you how to solve each problem the fastest way – "in real life," i.e., independent of the Paradigm.

For the last twenty examples, you will be entirely on your own.

So here, without further ado, are the first five problems, those on which I will give you some hints and advice:

Problem #1: 49 x 58

> *Real Life Solution: 49 x 58 = (50 x 58) – 58 = 2,900 – 58 = 2,842* ✔

LEVEL 1 **Step 2:** **49 x 58**

> ➤ $(60 \times 49) - (2 \times 49) = (60 \times 50) - (60 \times 1) - (2 \times 49)$

LEVEL 2   **Step 2:**   **49 x 58**

> $(50 - 1) \times (60 - 2)$

> $(50 \times 60) - (50 \times 2) - (60 \times 1) + 2$

LEVEL 3   **Step 1:**   **49 x 58 = 2,842**

   45 x 55 = 2,475

> $45 \times 55 = (4 \times 5) \times 100 + \left(\dfrac{4+4}{2}\right) \times 100 + 75 = 2,475$

> $\Delta_5 = 2,842 - 2,475 = 367$

   Step 2:   **49 x 58**

> $(49 \times 51) + (49 \times 7)$

> $\Delta_{10} \; 49|51 = (50 - 40) \times 4 - 4^2 = 24$

> $\Delta_5 \, (49|58) = \Delta_{10} + (49 \times 7) = 24 + 343 = 367$

   Step 4:   **49 x 58**

> $(49 \times 59) - (49 \times 1)$

> $\Delta_{10} \; 49|59 = (4 \times 100) + 4^2 = 416$

> $\Delta_5 \, (49|58) = \Delta_{10} - (49 \times 1) = 416 - 49 = 367$

LEVEL 4   **Step 1:**   **49 x 58**

> $(49 \times 64) - (49 \times 6)$

> $49 \times 6 = (50 \times 6) - 6$

LEVEL 5   **Step 1:**   **49 x 58**

> $\dfrac{49 \times 94}{2} + (11 \times 49)$

> $11 \times 49 = (10 \times 49) + 49$

Step 2:   **49 x 58**

> $\dfrac{(58 \times 85) + (58 \times 13)}{2}$

> $58 \times 13 = (58 \times 10) + (58 \times 3)$

<u>**LEVEL 6**</u>   **Step 1:**   **49 x 42** $= (50 \times 42) - 42$

Step 2:   **58 x 51** $= (58 \times 50) + 58$

<u>**LEVEL 7**</u>   **Step 1:**   **49^2**

> $50^2 - (50 + 49) = 50^2 - 99$

> $49 \times 58 = 49^2 + (9 \times 49)$

> $9 \times 49 = (10 \times 49) - 49$

Step 2:   **58^2**

> $60^2 - (4 \times 60) + 2^2$

<u>**LEVEL 8**</u>   **Step 1:**   **24½ x 29**

> $(25 \times 29) - (½ \times 29)$

Remember: To multiply by 25, divide by 2 and again by 2 and then multiply by 100.

Step 2:   **Too close for common denominator. Start with 50 x 60.**

Step 3:   **98 x 29**

> $(100 \times 29) - (2 \times 29)$

Step 4:   **24½ x 116**

> $(24 \times 100) + (24 \times 16) + (½ \times 116)$

> $2,400 + 384 + 58$

> Note: $24 \times 16 = 20^2 - 4^2$

LEVEL 9   **Step 3:**   **39 x 48**

> ➤ $(39 \times 50) - (39 \times 2)$ *or*

> ➤ $(40 \times 48) - 48$

         Step 4:   **59 x 68**

> ➤ $(60 \times 68) - 68$

LEVEL 10   **Step 3:**   **84**
                            x95

> ➤ $(84 \times 100) - (84 \times 5)$

         Steps 4/5:   **45**
                            x89

> ➤ $(45 \times 100) - (45 \times 11)$ *or*

> ➤ $(50 \times 89) - (5 \times 89)$

         Steps 6/7:   **98**
                            x54

> ➤ $(100 \times 54) - (2 \times 54)$

LEVEL 11   **Step 1:**   **17 x 49**

> ➤ $(50 \times 17) - (1 \times 17)$

         Step 2:   **17 x 58**

> ➤ $(60 \times 17) - (2 \times 17)$

LEVEL 12   **Step 1:**   **94**
                            x85

> ➤ $(100 \times 85) - (6 \times 85)$

         Steps 2/3:   **45**
                            x98

> ➤ $(45 \times 100) - (45 \times 2)$

         Steps 4/5:   **89**
                            x54

> ➤ $(100 \times 54) - (11 \times 54)$

> ➤ $5{,}400 - 594 = 5{,}406 - 600$

424

<u>LEVEL 13</u> **Step 1:** $(53\tfrac{1}{2})^2 - (4\tfrac{1}{2})^2$

➢ $(53\tfrac{1}{2})^2 = (50)^2 + (7 \times 50) + (3\tfrac{1}{2})^2$ $[(3\tfrac{1}{2})^2 = 12(.25)]$.

Step 2:   **49 x 58**

➢ $2{,}500 - 1^2 + (49 \times 7)$

Step 3:   **49 x 58**

➢ $2{,}500 - 8^2 + (58 \times 7)$

<u>LEVEL 14</u> **Step 1:**   **49 x 58**

➢ $(49 \times 51) + (49 \times 7)$

➢ $(60 \times 40) + (9 \times 20) - (9^2) + (49 \times 7)$

➢ $2{,}400 + 180 - 81 + 343$

<u>LEVEL 15</u> **Step 1:**   **49 x 58**

➢ $(49 \times 59) - (49 \times 1)$

49 x 58

➢ $(40 \times 50) + (90 \times 9) + 9^2 - 49$

<u>LEVEL 16</u> **Step 2:**   **49 x 58** becomes

-1 x 8

49 x 58

➢ $50^2 + 50(-1 + 8) + (-1 \times 8)$

➢ $50^2 + 350 - 8$

Problem #2: 43 x 67

__Real Life Solution:__ 43 x 67 = 55² – 12² = 3,025 – 144 = 2,881 ✓

Note right away that $3 + 7 = 10$. That means that in Level 3, Step 2 and 3 will merge into one.

And also, in Level 14, both Steps will merge into one.

And also, in Level 14, both Steps will merge into one.

In Levels 11 and 16, the multiplier will be 10, making things a lot easier.

In Level 13, the multiplier in Steps 2 and 3 will be 10, also easy.

In Level 15, the multiplier in Steps 3 and 4 is 10 --- easy.

LEVEL 1, LEVEL 2, and LEVEL 3 No help needed.

LEVEL 4   **Step 1:**   **43 x 67**

  ➤ $(43 \times 64) + (43 \times 3)$

LEVEL 5   **Step 1:**   **43 x 67**

  ➤ $2(43 \times 34) - 43$

LEVEL 6   **Steps 1/2:**   **43 x 33 and 67 x 57**, both by same last digit method.

LEVEL 7   **No help needed.**

LEVEL 8   **Step 2:**   **43 x 67**

  ➤ $(44 \times 66) - 66 + 43$

  ➤ $(22^2 \times 6) - 23$

LEVEL 9   **Step 1:**   **33 x 77**

  ➤ $11^2 \times 21$

  ➤ 121×21

  ➤ $2{,}100 + 21^2$

  ➤ $2{,}100 + 441$

LEVEL 10   **Step 3:** $\begin{array}{r} 74 \\ \underline{\times 36} \end{array}$

  ➤ $[(¾ \times 63) \times 100] - 36$, or

  ➤ $\left(\dfrac{74 + 36}{2}\right)^2 - 19^2 = 55^2 - 19^2$

426

> 3,025 – 361

Steps 6/7: 37 x 64

> 37 x 60 (the "37 rule") + (37 + 4)

<u>**LEVEL 11**</u>   **No help needed. 3 + 7, easy!**

<u>**LEVEL 12**</u> **Step 1:** $\begin{array}{r} 34 \\ \underline{x76} \end{array}$

> [(¾ x 34) x 100] + 34, or

> $\left(\dfrac{36+76}{2}\right)^2 - 21^2 = 55^2 - 21^2$

> 3,025 – 441

<u>**LEVEL 13**</u> **Step 1:**   **43 x 67**

> $55^2 - 12^2$ (real life solution)

    Step 2:   **43 x 67**

> $2,500 - 7^2 + (43 \times 10)$

    Step 3:   **43 x 67**

> $2,500 - 17^2 + (67 \times 10)$

<u>**LEVEL 14**</u> **Steps 1/2:**   **43 x 67**

> $(40 \times 70) + (3 \times 30) - 3^2$ **Merge into one.**

<u>**LEVEL 15**</u>   **No help needed.**

<u>**LEVEL 16**</u> **Step 2:**   **43 x 67** becomes

            -17 x 7

    43 x 67

> $60^2 + 60(-17+7) + (-17 \times 7)$

> 3,600 – 600 - 119

Problem #3: 48 x 63

Real Life Solution: $48 \times 63 = (50 \times 63) - (2 \times 63) = 3,150 - 126 - 3,024\checkmark$

Do you see anything special in this problem? Look again! The product of the tenners (4 x 6) is the same as the product of the oners (8 x 3). That means that in Levels 10 and 12 the horizontal derivative is the same as the solution to the problem itself. In Level 10, 43 x 68 = 34 x 86, and in Level 12, 48 x 63 = 84 x 36. That means that the results of Steps 4 through 7 of Levels 10 and Steps 2 through 5 in Level 12 will be the same.

LEVEL 1 **No help needed.**

LEVEL 2 **No help needed.**

LEVEL 3 **Step 1:** **48 x 63**
45 x 65

➢ $100\left[(4 \times 6) + \left(\dfrac{4+6}{2}\right)\right] + 25$ $= 2,925$

➢ $\Delta_5 = (3 \times 65) - (2 \times 48) = 195 - 96 = 99$

➢ $48 \times 63 = 2,925 + 99$ $= 3,024 \checkmark$

➢ $3,024 + \Delta_5 = 3,024 - 99$ $= 2,925 \checkmark$

LEVEL 4 **Step 1:** **48 x 63**

➢ $(48 \times 64) - 48$

Step 3: **48 x 63**

➢ $(48 \times 62\tfrac{1}{2}) + (\tfrac{1}{2} \times 48)$

➢ $(48 \times {}^5/_8 \times 100) + 24$

➢ $3,000 + 24$

LEVEL 5 **Step 1:** **48 x 63**
48 x 84

➢ $(40 \times 80) + 10(8^2 + 4^2) + (8 \times 4) = 4,032$

➢ $63 = \tfrac{3}{4}$ of 84

Step 2:   **48 x 63**
         36 x 63

➤ $(30 \times 60) + 10 (6^2 + 3^2) + (6 \times 3) = 2{,}268$

➤ $48 = \frac{4}{3}$ of 36

➤ $\therefore\ 48 \times 63 = 2{,}268 \times \frac{4}{3} = 3{,}024\ \checkmark$

LEVEL 6 **Step 1:**   **48 x 63**

➤ $4{,}800 - (48 \times 37)$

Rule of 37: **24 x 37**

➤ 888

48 x 37

➤ 1,776

48 x 63

➤ $4{,}800 - 1{,}776$

➤ $4{,}824 - 1{,}800 = 3{,}024\ \checkmark$

LEVEL 7 **Step 1:**   **48 x 63**

➤ $48^2 + (15 \times 48)$

48^2

➤ $50^2 - (4 \times 50) + 2^2 = 2{,}304\ \checkmark$

15 x 48

➤ $480 + 240 = 720$

➤ $48 \times 63 = 2{,}304 + 720 = 3{,}024\ \checkmark$

LEVEL 8 **Step 2:**   **(Closest common denominator is 16)**

48 x 63

➤ $(48 \times 64) - 48$

48x 63

➤ $(16^2 \times 12) - 48$

➤ $3{,}072 - 48 = 3{,}024$

(Note: $16^2 = 256$. $256 \times 12 = (250 \times 12) + (6 \times 12) = 3{,}000 + 72$.)

LEVEL 9 **Step 1:**   **38 x 73 (Δ 48|63 = 15)**

➤ $(38 \times 75) - (38 \times 2)$

➤ $(38 \times \tfrac{3}{4} \times 100) - 76 = 2{,}774$

48 x 63

➤ $(38 \times 73) + 250 = 2{,}774 + 250 = 3{,}024$

LEVEL 10 **Step 2:**   43
    x68

➤ $(8 - 3) \times (60 - 40) = 5 \times 20 = 100$ less than 48 x 63

Step 3:   **Horizontal derivative 34
    x86**

is same, because the product of the tenners (4 x 6) is the same as the product of the oners (3 x 8).

Steps 4/5:   Solve 46 x 38 by square of half sum = $42^2 - 4^2$

Steps 6/7:   83
    x64

➤ $64 = 2^6$

➤ $166 \rightarrow 332 \rightarrow 664 \rightarrow 1{,}328 \rightarrow 2{,}656 \rightarrow 5{,}312$, **or**

    83
    x64

➤ $(80 \times 64) + (3 \times 64) = 5{,}120 + 192 = 5{,}312$

LEVEL 11 **Step 1:**   **48 x 63**

➤ $(40 \times 60) + (11 \times 48) + (8 \times 20) - 8^2$

➤ $2{,}400 + 528 + 160 - 64 = 3{,}024 \checkmark$

430

LEVEL 12 Step 1:   84
                                     x36

    ➢ $60^2 - 24^2 = 3,600 - 576 = 3,024$ ✓

    ➢ **Why is the horizontal derivative the same as the original product? Remember, since the product of the tenners is the same as the product of the oners, the horizontal derivative is the same as the original product.**

    Steps 2/3:   46
                                     x 83

    ➢ $(50 \times 83) - (4 \times 83)$

    ➢ $4,150 - 332 = 3,818$

    Steps 4/5:   38
                                     x 64

    ➢ 76 → 152 → 304 → 608 → 1,216 → 2,432 ✓, or

    ➢ $(40 \times 64) - (2 \times 64) = 2,560 - 128 = 2,432$ ✓

LEVEL 13 Step 1:   **48 x 63**

    ➢ $\left(\dfrac{48 + 63}{2}\right)^2 - 7\frac{1}{2}^2$

    ➢ $55\frac{1}{2}^2 = 7\frac{1}{2}^2$

    ➢ $3,080 - 56$

    Step 3:   **48 x 63**

    ➢ $2,500 - 13^2 + (63 \times 11)$

    ➢ $2,500 - 169 + 693 = 3,024$ ✓

LEVEL 14 Step 1:   **48 x 63**

    ➢ $(48 \times 62) + 48$

    ➢ $(40 \times 70) + (8 \times 30) - 8^2 + 48$

    ➢ $2,800 + 240 - 64 + 48 = 3,024$ ✓

LEVEL 15 Step 1:   **48 x 63**
                        48 x 68

➢ (48 x 68) – (48 x 5)

➢ (40 x 60) + 8 (40 + 60) + 8^2 – 240

➢ 2,400 + 800 + 64 – 240 = 3,024

LEVEL 16 Step 2:   **48 x 63 becomes**

                        – 12 x 3

48 x 63

➢ 60^2 + 60 (-12 + 3) + (-12 x 3)

➢ 3,600 + 60 (-9) + (-36)

➢ 3,600 – 540 – 36 = 3,024

Problem #4: 37 x 84

Real Life Solution (Special "37 Rule"): *37 x 84 = (37 x 90) – (37 x 6) = 3,330 – 222 = 3,108* ✓

Notice right away that we'll be able to apply the "37 rule" for this problem. 37 x 9 = 333: Therefore, 37 x 90 = 3,330. 33 x 6 = 222. Thus, 37 x 84 = 3,330 – 222 = 3,108. You should see this instantly and solve this problem and similar ones (in real life) in seconds.

Let me give you a few hints through the levels, though I'll give you less help than with the previous problems.

LEVEL 1   **No help needed.**

LEVEL 2 Step 2:   **37 x 84**

➢ (40 x 90) – (3 x 90) – (6 x 40) + 18

➢ 3,600 – 270 – 240 + 18

LEVEL 3   **Step 1:**   **35 x 85**

> $100\,(3 \times 8) + 100\left(\dfrac{3+7}{2}\right) + 75$

> $2{,}400 + 500 + 75 = 2{,}975$

> $\Delta_5 = (2 \times 85) - (1 \times 37) = +133$

> $2{,}975 + 133 = 3{,}108$ ✓

LEVEL 4   **Step 1:**   **37 x 84**

> $111 \rightarrow 333 \rightarrow 999 \rightarrow 2{,}997$

> $2{,}997 + 111 = 3{,}108$ ✓

LEVEL 5   **Step 1:**   **37 x 84**

> $(37 \times 73) + (37 \times 11)$

 37 x 73

> $(30 \times 70) + 10\,(7^2 + 3^2) + (7 \times 3)$

> $2{,}100 \quad + \quad 580 \quad\quad + \quad 21$

37 x 11

> $370 + 37$

LEVEL 6   **Step 2:**   **37 x 84**

> $8{,}400 - (84 \times 63)$

84 x 63

> $(80 \times 63) + (4 \times 63)$

> $5{,}040 + 252 = 5{,}292$

37 x 84

> $8{,}400 - 5{,}292$

> $8{,}408 - 5{,}300 = 3{,}108$ ✓

LEVEL 7   **Step 1:**   37 x 84

➢ $(2 \times 37^2) + (10 \times 37)$

37^2

➢ $40^2 - (6 \times 40) + 3^2$

➢ $1,600 - 240 + 9 = 1,369$ ✓

37 x 84

➢ $(2 \times 1,369) + 370 = 2,738 + 370 = 3,108$ ✓

LEVEL 8   **Step 1:**   18½ x 42

➢ $(18 \times 42) + (½ \times 42)$

 18 x 42

➢ $30^2 - 12^2 = 900 - 144 = 756$

18½ x 42

➢ $756 + 21 = 777$

37 x 84

➢ $4 (18½ \times 42) = 777 \times 4 = 3,108$ ✓

Step 2:   **Closest common denominator = 37. Therefore, this step is the same as Level 7, Step 1.**

LEVEL 9   **Step 4:**   37 x 84
                          47 x 94 (Σ = 121)

➢ $(47 \times 100) - (47 \times 6)$

➢ $4,700 - 282 = 4,418$, **or**

➢ $47 \times 94 = 2 \times 47^2 = 2 \times 2,209 = 4,418$

➢ $4,418 - 1,310 = 3,108$ ✓

LEVEL 10 **Steps 6/7:**   74
                          x 83

➢ $(73 \times 83) + 83$

73 x 83

➤ $(70 \times 80) + (3 \times 150) + 9$

➤ $5,600 + 450 + 9 = 6,059$

$$\begin{array}{r} 74 \\ \times\, 83 \\ \hline \end{array}$$

➤ $6,059 + 83 = 6,142$

LEVEL 11 Step 2:   **37 x 84**

➤ $(30 \times 80) + (11 \times 84) - (4 \times 50) - 4^2$

➤ $2,400 + 724 - 200 - 16 = 3,108$ ✓

LEVEL 12 Steps 4/5: $\begin{array}{r} 47 \\ \times\, 83 \\ \hline \end{array}$

➤ $\left(\dfrac{47+83}{2}\right)^2 - 18^2$

➤ $65^2 - 18^2 = 4,225 - 324 = 3,901$

LEVEL 13 Step 1:   **37 x 84**

➤ $60\,\tfrac{1}{2}^2 - 23\tfrac{1}{2}^2 = 3,660 - 552 = 3,108$ ✓

LEVEL 14 Step 1:   **37 x 84**

➤ $(37 \times 83) + 37$

37 x 84

➤ $(30 \times 90) + (7 \times 60) - 7^2 + 37$

➤ $2,700 + 420 - 49 + 37 = 3,108$ ✓

LEVEL 15 Step 3:   **37 x 84**

➤ $(37 \times 34) + (37 \times 50)$

➤ $30^2 + (11 \times 30) + (7 \times 4) + 1,850$

➤ $900 + 330 + 28 + 1,850 = 3,108$ ✓

LEVEL 16 Step 1:   **37 x 84 becomes**

                             7 x 54

                             37 x 84

> $30^2 + 30 (7 + 54) + (7 \times 54)$

> $900 + 1{,}830 + 378 = 3{,}108$ ✓

Problem #5: 38 x 95

Real Life Solution: *$38 \times 95 = (38 \times 100) - (38 \times 5) = 3{,}800 - 190 = 3{,}610$* ✓

Anytime when (in "real life") you get a problem, you should stand back for a moment and see how it can quickly be solved. Anytime that one of the factors is as close to 100 as in this case, the easiest way is usually to multiply the other factor by 100 and then subtract from that intermediate result that factor times the other factor's difference from 100. That is what we're doing here in the "real life" procedure.

Before we run this problem through the 16-Level Paradigm, we should note two other things that make it easier for us as we move along.

- One of the factors (95), ends in 5.

- The two factors have a common denominator, namely 19. 38 is 2 x 19, and 95 is 5 x 19.

LEVEL 1   **No help needed.**

LEVEL 2 Step 2:   **38 x 95**

> $(40 \times 100) - (2 \times 100) - (5 \times 40) + (2 \times 5)$

> $4{,}000 - 200 - 200 + 10 = 3{,}610$ ✓

LEVEL 3 Step 1:   > $\Delta_5 = (3 \times 95) = 285$

LEVEL 4 **Step 3:**   **38 x 95**

➢ $(37\frac{1}{2} \times 95) + (\frac{1}{2} \times 95)$

37½

➢ $100 \times \frac{3}{8}$

95 x ⅜

➢ $11\frac{7}{8} \times 3 = 33 + {}^{21}\!/_{8} = 35\frac{5}{8}$

35⅝ x 100

➢ $35.625 \rightarrow 3,562\frac{1}{2}$

38 x 95

➢ $3,562\frac{1}{2} + 47\frac{1}{2} = 3,610$ ✓

LEVEL 5 **Step 1:**   **38 x 95**

➢ $(38 \times 83) + (38 \times 12)$

38 x 83

➢ $(30 \times 80) + 10\,(3^2 + 8^2) + (8 \times 3)$

➢ $2,400 + 730 + 24 = 3,154$

38 x 12

➢ $(40 \times 12) - (2 \times 12) = 480 - 24 = 456,$ **or**

$$\left(\frac{50}{2}\right)^2 - 13^2 = 625 - 169 = 456$$

38 x 95

➢ $3,154 + 456 = 3,610$ ✓

LEVEL 6 **Step 1:**   **No help needed.**

LEVEL 7 **Step 2:**   **38 x 95**

➢ $95^2 - (57 \times 95)$

57 x 95

> $5,700 - 285 = 5,415$

95^2

> $9,025$

38 x 95

> $9,025 - 5,415 = 3,610$ ✓

LEVEL 8   **Step 2:**   **38 x 95**

(Note: $38 = 2 \times 19$; $95 = 5 \times 19$)

> $19^2 \times (2 \times 5) = 19^2 \times 10 = 3,610$ ✓

LEVEL 9   **Step 3:**   **38 x 95**
                             48 x 105   **($\Sigma = 133$)**

> $4,800 + 240 = 5,040$

> $5,040 - 1,430 = 3,610$

LEVEL 10   **Step 2:**   **38**
                            x 95

                            35
                            x 98

> $(35 \times 100) - (35 \times 2) = 3,500 - 70 = 3,430$ ✓

> $(8 - 5) \times (90 - 30) = 180$

> $3,430 + 180 = 3,610$ ✓

Step 3 (Horizontal Derivative):

                            53
                            x 89

> $5,300 - 583 = 4,717$

> $(3 \times 9) - (5 \times 8) = 27 - 40 = -13$

> $4,717 - 1,300 + 13 = 3,430$ ✓

LEVEL 11   **Step 1:**   **38 x 95**

> $(30 \times 90) + (13 \times 38) + (8 \times 60) - 8^2$

➢ $2{,}700 + 494 + 480 - 64 = 3{,}610$ ✓

LEVEL 12 **Step 1 (Horizontal Derivative):**

$$\begin{array}{r} 83 \\ \underline{\times 59} \end{array}$$

➢ $(83 \times 60) - 83 = 4{,}980 - 83 = 4{,}897$ ✓

➢ $4{,}897 - 1{,}300 + 13 = 3{,}610$ ✓

Steps 2/3:

$$\begin{array}{r} 39 \\ \underline{\times 85} \end{array}$$

➢ $(40 \times 85) - 85 = 3{,}315$

➢ $\Delta_1 = 9 \mid 8 = 1$

➢ $\Delta_2 = 5 \mid 3 = 2$

➢ $3{,}315 + 300 - 5 = 3{,}610$ ✓

➢ $3{,}315 + 1{,}600 - 18 = 4{,}897$ ✓

LEVEL 13 **Step 3:** **38 x 95** $\quad \Sigma = 133$

➢ $2{,}500 - 45^2 + (95 \times 33)$

➢ $2{,}500 - 2{,}025 + 3{,}135 = 3{,}610$ ✓

(Note: $45^2 = 100 \times (4 \times 5) + 25 = 2{,}025$)

95 x 33

➢ $3{,}300 - 165 = 3{,}135$

LEVEL 14 **Step 1:** **38 x 95**

➢ $(38 \times 92) + (38 \times 3) = (30 \times 100) + (8 \times 70) - 8^2 + 114$

➢ $3{,}000 + 560 - 64 + 114 = 3{,}610$ ✓

LEVEL 15 **No help needed.**

LEVEL 16 **Step 2:** **38 x 95 becomes**

-52 x 5

> $90^2 + 90 \,(-52 + 5) + (-52 \times 5)$

> $8,100 - (90 \times 47) - 260$

> $8,100 - 4,230 - 260 = 3,610$ ✓

(Note: $90 \times 47 = (100 \times 47) - (10 \times 47) = 4,700 - 470 = 4,230$)

I expect you to do or to have done the foregoing five examples and that you have taken each one of them through the "rigors" of the 16-Level Paradigm.

I have given you quite a bit of help, though you shouldn't have had too much trouble with them

As I told you earlier in this section, I am now giving you twenty more problems on which you will be quite on your own. In each case I give you my opinion on how I would solve the problem in "real life." I say *opinion* because in many cases, problems can easily be solved in more than one way. You will note that in many, if not in most cases, the easiest way to solve a problem is by Level 1 ("Easiest") method. This book is about sharpening your mind and about enhancing your memory. It is not meant to make you a calculating wizard. But if you have stuck with me so far, you will inevitably become or will already have become a lightning calculator.

Here are your final homework problems:

Problem #		Real Life Solution
6.	23 x 68	$(20 \times 68) + (3 \times 68)$
7.	49 x 82	$(50 \times 82) - 82$
8.	52 x 76	$(50 \times 76) + (2 \times 76)$

9.	43 x 92	(43 x 100) – (43 x 8)
10.	24 x 78	(25 x 78) – 78 = 1,950 – 78
11.	82 x 91	8,200 – (9 x 82)
12.	56 x 84	$70^2 - 14^2 = 4,900 - 196$
13.	36 x 84	(30 x 80) + (6 x 80) + (6 x 4), or $60^2 - 24^2$
14.	48 x 52	$50^2 - 2^2$
15.	37 x 66	Rule of 37: (37 x 60) + (37 x 6)
16.	35 x 72	(30 x 72) + (5 x 72), or $2(35^2) + 70$
17.	49 x 62	(50 x 62) – 62 = 3,100 – 62
18.	34 x 85	17^2 (2 x 5) = 289 x 10
19.	22 x 57	(20 x 57) + (2 x 57)
20.	73 x 98	7,300 – (2 x 73) = 7,300 – 146
21.	28 x 73	(28 x 75) – (28 x 2) = 2,100 - 56
22.	47 x 58	(50 x 58) – (3 x 58) = 2,900 – 174
23.	53 x 75	(50 x 75) + (3 x 75) = 3,750 + 225
24.	42 x 58	$50^2 - 8^2$
25.	62 x 68	$60^2 + (10 \times 60) + (2 \times 8) = 3,600 + 600 + 16$, or $65^2 - 3^2$

Now on to something different. I'll show you how you can get your **Certificate of Achievement**.

Certificate of Achievement

I trust that you have tackled and finished the 25 problems that I gave you in this Section, that you have run all of them through the 16-Level Paradigm and that have you done it within two months? Also, have you promised yourself to maintain a schedule of problem solving by the 16-Level Paradigm? If you can answer "YES" to both questions, you are eligible to receive the **Certificate of Achievement**, a facsimile of which I reproduce for you on the following page. The Certificate is 8½ x 11 inches in size and is printed on vellum-like diploma paper. You will be proud to have it framed and to hang it in your study. It will be a spur to you to work the 16-Level Paradigm from here on out and to continue to sharpen your mind and to hone your memory.

To receive your **Certificate of Achievement**, please send us your check (or fax us your Visa/MasterCard number, including expiration date) in the amount of $10 to:

Jomira/Advance, Advance Books Division
470 Third Street, #211
San Francisco, CA 94107   Fax: (415) 356-7804

The $10 cost is inclusive of shipping and handling.

Copy this page and fill out the form below.

- -

❑ *I have fulfilled the stated requirements to receive the **Certificate of Achievement**.*

My name is: _____

I live at: _____

In _____ State _____ Zip _____

⭕ My check in the amount of $10 is enclosed.
⭕ Please charge my Visa/MC #_____ exp._____

_____   _____
Signature   Date

Certificate of Achievement

Let It Be Known By These Presents That:

John Tyler Smith

has successfully completed the 16-Level Paradigm Course, that he/she has diligently fulfilled the requirements to obtain this certificate, and that he/she has undertaken to pursue a program of continuing exercises in the 16-Level paradigm, in order to bring his/her mind to razor sharpness and to bring his/her memory to steel-trap perfection.

In testimony of which we have given our hand and seal this **April 28, 2000**, in San Francisco, California.

Gerardo Joffe
Author and Director

Casey Shaw
Alumni Coordinator

How to Get This Book for Free

I told you in the foreword that you could get this book for free – in fact, I'll show you how you can not only get it for free, but actually make a nickel in the transaction.

Here's how:

Advance Books, the publisher of this book, is a subsidiary of Jomira/Advance of which Haverhills, a national mail-order house, is also a subsidiary.* I am the president of Jomira/Advance.

On the next page is a <u>Merchandise Certificate in the amount of $30.00</u>. You may apply it to any purchase from Haverhills within a year, provided that the merchandise value of your purchase (exclusive of tax and shipping/handling) is a minimum of $60.00 ($59.95).

The page after that is an Order Form and the pages that follow show you some of Haverhills current best sellers. <u>Photo copy both the $30.00 Merchandise Certificate and the Order Form, fill out the order form and mail it or (if you wish to charge your purchase to Visa/MC, you may fax to us). Only one Certificate per customer, please.</u>

So you see, you paid $29.95 for this book and you're getting a credit for $30.00. You are making a nickel on the transaction. What a deal!

---

*I have in the meantime sold the Haverhills Division. But that does not affect the validity of your Merchandise Certificate.

RE: MERCHANDISE CERTIFICATE

Dear Reader:

To take advantage of your **$30 Merchandise Certificate**, please photocopy it, clip it, and mail or fax it to us with your check or Visa/MasterCard number (remember to include expiration date).

Our "800" answering service is ***not aware*** of this promotion and <u>cannot accept your Certificate</u>. The **Certificate** is <u>only valid for orders with a minimum merchandise value of $60</u> ($59.95).

Also, please note that the **Certificate** is valid for one-time use only.

Thank you and sincerely yours,

Gerardo Joffe

MERCHANDISE CERTIFICATE

DO NOT DEPOSIT – NOT A BANKABLE ITEM

haverhills
5575 West 78th Street
Edina, MN 55439

Certificate #: <u>25234</u>

$30.00-------

CREDIT TO THE ORDER OF: **BEARER**

Thirty and 00/100- DOLLARS

You may use this **Certificate** for *one purchase with a minimum merchandise value of $60 ($59.95)* from the accompanying product sheets. Only mail or fax (952-942-7999) orders will be accepted – this **Certificate** is *not* valid for orders placed through our "800" service. This **Certificate** may not be used to purchase additional books through the **advance books** division.

VALID FOR ONE-TIME USE ONLY

Chris Simpson

since 1967
haverhills® Order Form

Please note: No other discount or credit beyond your $30 Merchandise Certificate is applicable to this promotion!

5575 West 78th Street • Edina, MN 55439 • Phone: (952) 942-8010 • Fax: (952) 942-7999

*P*lease fill out this **Order Form** and mail or fax it to us, together with your **$30 Merchandise Certificate**. Please note that the **Certificate** is applicable only for minimum merchandise value of $60 ($59.95) and can be used only once.

Qty.	Item #	Name of Item	Unit Price	Merchandise Value
			$	$
			$	$
			$	$
			$	$
			$	$
			$	$
			$	$

Total Merchandise Value	$
Plus MN sales tax (6.5%) *(MN deliveries only)*	$
Plus shipping/insurance ($6.95)✦	$
*Overnight or Second Day Air Surcharge**	$
Less: Merchandise Certificate	$ (30.00)
TOTAL	$

✦Note: Standard shipping/insurance is **$6.95** for all shipments to the continental U.S., in quantities up to six units☆. Add **$5** surcharge for shipments to AK and HI, **$10** surcharge for shipments outside the U.S.

Note: A higher standard shipping charge applies to the following "heavy" items, as indicated *(AK, HI, foreign residents add applicable surcharges)*:

♦   **Admiral Nelson's Telescope™**, **Car Starter III™**, **Mole-Ex VI™**, and **Rodelsonix IX™**: **$9.95** up to three units☆.

♦   **Night Piercer II™**: **$19.95** up to three units☆.

☐ **My check in the full amount is enclosed.**

☐ **Bill my VISA/MC acct.#:** _____ **exp.** _____

Phone:_____

My name is: _____

I live at: _____

City _____ **State**_____ **Zip**_____

**Contact customer service at (952) 942-8010 for Overnight Air or Second Day Air shipping surcharges.

☆For larger quantities, please contact customer service at (952) 942-8010 for shipping charges.

NOTE: Please mail your order to the address shown above or, for fastest service, fax it to (952) 942-7999. Be sure to fax your **Merchandise Certificate** also!

We do not refund or credit shipping/insurance charges.

IMPORTANT: Our "800" answering service cannot accept your $30 Merchandise Certificate under this promotion. Please do not call them!

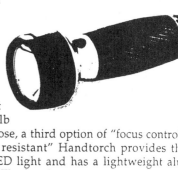
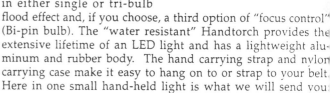
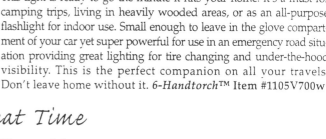

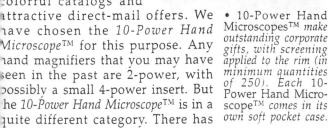
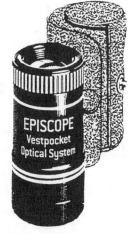

Mole-Ex VII™

Get rid of moles, gophers and other burrowing pests, with...

only $59.<u>95</u>

It's annoying to see your beautiful lawn being ruined by burrowing pests. You may have tried pouring poison down their holes or getting rid of them with other nostrums. Nothing really works. Now comes *Mole-Ex VII*™, the revolutionary electronic solution to this age-old problem. Spike *Mole-Ex VII*™ into your lawn. It emits short, high-pitched shrieks (at the threshold of ultrasound) in 30 sec. intervals. They are barely audible to humans, but they are calibrated to be totally distressing to moles, gophers, and other burrowing pests. They can barely see, but their hearing is fine-tuned. Once they get a blast of *Mole-Ex VII*™, they'll scamper away and will never return. *Mole-Ex VII*™ is the state of the art in the control of burrowing rodents. It's made of virtually indestructible anodized aluminum and tough ABS plastic for years of rugged use. Get *Mole-Ex VII*™: It will get rid of that annoying pest problem once and for all! *Mole-Ex VII* ™ #1056V700h

•Mole-Ex VII™ protects about 1,000 sq. yds. against moles, gophers, and other pests. Do not confuse this advanced device with similar looking, but much less sophisticated and less powerful, units! Runs on 4 D-cells (not included).

PowerVox VII™ (Hearing Mate)

Increase your hearing range by a factor of 10x, and get top-notch FM stereo reception besides, with...

only $49.<u>95</u>

The instructions of *PowerVox VII*™ *(Hearing Mate)* caution you to have the control on "very low" when you first try it, because this instrument is truly amazing in its sound amplification—up to 10 times the actual level. You will be able to hear a pin drop 10 feet away, television, the movies, and the theater without any trouble, and every little sound in your surroundings. A walk through the woods will let you listen to birds, deer, squirrels, and even little crawly things. Tired of listening to the world or to people? Simply push the blue button and you will scan your choices of the FM stations in your area, in truly marvelous stereo fidelity. *PowerVox VII*™ *(Hearing Mate)* comes with belt/pocket clip and two AAA batteries included. *PowerVox VII*™ *(Hearing Mate)* #1076V700

• PowerVox VII™ (Hearing Mate) does for hearing what binoculars do for seeing. I brings everything 10-time closer. PowerVox VII™ i: not a medical hearing device It is a way for you to experi ence the world of soun(around you—and to enjoy out standing FM stereo reception

---

Rechargeable Solar Fluorescent Light™ only $59.<u>95</u>

Brilliant light without electricity...

You can now add charm, beauty, and security to your property – without electricity. The super-efficient solar panel of this unit will supply four hours of bright light, with just six hours of charging in sunshine. The clever reflector triples the luminosity of the fluorescent tube. But the *Rechargeable Solar Fluorescent Light*™ isn't just for outdoors. Detach the solar panel and use the *Light* as a study lamp, as a garage lamp, or for any indoor purpose. And, of course, you can switch it off and on, saving the solar power for when it is needed.

• This unit comes with complete hardware for spiking the light outdoors and for mounting indoors. An optional AC/DC Adapter - $9.95 for one or $19.90 for three (for the price of two) – is available for use in bad weather or to power the unit for an extended time. The housing of the Rechargeable Solar Fluorescent Light™ is fully weather-proof. Size: 8"x 5".

Make yourself independent of electricity, add beauty and security to your property, and illuminate your outdoors and any places in your home with *Rechargeable Solar Fluorescent Light*™. *Rechargeable Solar Fluorescent Light*™ $59.95 #1090V700j *AC Adapter for Solar Fluorescent Light*™ $9.95 #1091V700k

---

Minifold™ Eyeglasses

Fall in love with our elegant folding reading glasses . .

only $59.<u>95</u>

The "Minifold" is the World's Best Seller in folding reading glasses. These eye glasses can be discreetly tucked away in a beautiful and compact case. The patented hinge guarantees ease of operation. The "Minifold" folds up into an approximately 1 1/2-in. size, and fits into a small case for your pocket or purse. Our stylish frames will make you the envy of all those who purchase expensive designer eyewear. Our glasses have the following key features

- Scratch resistant, asperical crown glass lenses
- Silicon nose pads and temple tips
- Powers: +1.00, +1.50, +2.00, +2.50, +3.00, +3.50
- Cases: Black or Tortoise
- Frame: Pewter or Gold

Here's a way to conveniently always have your reading glasses with you and look like you spend a fortune or designer eyewear when you didn't! This gem is affordable when compared to quality eyewear purchased though your clinic or retail outlet. By two and change your look whenever you feel like it. *Minifold*™ *Eyeglasses* **(with Pewter Frame #1106V700l** *with Gold Frame* **#1106V700m**

How to Determine the Day of the Week for any Date of the Twentieth & Twenty-first Centuries

I told you that I was going to show you this, so here it is.

To determine the day of the week for any date in the 20th century – from 1900 to 1999 – proceed as follows:

1. Take the last two digits of the year. For instance 1903 become 3, 1928 becomes 28, and 1987 becomes 87.

2. Add the number of leap years to that date. You get that by dividing the last two digits by 4, disregarding any remainder. For instance, you add nothing for 1903, because 4 doesn't go into 3. You add 3 for 1912, because 4 goes 3 times into 12. And you would also add 3 for 1913, 1914 and 1915, because 4 goes into them also 3 times (though there is a remainder, which we disregard). You would add 23 if the year is 1995, because 95 divided by 4 is 23 (with a remainder of 3, which you disregard).

    Leap years are all years that are divisible by 4, such as 1900, 1904, 1908, 1912…1996, 2000, 2004, 2008…2096.

3. Subtract 1 for the months of January and February in leap years.

4. Add the "month number" (see below).

5. Add the date (day of the month).

6. Determine whether the resulting number is divisible by 7. If it is, the day of the week is Sunday. If the number is not divisible by 7, determine the next lowest number divisible by seven and note the remainder.

    Depending on the remainder, the day of the week will be as follows:

Remainder 1	Monday
Remainder 2	Tuesday
Remainder 3	Wednesday

Remainder 4	Thursday	
Remainder 5	Friday	
Remainder 6	Saturday	

7. Do exactly the same for 2000+ (21st century) dates, except add 6 to your result. For instance, 2003 would be 6 + 3 = 9; 2021 would be 6 + 21 = 27, etc.

Here are the numbers of the months.

Jan	Feb	Mar	April	May	June	July	Aug	Sept	Oct	Nov	Dec
0	3	3	6	1	4	6	2	5	0	3	5

How can you possible remember those numbers? Make up a nonsense sentence and you won't forget. Let me give you some examples that I've made up (keep in mind that none of them make any sense --- they are not expected to). In all cases the word "oh" corresponds to zero.

Jan	Feb	Mar	April	May	June	July	Aug	Sept	Oct	Nov	Dec
0	3	3	6	1	4	6	2	5	0	3	5
Oh,	the	man	steers	a	boat,	drives	no	buggy,	oh,	the	shame!
Oh,	you	can	simmer	a	soup,	pickle	an	olive,	oh	the	taste!
Oh,	you	use	people.	I	have	spoken	no	words,	oh	you	devil!

Take your pick or make up your own nonsense sentence.

Now let's try a few examples.

1. October 25, 1987
    1) Last two digits of year   87
    2) Divided by 4 (remainder 3)   21
    3) January, February leap year deduction   N/A
    4) Month number (October)   0
    5) Date   <u>25</u>
                        Total   133

This number is divisible by 7 (133/7 = 19); therefore, this date is Sunday.

2. June 22, 1920
    1) Last two digits of year   20
    2) Divided by 4 (no remainder)   5
    3) January, February leap year deduction   N/A
    4) Month number (June)   4
    5) Date   <u>22</u>
                                    Total   51

Next lower number divisible by 7 is 49 (49/7 = 7) and remainder is 2. Day of the week is Tuesday.

3. February 5, 1992
    1) Last two digits of year   92
    2) Divided by 4 (no remainder)   23
    3) January, February leap year deduction   (1)
    4) Month number (February)   3
    5) Date   <u>5</u>
                                    Total   122

Next lower number divisible by 7 is 119[*] (119/7 = 17) and remainder is 2. Day of the week is Tuesday.

4. July 18, 1927
    1) Last two digits of year   27
    2) Divided by 4 (remainder 3)   6
    3) January, February leap year deduction   N/A
    4) Month number (July)   6
    5) Date   <u>18</u>
                                    Total   57

Next lower number divisible by 7 is 56 (56/7 = 8) and remainder is 1. Day of the week is Monday.

5. March 7, 2004
    1) Last two digits of year (4) plus 6 for 20xx   10
    2) Divided by 4 (4/4)   1
    3) January, February leap year deduction   N/A
    4) Month number (March)   3
    5) Date   <u>7</u>
                                    Total   21

This number is divisible by 7. Day of the week is Monday.

• Do you remember how you can instantly determine whether a number is divisible by 7? If not, go back to Section I. Double the number before the last two digits and add the result to the last two digits. In this case, the number before the last two digits is 1, doubled it becomes 2. Add 2 to 19 and you get 21. 21 is divisible by 7; therefore, 119 is divisible by 7.

6. June 24, 2017
    1) Last two digits of year (17) plus 6 for 20xx 23
    2) Divided by 4 (17/4 remainder 1)   4
    3) January, February leap year deduction   N/A
    4) Month number (June)   4
    5) Date   <u>24</u>
                              Total   55

Next lower number divisible by 7 is 49 (49/7 = 7) and remainder is 6. Day of the week is Saturday.

7. September 3, 2025
    1) Last two digits of year (25) plus 6 for 20xx 31
    2) Divided by 4 (25/4 remainder 1)   6
    3) January, February leap year deduction   N/A
    4) Month number (September)   5
    5) Date   <u>3</u>
                              Total   45

Next lower number divisible by 7 is 42 (42/7 = 6) and remainder is 3. Day of the week is Wednesday.

8. January 11, 2035
    1) Last two digits of year (36) plus 6 for 20xx 42
    2) Divided by 4 (36/4)   9
    3) January, February leap year correction   N/A (2035 is not a leap year)
    4) Month number (January)   0
    5) Date   <u>11</u>
                              Total   62

Next lower number divisible by 7 is 56 (56/7 = 8) and remainder is 6. Day of the week is Saturday.

I give you a few examples for you to work out yourself and I give you the answer in each

case. See if you can arrive at the proper answer by the method I have shown you.

Practice this and learn to do it quickly in your head. You will amaze friends, relatives and

acquaintances.

1. March 19,   1982   Friday   ✓
2. October 12,   1993   Tuesday   ✓
3. June 25,   2007   Monday   ✓
4. July 8,   2013   Monday   ✓
5. February 23, 2028   Wednesday ✓

Bonus: An Extra Step for Level 6 and a Whiff of Calculus

An Extra Step for Level 6

Here is a little bonus -- an extra step for Level 6. I think you will find it stimulating and enjoyable.

What is the product of the complements to 100 of two 2-digit numbers -- or rather: how does that product compare to the product of the original numbers?

Here is the rule:

> *The product of the complements of two 2-digit numbers to 100 is the*
>
> *product of the original numbers plus/minus the difference between the sum*
>
> *of the those two numbers times 100 -- plus if the sum of these numbers if*
>
> *less than 100 and minus if the sum of these numbers if more than 100.*

For instance, take our old friend

$$37 \times 82 = 3{,}034$$

The sum of these two numbers is 119, which is 19 more than 100. Therefore, according to the rule, products of the complement to 100 of these numbers, which is

$$63 \times 18$$

should be 1,900 less, i.e., 1,134, which, sure enough, it is. Figure it out.

$63 \times 18 = (60 \times 18) + (3 \times 18) = 1{,}080 + 54 = 1{,}134$ ✓ q.e.d.

Let's try it with a couplet, the sum of which is less than 100, say

$$23 \times 64 = 1{,}472$$

The sum of the factors is 87, which is 13 less than 100. Therefore, according to the rule, the product of the complements of the factors to 100 which is

77 x 36

should be 1,300 more, i.e., 2,772, which indeed it is. Let's prove it:

77 x 36 = (70 x 36) + (7 x 36) = 2,520 + 252 = 2,772 ✓ q.e.d.

By the way, since one of these complementing factors is 77, which itself is the product of 7 x 11, the result (2,772) should be divisible by both 7 and 11. Is it? Do you remember how to test for divisibility by 7 and by 11, respectively?

A little review might be in order.

For 7: Separate the last two digits, double the number before that separation line and add that sum to the number formed by the last two digits. Repeat this process if necessary until only a 2-digit number remains. If that 2-digit number is divisible by 7, the original number is divisible by 7. If it is not, the original number is not divisible by u.

Let's try it with our result:

2,772

It becomes   27|72

                                   1|26

                                       |28,

which is divisible by 7. Therefore, as expected, 2,772 is divisible by 7.

Let's test it for divisibility by 11. You recall (I hope!) that a number is divisible by 11 if the difference of the sum of the alternative digits is either 0 or 11 or a multiple of 11. Let's try it with our number:

2<u>77</u>2

It's clear: $2 + 7 = 9$ and $7 + 2 = 9$; they are both the same. So, 2,772 is (of course) divisible by 7.

But wait: How about the other factor of 77 x 36? It's 36, itself the product of 4 and 9. Therefore, 2,772 should also be divisible by both 4 and by 9, shouldn't it? Of course, you remember how to test for divisibility for both.

For 4: The last two digits have to be divisible by 4. Are they? Yes, 72 is divisible by 4, so 2,772 is divisible by 4.

For 9: The sum of digits has to be 9. let see:

$2 + 7 + 7 + 2 \rightarrow 18 \rightarrow 9$. So yes, 2,772 is divisible by 9.

I hope you didn't mind this little refresher into divisibility.

But let's try a few more examples of complements to 100.

- 43 x 68 = 2,924. Σ 43 + 68 = 111.   111 - 100 = 11.

  57 x 32 = 1,824.   1,824 = 2,924 - 1,100 ✓ q.e.d.

- 37 x 88 = 3,256. Σ 37 + 88 = 125.   125 - 100 = 25

  63 x 12 = 756.   756 = 3,256 - 2,500 ✓ q.e.d.

- 24 x 67 = 1,608. Σ 24 + 67 = 91.   91 - 100 = -9

  76 x 33 = 2,508.   2,508 = 1,608 + 900 ✓ q.e.d.

Now try a few on your own.

- 42 x 87
- 29 x 53
- 73 x 91
- 38 x 69
- 24 x 47

Let's look at the algebra of this step.

If A and B, respectively, are the original factors, their product is AB.

The product of the complements is:

$$(100 - A)(100 - 3) = 10,000 - 100A - 100B + AB$$

and the differencc between the two, i.e., subtracting this expression from AB is:

$$-10,000 + 100A + 100B.$$

That is equivalent to

$$100(A + B - 100)$$

Let's take two examples, one in which A + B < 100, and one is which A + B > 100

1. A = 26, B = 87.   A + B = 113 (A + B − 100) = 13.

-(AB) = -(26 x 87)	=	-2,262
(100 − A)(100 − B) = 74 x 13	=	+<u>962</u>
Δ	=	-1,300
-100(A + B − 100) = -100 x 13	=	-<u>1,300</u> ✓ q.e.d.

2. A = 24, B = 53 A + B = 77   (A + B − 100) = -23

-(AB) = -(24 x 53)	=	-1,272
(100 − A)(100 − B) = 76 x 47	=	+<u>3,572</u>
Δ	=	+2,300
-100(A + B − 100) = -100 x (-23)	=	+<u>2,300</u> ✓ q.e.d.

A Whiff of Calculus

No, don't worry! We are not going to wind up with a calculus lesson. But I thought you might enjoy it if, to conclude, I acquainted you with just one very interesting concept of calculus: Maxima and Minima.

Maxima and Minima play such a great role in our lives. Many decisions depend on it, though, admittedly, many such problems are solved "intuitively" or by trial and error, rather than by calculus. That's what we're going to do here now.

Let's take for example:

Your rich father-in-law, a prominent rancher, gives you 100 acres (4,356,000 square feet) of grazing land as a wedding present. You can pick the acreage. He only makes two conditions. 1. Your lot must be a regular polygon. 2. The lot must be fenced.

A regular polygon can range from an equilateral triangle (1), a square (2), a pentagon (3), hexagon (4), etc. all the way to a circle (5), which is a regular polygon with an infinite number of sides (of infinitesimal small width).

Let's see what it looks like.

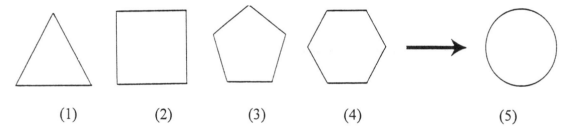

(1)   (2)   (3)   (4)   (5)

The fence that your father-in-law insists you put up costs $10/ft. The question is: What shape of lot (regular polygon) should you pick to minimize your fencing costs. And, how much would the fencing cost you?

But wait! The wily fencing salesman sidles up to you and tells you that he would like to sell fencing to the father-in-law, to fence in the whole ranch. It would be a tremendously profitable deal for him. He wants you to talk your father-in-law into the deal -- and he makes you an offer: In order to induce you, he offers to give you the fence for your acreage, not just for free, but he'll pay you a commission of $5/ft for every foot of fence you need to fence in your lot. You accept the deal and you now have to decide what shape to give your lot.

1. To minimize your fencing cost if the salesman hadn't come along, and what would be that cost, and

2. To maximize your commission if you accept the salesman's proposition, and what would be the commission?

One more:

You are supposed to lay a pipe through two adjoining square lots. Each lot is the size of 1,000 x 1,000 feet. Thus, the two lots together measure 2,000 x 1000 feet.

Here is the picture.

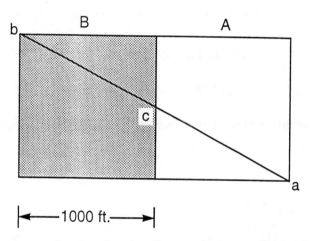

Here's the problem: You are supposed to lay the pipe from point a to point b. It costs $50 per foot for the pipe and for laying it. Lot A belongs to the City and they don't charge you for any right of way. Lot B belongs to a private landowner and he wants $20 per foot for the right of way. How should you lay the pipe for the least cost?

Look at the picture. A straight line from a to b would be the shortest. But it certainly would not be the least expensive way to do it. The straight line intersects the dividing line between the two lots at c. The question boils down to: How many feet below or above point c should the pipeline cross to give you the least expensive route?

This can only be solved by calculus. But if you don't know calculus or if you have forgotten it, figure it out by trial and error and let me know what you come up with. You know my address. It's on pages 412 and 417.

—————————————————————— o ——————————————————————

So this is it. This is the final good-bye. I hope you enjoyed this extended exercise as much as I enjoyed writing this book and as much as I enjoyed having you as my pupil.

I know that there must have been times when you read this book and worked through the exercises that you wanted to give up, that you wanted to throw in the towel. Don't do it – stay with it. Do <u>at least</u> one full 16-Level Paradigm every other day. You will be surprised what it will do for your mind. It will really be razor-sharp and your memory will be like that proverbial steel trap. That is my promise to you!

With best regards,

Gerardo Joffe